16.00

# Heroin Addiction

## Treatment and control in Britain

# Heroin Addiction

## Treatment and control in Britain

*Gerry V. Stimson*
*and*
*Edna Oppenheimer*

Tavistock Publications
London and New York

*First published in 1982 by*
*Tavistock Publications Ltd*
*11 New Fetter Lane, London EC4P 4EE*
*Published in the USA by*
*Tavistock Publications*
*in association with Methuen, Inc.*
*733 Third Avenue, New York, NY 10017*


*Phototypeset in Great Britain by*
*Servis Filmsetting Ltd, Manchester*
*Printed in Great Britain*
*at the University Press, Cambridge*



British Library Cataloguing in Publication Data

*Stimson, Gerry V.*
*Heroin addiction: treatment and control in Britain.*
*1. Heroin habit – Great Britain*
*2. Narcotics, Control of – Great Britain*
*I. Title II. Oppenheimer, Edna*
*362.2'93'0941 HV5822.H4*
*ISBN 0–422–77890–7*

Library of Congress Cataloging in Publication Data

*Stimson, Gerry V. (Gerry Vivian)*
*Heroin addiction.*

*Bibliography: p.*
*Includes indexes.*
*1. Heroin habit – Treatment – Great Britain.*
*2. Heroin habit – Government policy – Great Britain.*
*I. Oppenheimer, Edna. II. Title.*
*RC568.H4S76 362.2'93'0941 82-3193*
*ISBN 0-422-77890-7 AACR2*

# Contents

# *Acknowledgements*

The major part of this work was conducted at the Addiction Research Unit of the Institute of Psychiatry in London and we would like to thank the Department of Health and Social Security and the Medical Research Council for financing the major part of the research from 1968 to 1971 and from 1975 to 1978, and for continuing support through to 1980. We are grateful, too, for financial support in 1980 from the University of London Goldsmiths' College Research Fund. We would also like to thank Griffith Edwards, Director of the Addiction Research Unit, who has supported and advised on our work since it was conceived in the late 1960s.

There are numerous people who have helped and advised over the years and we would like to extend our thanks to them all. The initial study of addicts and London Clinics, in 1969, was conducted with Alan Ogborne and the follow-up study, from 1975 to 1977, with Anthony Thorley. We are grateful to Jacqueline May who was project secretary from 1975, Rolf Wille for collaboration on follow-up material, Colin Taylor for computing assistance, Richard Hartnoll for help with interviewing, Carol Stimson for help with the manuscript, and Barry Carman for help with newspaper sources. We have had many helpful comments on our work from Michael Ashton, Virginia Berridge, Herb Blumberg, John Mack, Martin Mitcheson, David Robinson, Margaret Sheehan, and Jasper Woodcock. We have also received valuable help from staff at drug treatment centres, the Department of Health and Social Security, the Home Office Drugs Branch, and the Institute for the Study of Drug Dependence. We would also like to thank the addicts and ex-addicts who have been interviewed by us in the course of our research.

# Introduction
## *What happens to heroin addicts?*

This book is about what happens to heroin addicts in Britain. It is based on the lives of 128 people who were heroin addicts in the 1960s. For a period of ten years, from 1969, we followed them to see where their lives led. We found out about those who were still addicted, about the ones who died, and about the ones who gave up heroin and other drugs.

### THE ADDICTS

The British drug scene has changed in many ways in the last twenty years. In the early 1960s, when many of these people first became addicted, heroin was relatively easy to obtain and could be legally prescribed to addicts by any medical practitioner, although few did so. A significant change in British policy occurred towards the end of the 1960s, and resulted in the setting up, in 1968, of special drug treatment centres (the 'Clinics'), and the restriction of the prescribing of heroin and cocaine to specially licensed doctors. Since Britain is one of the few countries in the world to allow doctors to prescribe heroin for addicts we were interested to see what sort of people came to the Clinics and how they managed their lives whilst addicted to heroin. In the first full year of the operation of the Clinics, in 1969, we interviewed people who were receiving prescriptions for heroin. What struck us then was the diversity we found among these patients. There were some who lived the life of the *junkie*, spending much of their time in poverty, suffering from infections, and going the rounds of doctors, chemists, and Piccadilly Circus, and occasionally being arrested and imprisoned. But there were others who were more like the *stable* addict described in the early twentieth-century literature on addiction. These people, although addicted, led reasonably ordinary lives; they were inconspicuous in dress and manner, kept themselves apart from other addicts, and suffered few problems. Others were somewhere between these two extremes.

Some years later, in 1976 and 1977, we set out to see what had happened to all these people. Were they, as might have been predicted, now dead, or at the best still chronically addicted, or had they ceased to be addicted? To answer these questions we hoped to recontact as many of them as possible. We were fortunate to find most of those who were still alive, spending many hours talking to them, and we continued to follow them, through official records, up to 1979. This book is about what happened to these people over the ten years from 1969 to 1979.

### HEROIN

Our initial focus was on heroin for most of these people saw themselves as heroin addicts. It was the drug they preferred, even if it was not the only one they used. Heroin is one of a group of drugs derived from and similar to opium. The opiates, as the group is called, include opium, its derivatives, such as morphine, codeine, and heroin, and synthetic opiates such as methadone. These drugs are used in medicine mainly for the relief of pain, sedation, and the reduction of anxiety. Of all the opiates heroin probably has the greatest analgesic action and its medical use in Britain is usually confined to the control of pain in major surgery and terminal illnesses. Other uses of the opiates are in the treatment of coughs and diarrhoea, and many fairly common medicines for the treatment of these conditions contain, or used to contain, small traces of opiates. In a neurophysiological sense opiates are depressants, acting on certain physiological functions such as respiration and cardiac activity. In high doses, the effects can so reduce such activity that insensibility and death may follow. But opiates can also produce gratifying and euphoric experiences: in certain conditions they can be pleasurable drugs to take. Thus in addition to their use in medicine they are in worldwide use as drugs of 'recreation'.

In Britain two main types of heroin are used by addicts. The first, which is becoming increasingly rare, is medicinal heroin. This is manufactured for medical use under the official pharmaceutical name of diamorphine. It is produced as small white pills of 5 mgs and 10 mgs. These pills can be taken by mouth, but are more commonly dissolved in water and injected subcutaneously (under the skin) or intramuscularly (into a muscle). An initial therapeutic dose would be in the region of 10 mgs. When used by addicts diamorphine is usually injected into a vein – intravenously – because this results in more rapid effects. The dose for seasoned users can be many times the initial therapeutic dose. Medicinal heroin is available to addicts on prescription, in circumstances that we discuss later. It is also sold on the black market.

The other type of heroin is smuggled into the country. This heroin has been illegally manufactured and is usually available as a brownish-white powder. Because the conditions of manufacture are not known, nor the extent to which it has been diluted ('cut') with other substances, its strength is variable. Most of the illegally imported heroin in Britain has been produced from opium poppies grown in Turkey, in the 'Golden Triangle' area of Burma, Laos, and Kampuchea, or, more recently, in Iran. The current price is in the region of £100 to £120 per gram.

Another drug commonly used by addicts is methadone, also known in Britain as Physeptone. Methadone is a synthetic drug, similar to the opiates but with a more protracted span. Whilst the effects of heroin will be wearing off within two or three hours, the effects of methadone may continue for twelve to twenty-four hours thus requiring less frequent injections. It was originally introduced as a treatment for heroin addiction in the US. Given orally in the form of a linctus or flavoured syrup it was intended to obviate the need to inject heroin, and to 'block' the effects of heroin, that is, if heroin was subsequently injected it would have no euphoric effect. It is in wide use in the US in Methadone Maintenance Programs where addicts are maintained on low doses. In Britain up until the mid-1970s, it was prescribed to addicts by doctors in Clinics more frequently in the form of ampoules to inject. However, in the last few years most of the methadone prescribed in Britain has been in linctus form.

When any opiates are regularly administered to or used by individuals certain changes in physiological activity take place. The most important changes are the development of physical dependence and of tolerance. Physical dependence is indicated by certain observable signs and reported symptoms that occur when administration of the drug is stopped. These symptoms are known as the abstinence or withdrawal syndrome. Characteristic symptoms of withdrawal are feeling unwell, experiencing distress, craving for the drug, restlessness and discomfort, yawning, tears, perspiration, a runny nose, gooseflesh, dilated pupils, increased blood pressure, vomiting, diarrhoea, raised temperature, and insomnia. These withdrawal symptoms are relieved by continued or renewed administration of the original opiate or any other opiate. If no opiate is taken symptoms reach a peak at 36 to 72 hours after the last dose. Most of the symptoms disappear within seven to ten days.

Tolerance refers to the diminishing effect of the same dose of the drug when it is repeatedly administered. Tolerance to the euphoric or pleasurable effects is gained relatively quickly, tolerance to the analgesic effects comes relatively slowly, and it is never acquired for the effects on intestinal activity (such as constipation). People who are tolerant to the effects of the drug are able to take much more of it without overdosing than are those with a lower level of tolerance. One person we interviewed in 1969 was prescribed 1140 mgs of heroin each day and had been observed taking this amount in a twenty-four hour period in hospital. In a non-tolerant individual a dose of 10 mgs has been known to lead to respiratory failure.

Does the long-term use of opiates cause any physical damage? This is difficult to determine because few addicts use only opiates, but it would seem that there is little evidence to show that pure opiates themselves cause any direct physical damage when used over long periods. Most of the physical damage is caused by the manner in which the drugs are administered and the accompanying life style. The opiates used by addicts in this country are generally administered by injection and the physical complications frequently found among addicts are septicaemia, abscesses, and hepatitis. These are the result of unsterile injection practices, the sharing of syringes, the injection of drugs such as the barbiturates which are not designed to be injected, and also infection caused by contaminants found in illicitly manufactured heroin. Vein thrombosis and atrophy of muscle are caused by repeated injection in one site. Heroin does cause suppression of testosterone secretion and a reduction or cessation of menstruation and may cause endocrinal damage. However, there is no evidence that opiates cause damage to the central nervous system or that addiction is associated with an increased incidence of psychosis or of intellectual deterioration. As a group addicts suffer a high degree of morbidity and mortality. Follow-up studies in Britain and the US have suggested a mortality rate of several times the expected rate of the general population. Overdose is a frequent cause of death and if not culminating in death may result in permanent brain damage. It appears that overdose occurs most often after the addict has been institutionalized and tolerance to the effects of opiates has been reduced. It is very often complicated by the use of barbiturates and alcohol. Despite the high incidence of morbidity and mortality it must be said that an addict on a maintenance regime, with a regular supply of drugs, who uses sterile injection techniques or methadone linctus and who takes good care of food and health, should, theoretically, live out a normal life span.

## THE RESEARCH

The research reported in this book shows what has happened to one group of heroin addicts over the period of ten years in which we followed them. Since we gathered material on the lives they led before addiction, we have, in many cases, detailed information over entire life spans. The addicts are now, in 1981, on average thirty-seven years old.

The people we talked to were a one-in-three representative sample of all the addicts who in 1969 were attending London Clinics as out-patients and who were receiving prescriptions for heroin. There were 128 people in the sample, which comprised approximately 11 per cent of all Clinic patients in England and Wales in that year. Fuller details of the selection of the sample will be found in the Appendix, and in a previous book, *Heroin and Behaviour* (Stimson 1973). Details of the personal follow-up in 1976/77, from which most of the material for this book is derived, as well as the various follow-ups between 1969 and 1979 using written records will also be found in the Appendix.

We found that after ten years approximately *38 per cent of the original sample had become abstinent from opiates* and were leading reasonably ordinary lives with no major problems with other drugs. Also, ten years on, there was a same-sized group (38 per cent) still attending Clinics and still receiving prescriptions, and a further 15 per cent who had died. The remaining 9 per cent were of equivocal or uncertain status.

There is no easy way to do research. Despite the recipes offered in the research textbooks, the actuality involves countless decisions about what sort of material to collect, how to collect it, how to use it, and how to write about it. Data do not just appear before the investigator, to be collected and then reported for the reader. Rather we think it more realistic to view data as actively generated, assembled, or produced. Research is a way of acting on the world, and because we can act on the world in so many different ways we can therefore produce different accounts and versions of it. Hence when we come to undertake a study of what happens to heroin addicts, the way we proceed becomes an exercise in method.

Some of the time we worked within the traditional survey research model. We conducted formal structured interviews in 1969 and collected material from official records in order to assess the quality of the interviews. In addition, to get some idea of what had been happening to our sample, we used official records over the years 1969 to 1979. Such records, though, are no substitute for personal contact, so we arranged to meet our people again in 1976/77. In the follow-up interview we asked them questions about their current lives and attempted to systematically plot with them an account of their activities during each year since our introduction. We have presented this material in the Appendix as the results of a *longitudinal study*, and make statements there about the status of the sample at different points in time.

One view of the classic survey research model forces us to consider materials as data only if they have been collected according to certain prescriptions supposed to reduce the risk of bias and error in data gathering. We found this view somewhat restrictive and a poor reflection of how researchers generate data and ideas. Formal structured interviews produce much of worth, but so, too, do extensive conversations with people, what the textbooks would refer to as 'in-depth' or loosely structured interviews. Thus, using a prepared 'hidden' agenda, we also collected a vast amount of conversational material in the follow-up. The interviews were mostly tape-recorded and people were encouraged to talk about various aspects of their lives. These interviews often lasted several hours and gave people the opportunity to reflect on the last ten, fifteen, or more years of their lives: on how they 'got into' using heroin in the first place, on the doctors they had consulted, on their friends, on changes over the years, on how they 'got off' heroin (if they did), and on how they currently saw their lives. We ended up with several hundred hours of taped interviews, 2000 pages of transcripts and field notes, the formal interviews we had made in 1969 and 1976/77, a variety of records from hospital case notes, criminal records, material from the Home Office Drugs Branch, and notes of conversations with doctors, addicts' friends, parents, and spouses.

This material has been used to examine the life histories of the addicts. Sociological interest in life history has been rather limited and it has been a relatively neglected technique in research. What can life history research offer? First, it can be used to emphasize the perspective of the people studied, allowing people to describe their own experiences and feelings. Second, life histories can be used to describe process: there are few techniques in social research suitable for portraying the dynamic of everyday life and the development of the person. Surveys provide static snapshots; participant observation freezes people in specific locations. Life history research should be able to provide a moving and changing perspective. Third, assembling research material in the form of life histories is a convenient device for linking the personal experiences of the people studied with the social and historical circumstances in which they lead their lives. For our sample it was a device that enabled us to locate the addicts in the stormy days of the 1960s when most of them first used heroin, and to bring them up to date through the various changes in the drug scene in the 1970s. It also enabled us to set their lives in the context of the institutional arrangements for the treatment and control of addiction. These people's lives were intimately bound with the policies that made up the 'British approach to heroin addiction'. As these policies changed, so did people's lives change.

We have used two life history techniques in this work. The first presents material as short *biographies*. We chose four people, not as typical examples of different types of addicts, but more to illustrate important experiences that have been shared by others. For example, Robert Jones was still an addict and was chosen to illustrate some of the problems encountered by people who continue addicted and some of the strategies that may be used to solve their day-to-day problems. Robert Jones, in his own words, tried to live a reasonably 'normal life'. Kevin Cummings also remained an addict and was in contact with the Clinic doctor who first saw him in 1968. His life had been linked to the changes in treatment policies and illustrates the problems that arise in the drug Clinics between doctors and patients where the relationship between the two seems to be marked by conflict. Gillian Morris was one of the people who died from an overdose, and we were able to reconstruct the events leading to her death. Susan Hughes had been off heroin for several years, and her history illustrates the way in which people can give up heroin and change their lives. So these biographical chapters represent individual life histories, sometimes spanning several years of a person's life and sometimes focusing on a period when significant events occurred.

In sociological research life history has been used more often in another way. Rather than focusing on individual biography the focus has been on the processes shared by people who engage in similar activities and who move in and out of various institutional arrangements. We refer here to those interactionist studies which were influenced by the Chicago school of sociology under Everett Hughes. These likened people's passage through life to a *career*, this occupational analogy being used to show the shape and passage of people's lives as they move through various 'occupations' and activities. The occupational analogy has been extended to occupations as bizarre as cheque forging, prostitution, homosexuality, nudism, and smoking marijuana, as well as the more mundane ambit of hospital patients and medical students. The career studies emphasize socialization, process, and change.

We, too, used our research material in this way. The material has been developed and presented as different stages in a hypothetical *career* of addiction, dealing with questions such as how people first started on heroin, the problems they faced living a life on heroin, problems between patients and doctors in drug Clinics, the ways in which people handled the hazards of addiction, the ways in which they stopped using heroin, and what life was currently like for them. These stages in the hypothetical career of the addict are our construction of what we see as relevant in describing what happens to heroin addicts and is our way of putting together a sensible account from the data collected.

As we have indicated, we do not think it is possible to present *longitudinal*, *career*, or *biographical* studies without paying special attention to the social and historical circumstances of people's lives. In the last twenty years there have been major changes in drug use in Britain and, more especially, in the policies that have been designed to treat and control addiction. The lives of the people we have studied are intimately bound up with these policies. Addicts come up against many whose job it is to implement policy and who thus influence their lives: chemists, police, court workers, social workers, medical workers. Foremost among these are doctors, nurses, social workers, and receptionists who work in the Clinics. The people we followed were all patients at Clinics in 1969, and many remained so. They had been required to attend Clinics frequently and were on the receiving end of the ways in which Clinic staff decided to treat addicts. Furthermore, as we show later, policies aimed at addiction have intentional elements of both medical treatment and social control.

Thus a major focus in the book is on the *policies* and *practices* concerning heroin addiction and drug use. We have brought together material on the formal written policies on addiction, expressed in legislation and the commentaries of the policy makers. We look at the way in which British policies on addiction emerged in the nineteenth century, how the shape of British policy crystallized in the 1920s, and at how these policies developed and changed in the 1960s and 1970s. The policies cannot be understood entirely through the formal legislation and we have to see how they are implemented in the day-to-day rounds of Clinic work. We have, therefore, recorded our observations on our visits to Clinics and our conversations with Clinic workers, and provide an ethnography of some aspects of the work of these centres.

## A NOTE ON THE TEXT

We have made extensive use of transcripts from tape-recorded interviews. Anyone who has worked with such material knows the problems of producing intelligible written quotations from conversational speech. Few people speak grammatically, they repeat themselves, pause, refer forward and backwards, and intersperse sentences with 'mmm', 'you know', 'right', and so on. When speech is recorded it loses the kinetic features – gestures that add sense to language. When we transform speech to writing we lose inflection and rhythm. Since we are mainly interested in the content of interviews, in details of what people have said about their lives, we have chosen to edit the transcripts to produce intelligible quotations, though this has not always been necessary. We have removed the majority of 'you knows' where they interrupted the flow of the quotation. We have also omitted sections that were unintelligible within the limits of the quote, irrelevant to the point being made, repetitious, or that were interruptions by the interviewer. These omissions are always indicated by three dots. We have often used colloquial expressions in the text where these were in general usage by addicts or doctors and where these expressions more adequately describe or give the flavour of the experiences reported. The first use of a colloquial expression is generally indicated by inverted commas.

In Chapters 4 to 10 we have disguised people for, particularly in the detailed biographical and ethnographic chapters, they might otherwise be identified. Some would not like this and we made the customary promise to them that they would not be identified. Addicts, ex-addicts, practising doctors, and Clinic workers have been given pseudonyms. Place names have been changed where necessary. But to retain historical authenticity we have, where possible, used the names of the doctors who prescribed heroin in the 1960s. Their names are in any case well known through newspaper articles and television programmes. We have also retained the names of important places and institutions such as Piccadilly Circus and Phoenix House, which if changed would alter the sense of some statements. Pseudonyms have not been used in our discussion of policies in Chapters 1, 2, 3, and 11.

### A NOTE ON DRUG DOSES

We have often been able to give precise details of the amount of drugs used by and prescribed for Clinic patients. We have tried to give these doses in milligrams (mgs). Addicts now usually refer to heroin doses in terms of pills, or colloquially as 'jacks'. In the 1960s addicts were accustomed to receiving larger prescriptions than at present and doses were often described in terms of 'grains'. One grain of medicinal heroin is six 10 mg pills. Methadone is often prescribed as a linctus to be taken orally. The dose is also expressed in milligrams. It is also prescribed as 5 mg pills and 10 mg ampoules: the pills can be dissolved in water for injection, the ampoules can be injected without further dilution. We are not in a position to know the doses of illegally manufactured heroin.

# Part One
# *Policy*

# 1

# *The emergence of a policy of drug control*

'Among the remedies which it has pleased Almighty God to give to man to relieve his sufferings, none is so universal and so efficacious as opium.'

(Thomas Sydenham 1680)

Opium was in extensive use as a medicine and recreational drug for many thousands of years before controls and limitations on its use were attempted. In the last 200 years opium and its various preparations and derivatives have passed from being socially commonplace and accepted substances to being drugs which are now outlawed and condemned, except when used under medical surveillance. The opiates are now covered by strict legislation, their excessive use a problem handled by the medical profession, and their worldwide use a matter of international policy and diplomacy. In Britain, competing and changing conceptions of the opiates have resulted in a social policy on addiction that is a mixture of penal and medical ideas on the nature of addiction and the appropriate social response to it.

Heroin, one of several drugs derived from opium, only came to prominence as a problem in Britain in the 1960s, but since the legislation and policies relevant to its contemporary control have developed from nineteenth-century attempts to control drugs, a history of heroin must begin with a history of these earlier legislative moves, and with the way in which the use of opiates emerged to consciousness as a social problem.

## THE OPIATES

Opium, the base drug from which opiates are derived, is a brown, sticky, cake-like substance and is obtained from the opium poppy. A few days after the flower petals fall, the unripe, green seed pod is slit by a sharp, multibladed knife. From the cuts there exudes a milky juice which coagulates within twenty-four hours. This is scraped off, cleaned, and shaped into blocks of crude opium.

The opium poppy was called *papaver somniferum* by Linnaeus, its name pointing to its property of inducing sleep. First found in the Eastern Mediterranean, its use was well known in ancient civilizations. Sumerian tablets inscribed 6000 years ago mention the use of opium in bringing sleep and an end to pain (Emboden 1972). Ancient Assyrian lists of herbs and medicaments which survive in cuneiform writings refer to the opium poppy plant and to opium, which was called 'lion fat'. Homer relates in the *Odyssey* that Helen offered Telemachus nepenthe, or opium, which indicates that it was known for its effect on the elevation of mood. *Opion* is Greek for poppy juice, the pharmacologically active milky sap from the pods of poppy seed. In the eighth century BC, Hesiod wrote of a town named Mekone, or 'town of the poppy', near Corinth. Hippocrates, the Greek physician, suggested poppy wine as a medicine. The opium poppy is mentioned by nearly all major Greek and Roman writers including Aristotle, Dioscorides, Theophrastus, Virgil, and Pliny the elder. The Roman physician Galen, who lived in the second century AD, was an enthusiastic advocate of its virtues and his works were authoritative for hundreds of years. After the decline of the Roman Empire, the use of opium spread, with Islam, through the Middle East. Avicenna, the Arab physician, died of opium intoxication in 1037 in Persia.

Opium was probably introduced into India as late as the eighth century AD, by Arab and Turkish traders. By the fifteenth century, during the rule of the Mogul Emperor Akbar the Great, poppies were widely cultivated in Bengal. In China, which in the popular mind has often been associated with opium smoking, the poppy was grown mainly as an ornamental plant until the seventeenth century. It was only when the smoking of tobacco spread from the New World to Europe, and later to China, that opium was first smoked by mixing it with tobacco. Later, small pipes were used for smoking it on its own. The exercise became a widespread social habit in China in the eighteenth and nineteenth centuries, and this country saw the first major national efforts to control its use. The sale and smoking of opium was first prohibited in 1729 and further attempts to forbid its importation and sale were made by various Ching dynasty emperors from 1796 onwards. However, despite efforts to control its usage, opium was extensively smuggled into China with the help of the British East India Company. Imports rose dramatically between 1790 and 1830. British merchants, anxious to find a product that could be traded for Chinese silk and tea, used opium for this purpose. The opium trade was deliberately fostered by the British, using opium specially grown in Bengal. Extensive misery from addiction, and a massive outflow of silver from China as payment for opium led to attempts by the Chinese authorities to suppress the trade (Compilation Group for the History of Modern China 1976). The French writer Huc, recording his travels in *The Chinese Empire* (1865), mentioned the 'idleness, debauchery, poverty' of the opium smokers, 'the ruin of their physical strength, the complete prostration of the intellectual and nerve facilities', and the 'disgusting apathy' in which they were sunk. British attempts to pursue the trade and preserve their business interests led to the First Opium War of 1839 to 1842, and resulted in the opium trade continuing for the rest of the nineteenth century.

For most of its history opium was used in its raw state, but this was gradually supplanted by a number of preparations and derivatives which were developed in Europe. Paracelsus, at Basle in the fifteenth century, combined opium with alcohol to produce *laudanum*, a tincture of opium. Le Mort, a professor of chemistry at Leyden at the beginning of the eighteenth century, combined opium with camphor to produce *paregoric*, which was used to control diarrhoea. Serturner, a German apothecary, isolated the alkaloid *morphine* from opium in 1803: he tested it on animals and on himself and named it after Morpheus, the god of dreams. Others, like Derosne and Seguin, worked on similar lines. There was a subsequent search for other pure material in opium that might be used in place of the crude product. Eventually two dozen alkaloids were discovered, including codeine and thebaine, and by the nineteenth century opium, its preparations, and various derivatives were in recognized and often common use. Heroin – diacetylmorphine or diamorphine – a semi-synthetic derivative of morphine, was first made from morphine at St Mary's Hospital, London, in 1874 but was not introduced into medical practice until 1898, by the Bayer Company of Germany. It was sold as a remedy for coughs.

## OPIATES IN NINETEENTH-CENTURY BRITAIN

Opium was one of the most widely used drugs in nineteenth-century Britain. It was rarely smoked, but was available in various forms, mainly to be taken by mouth, a practice sometimes referred to as 'opium eating'. It was sold in crude form, shaped into small pills or cut into square lumps, as laudanum (containing approximately 1 to 2 per cent opium), and as paregoric, and was in numerous patent medicines such as Godfrey's

Cordial, Dalby's Carminative, and Collis Brown's Chlorodyne. A price list from George Meggeson 'Druggist and Manufacturer of Medicated Lozenges, Refined Liquorice, Pate de Jujubes' included lozenges made with opium, opium and chalk, opium and fruit, morphia, morphia and ipecacuanha, poppy, and paregoric. It is perhaps hard for us to appreciate the extent to which opium products were used. They were everyday household items, available from any sort of shop without legal restriction, until 1868, and with only limited restriction thereafter. Opium was said to be cheaper than beer or gin, and indeed was sometimes mixed with alcoholic drinks. In the mid-nineteenth century laudanum sold for sixpence an ounce, and crude opium for one shilling and four pence, and were thus available to most workers. Thirty grains of laudanum, the average daily dose for a regular user, was a pennyworth. It was sold in grocers' shops, general stores, market stalls, and even village to village by itinerant vendors (Berridge 1979a). This widespread use can perhaps be understood when one recalls that opium was one of the very few available effective drugs for the treatment of pain and such common ailments as fevers, diarrhoea, influenza, colds, bronchitis, and so on. In its popularity it may be likened to present-day use of drugs such as aspirin. Thomas De Quincey, writing his *Confessions of an English Opium Eater* in 1821, noted the widespread availability of such products. He gave two examples:

> 'Three respectable London druggists, in widely remote quarters of London, from whom I happened lately to be purchasing small quantities of opium, assured me that the number of *amateur* opium eaters (as I may term them) was, at this time, immense; and that the difficulty of distinguishing these persons to whom habit has rendered opium necessary, from such as were purchasing it with a view to suicide, occasioned them daily trouble and disputes. This evidence respected London only. But, (which will probably surprise the reader more), some years ago, on passing through Manchester, I was informed by several cotton manufacturers that their work-people were rapidly getting into the practice of opium eating; so much so, that on a Saturday afternoon the counters of the druggists were strewed with pills of one, two or three grains in preparation for the known demand of the evening. The immediate occasion of this practice was the lowness of wages, which at this time would not allow them to indulge in spirits; and wages rising, it may be thought that this practice will cease; but, as I do not readily believe that any man, having once tasted the divine luxuries of opium, will afterwards descend to the gross and mortal enjoyment of alcohol, I take it for granted "that those who eat now, who never ate before; and those who always ate, now eat the more".'
>
> (De Quincey 1978 edn: 31–2)

Most of the opium was imported (though it was grown successfully in some parts of Britain) and estimates of consumption can be made from trade statistics on import and export kept from the 1820s onwards. In 1827 the actual home consumption amounted to 17,000 pounds which, converted into today's metric measure, amounts to nearly 600 mgs of opium per person per annum. In 1859 home consumption was 61,000 pounds, or 1410 mgs per person (Berridge 1979b). Opium products were used by all classes and in all geographical areas. For example, the Fenlands, in the counties of Lincolnshire, Cambridgeshire, Huntingdonshire, and Norfolk, were especially well known for opiate use in the first seventy years of the nineteenth century. Opiates were used mainly by agricultural labourers in isolated hamlets, and it was said that use was associated with the poverty and ill-health of the low-lying damp fens (Berridge 1977). Opiates were also in common use in industrial towns in Lancashire and in Sheffield, Birmingham, and Nottingham. A druggist in the town of Thorpe told Coleridge that he sold a gallon of laudanum and 2 or 3 pounds of opium on market-day. Opium and its products were also used by many public and literary figures. De Quincey mentioned Wilberforce, who fought for the abolition of slavery; Coleridge; the diplomat Henry Addington; and Isaac Milner, Dean of Carlisle and President of Queens' College, Cambridge. It was also used by Clive of India, Poe, Crabbe, and Rossetti.

Opium and its preparations were used in many ways as they were broad palliatives for all sorts of ailments and anxieties. They were specifically used to dull pain (there were few alternative pain killers), to reduce coughing, to control diarrhoea, and to induce sleep. They were given to children in 'infant calmers', 'soothing syrups', and 'infant preservatives'. In today's terms we would perhaps describe this as self-medication, but our present categories clumsily describe past practice. It was medication that often went beyond specific treatment to include palliation for general misery and lowness of spirits, much as alcohol was used. Opium was also certainly used by some as a recreational drug, as an intoxicant, or as an aid to the imagination (Hayter 1968), producing for De Quincey a 'sensual pleasure' and 'those trances, or profoundest reveries, which are the crown and consummation of what opium can do for human nature' (De Quincey 1978: 30; 81–2).

How was the use of opium viewed? In the first half of the nineteenth century its temperate use hardly occasioned comment, indeed its use as a medicament was indispensable. Discussion of possible harmful effects was rare, and debate was mainly centred around its therapeutic properties. Doctors and apothecaries were divided in their view as to the effects and, therefore, the most appropriate therapeutic use of opium. Some believed it to be primarily a sedative, while others saw it as a substance with stimulant properties. The question of potential hazards was little discussed though habituation, as we can read in De Quincey, was known.

Heavy use by the working class was mostly ignored, and use by the rich was seen as self-indulgence, a minor vice, or bad habit. Hayter, discussing the Romantic writers, said that the habit 'was not considered an exotic and secret vice, but the excess of normal indulgence, as drunkeness was' (Hayter 1968: 34), and Berridge (1979a), in one of many articles on nineteenth-century opium use, commented that the reaction against opium use was so weak as to be barely even moral condemnation. Moral tolerance might be a more apt description. For most Victorians opium-taking was a private matter and the habit was equated with personal indulgence. It was not seen as an illness requiring treatment, for this perception of opium habituation – opium use as an addiction – only properly emerged in the last quarter of the nineteenth century. In fact, there were some who thought that opium's beneficial properties were such that its side-effects should be kept from public knowledge. De Quincey, for example, quoted Awister, an eighteenth-century apothecary at Greenwich Hospital, who published his 'Essay on the Effects of Opium' in 1763. Awister thought that 'there are many properties in it, if universally known, that would habituate the use, and make it more in request with us than the Turks themselves', the result of which Awister considered 'must prove a general misfortune' (De Quincey 1978 edn: 32).

It took a legal wrangling to spur some doctors into an examination of their views and knowledge of opiate use. In 1828 the Earl of Mar died, two years after taking out an insurance on his life (Berridge 1979a). The insurance company refused to pay his heirs when it came to light that the Earl was an habitual opium user. It was said that he took as much as forty-nine grains (2940 mgs) of solid opium each day, and an ounce of laudanum. The insurance company argued that this habit had shortened his life. They lost the case on the ground that they had not shown sufficient care in their preliminary inquiries into his habits (Harrison 1854). There was some medical speculation about the case, and the question of whether opium could shorten life was raised. Professor Christison, professor of medical jurisprudence at Edinburgh, examined a number of cases of opium users in 1832 and concluded that many lived to a ripe old age. A Soho Square surgeon, writing in 1831–32 in the *Lancet*, came to the opposite conclusion: he maintained that opiate use shortened life in a similar way to excessive intake of alcohol. Others pointed out in the ensuing debate that there were stable opium eaters who adhered to a low consumption of the drug and who were able to lead normal lives. The medical debate focused on the possible effects and consequences of opium eating; the notion of opium habituation as a disease which required treatment had not yet emerged.

More information on the use and effects of opium came unexpectedly from a number of social inquiries into the lives of the industrial working class. Opium appeared to play a hitherto unsuspected part in their lives. The evidence concerning opium products was piecemeal, being referred to in the reports of the Committee and Commissions on Drunkeness in 1834, on Health in Towns in 1840, on Sanitary Conditions of the Labouring Population in 1842, on Children's Employment, and the Commission on the State of Large Towns in 1844. Edwin Chadwick, a nineteenth-century reformer, alleged that opium eating was a habit of large sections of the working population, though little evidence emerged of their seeing opium as a luxury or indulgence, rather than self-medication. For example, Mr Robertson, who gave evidence to the Factories Inquiries Commission, 1834, said 'Opium in any form is rarely (if ever) used by operatives as an article of luxury. I have been at pains to ascertain this fact' (Berridge 1978a). Most of the evidence indicated varied reasons for its use: there was widespread administration of proprietary preparations to children, there was self-medication to combat pain, sleeplessness, and stomach illnesses, and there was continued use as a general palliative. Evidence on mortality due to opium poisoning was given by the Registrar General. Deaths from opium, accidental and intentional, were recorded in the region of five per million in the 1840s, opium poisoning being the most common form of poisoning resulting in death. There were considerably higher rates for children than for adults, reflecting the widespread use of opium preparations as infant calmers. Some specifically local data show similar evidence. A medical officer at the London Hospital, in the East End of London, compiled figures on poisoning cases for the years 1846–56. He found that 228 people had been treated in his hospital and of these, 65 were poisoned from overdoses of laudanum (Berridge 1979b).

## DRUG CONTROL AND PROFESSIONAL MONOPOLY

It was the poisoning issue that was argued publicly as the case for drug regulation. There had been calls for controls over poisons in the first part of the nineteenth century and a Poisons Bill was presented to parliament as early as 1819. It aimed to establish regulations 'for the sale of poisonous drugs, and for better preventing the mischiefs arising from the inattention of persons vending the same', but failed to become law, being opposed by a lobby of chemists and druggists who feared that it would restrict their sales. Out of the discussions surrounding the Bill arose several ideas about controls over poisons, for example, the suggestion that arsenic and oxalic acid should only be sold with a 'poison' label, and that no-one should be allowed to sell poisons unless aware of the dangers of selling them to 'improper' or 'ignorant' persons.

By the middle of the nineteenth century, those engaged in selling drugs had begun to organize as professional bodies. The Pharmaceutical Society of Great Britain was established in 1841 and sought to bring together interests of chemists, druggists, and apothecaries. There were calls for professional standards of training, for the right to practise to be restricted to those who were especially licensed, and for controls of the sales of drugs and poisons. It was argued that only suitably qualified persons, in other words pharmacists, should be able to sell poisons. Early lobbying by the Society, which still represented only a small proportion of chemists and druggists, led to the first Act in this country to regulate the sale of a drug – the Arsenic Act of 1851. This Act required that sales of arsenic be properly recorded and witnessed, and that the buyer be known or personally introduced to the seller.

The issue was argued by pharmacists, doctors, and others as one of public safety, but the pressure to control drugs and poisons should, perhaps, more appropriately be seen in the context of emerging professionalization, for the issue centred on who should be allowed to *sell* drugs. The chemists and druggists were in competition with all sorts of other people, such as shopkeepers, market-stall holders, and itinerant vendors, for up to this time there were no restrictions on the sale of drugs and poisons. Any control in favour of the chemists and druggists would ensure them a lucrative commercial monopoly. Chemists and druggists were also in competition with doctors who often dispensed their own drugs. Both the Pharmaceutical Society and the General Medical Council hoped to be able to control the sales of drugs and poisons and wished to limit the sales of such drugs in general shops.

The passing of the 1851 Arsenic Act was followed by a period of lobbying in which the Pharmaceutical Society pressed for the sales of other drugs and poisons to be restricted. These attempts succeeded in the passing of the 1868 Pharmacy Act, which limited sales of certain drugs to pharmacists and ended sales in grocers, general stores, and other shops. Fifteen drugs were covered by the Act and these were put into two categories. Ten were covered by Part 1 of the poisons schedule which required that they could only be sold by a pharmacist to a person who was known or who had been properly introduced, and that the buyer sign the poisons register. Morphine and several other poisons, including potassium cyanide, prussic acid, and ergot, came within Part 1, but opium and its preparations came within the less restrictive Part 2 of the schedule to the Act which, although limiting sales to pharmacists, only required sale in a properly labelled container. It is said that opium was placed in this less restrictive category after representations from chemists in Cambridge, Norfolk, and Lincolnshire, who feared the commercial effect of restriction on sales. Patent medicines, such as paregoric and the children's soothing syrups, continued on sale without restriction in general shops and were specifically excluded from controls under Section 16 of the Act. The 1868 Act thus ensured pharmacists a monopoly over the sale of certain drugs and poisons but without those controls being so restrictive as to limit trade.

In the 1890s some of the opium-based patent medicines were brought within Part 2 of the Act as a result of court cases, particularly concerning Collis Brown's Chlorodyne. The subsequent 1908 Poisons and Pharmacy Act placed further restrictions on the sale of opiates, and all preparations containing more than 1 per cent of morphine were now placed in Part 1 of the poisons schedule. But it was still easy to purchase such drugs. Anyone wishing to buy opium, its preparations, and cocaine had only to be known by the pharmacist or be personally introduced, and to sign the poisons register. There were no restrictions on the possession of drugs and no need for a prescription. Crowley (1922b), for example, describing the period just prior to the First World War, told how he bought heroin and cocaine simply by signing the poisons register and paying sixteen shillings for 10 grams of cocaine and twenty shillings for a similar quantity of heroin.

To sum up, the poisons legislation was the first effort to control drugs in Britain. It was prompted by pharmacists' concerns to develop a monopoly in the sale and supply of drugs. The controls introduced ensured this monopoly but, at least initially, were not so restrictive as to severely limit pharmacists' sales. Potential harm from drugs and poisons was the overt issue, but the benefit to pharmacists was a commercial one.

## OPIATE USE AS A MEDICAL PROBLEM

There arose from the 1870s onwards a new medical interest in the effects of the opiates. For much of the century the excessive use of opiates had not been viewed as a medical concern, but in the last quarter of the century there were attempts to define the habitual use of opiates as a disease and therefore a subject within the scope of the medical profession. This emergent medical conception of addiction was closely tied to the development of the hypodermic needle and its use for administering morphine. The technique, first devised by Rynd and Wood in the mid-1850s and later developed by Hunter, led to a spread in the medical use of hypodermic morphine. Early reticence in its use was followed by wide adoption and concomitant warnings of possible abuse. The morphine 'epidemic' of the 1870s and after was undoubtedly exaggerated in the medical press of the period, but hypodermic morphine, unlike opium, had largely been a medically administered drug, and even self-administering patients had generally first been introduced to it by the medical profession. Any problems in its use were thus quite closely linked with the medical profession. There were also doctors who were said to be using morphine themselves.

What emerged from the debate about the growing problem of 'morphinomania' was a construction of habitual drug use as a disease. This new view was influenced by both the developing medical ideas about organic disease and by the Temperance movement. 'Morphinism' was linked to addiction to alcohol and to mental illness through the concept of 'inebriety'. 'Inebriety' was seen as a disease of the nervous system, similar to insanity, and characterized by an overpowering craving for the narcotic, be it alcohol or opium. The discussions of those connected with the Society for the Study of Inebriety, founded in 1884, showed a clear moral element to this medical formulation of addiction. Habitual opiate use was seen as a disease of the will, and thus a failure to achieve a cure was not a failure of medicine, but a failure of self-control (Berridge 1979a). Contemporary thinking about the causes of addiction was linked to ideas as to how it should be treated. Those who came down more heavily on the side of addiction as a moral failing tended to recommend harsher and more abrupt methods of treatment than those who put more emphasis on disease, who saw the desired treatment as gradual withdrawal or maintenance on low dosages of opiates. There was also a class basis to the new medical formulation of the nature of addiction: doctors were mainly discussing addiction among their colleagues or their peers in the middle class.

However, it was the problem of working-class self-medication, and not the problem of habituation that was the issue when the medical profession called for greater controls over opiates. The position of the medical profession, expanding in size and moving out from treating a relatively affluent clientele, was threatened by working-class drug use, since drugs could be bought from pharmacists without prescription. Even when a doctor's prescription was obtained it could be repeated without limit as the prescription remained the personal property of the patient. Doctors would have appreciated much stricter regulations over opiates than was provided in the 1868 Pharmacy Act. They were aiming at a monopoly on prescribing, and the Act did little to further this end. Self-medication was to become a frequent topic of discussion in medical journals in the last part of the nineteenth century. The British Medical Association campaigned against self-medication and discussed ways of making some drugs available only on prescription (Berridge 1978b). The introduction of limits to the supply of drugs through a restriction to prescriptions would obviously increase the monopoly of doctors over drug treatment. Many doctors thus favoured some control.

### OPIATE USE AS A SOCIAL PROBLEM

Doctors were not entirely successful in defining addiction as a disease as there were others who, from the turn of the nineteenth century, called for controls over opiate use on the grounds that it was a social problem. No longer just a matter of personal self-indulgence, the recreational use of opium was coming to be seen as a vice. Its consumption by Chinese in London's East End and the recreational use of cocaine, opium, and heroin in artistic, literary, and theatrical circles in London's West End, although numerically small, received occasional graphic description in the popular press. Recreational use of opiates was seen as an exotic, yet evil, vice which needed to be controlled. At the same time, there was an American-inspired international narcotics control movement, which was promoted as a drive against opiate use among Chinese workers in North America and opium use in China. There was a number of meetings, beginning in Shanghai in 1909, that Britain, under pressure from the US, attended. These meetings culminated in the First Opium Convention in The Hague in 1912 to which Britain was one of the signatories. Under this Convention, signatory nations agreed to examine the world's need for opium derivatives, to reduce production where desirable, and to adopt a system of controls over opium, morphine, and cocaine. It was agreed that the use of such drugs should be confined to legitimate medical purposes. These suggestions were in many ways welcomed by the British medical profession for, if acted upon, they would severely limit self-medication, and would ensure that such drugs were only available on prescription and so increase the monopoly position of doctors. Between 1912 and 1914 representatives of different government ministries in Britain, along with representatives of the medical and pharmaceutical professions, met to discuss the shape of the proposed narcotics legislation. The debate had now moved from the pharmacists' earlier concerns about who should be allowed to sell opiates, and from the problem of addiction as a disease, to the question of the circumstances in which people should be allowed to *possess* drugs. It was proposed that control might be achieved within some form of professional self-regulation, but discussions were interrupted by the outbreak of war in 1914.

By 1914 there were two views on opiate use in Britain, one which saw addiction as a medical problem and viewed control as being a matter for the medical profession, and the other which saw addiction as a vice to be controlled penally. During the war there was a shift in the direction of the latter view, where drug use and addiction were predominantly seen as social problems in need of prohibition. Two immediate issues were brought into the public debate. First, there was evidence of smuggling opium and morphine to China and the US on British ships, which was a cause of international embarrassment. Second there was the issue of cocaine and army efficiency, for it was rumoured that cocaine was being used by soldiers on leave (Spear 1969). Early in 1916 an order prohibited the gift or sale of cocaine to soldiers except on prescription, but there was no restriction on sale or possession by civilians and cocaine sellers could easily acquire it and sell it (illegally) to soldiers. The Home Office decided that there was need for more widespread measures and in July 1916 introduced controls under Defence of the Realm Regulation 40B (DORA 40B). It now became an offence for anyone except members of the medical, pharmaceutical, and veterinary professions to possess cocaine and it could only be supplied on prescription. The passage of DORA 40B was greatly influenced by Sir Malcolm Delevingne, Assistant Under-Secretary at the Home Office, who was anxious to press for controls over cocaine and opiates as required by The Hague Convention. The issue of drug use was now being successfully argued as one of smuggling and public order, a policing issue, and hence under the remit of the Home Office.

This war-time legislation was a major step in drug control in Britain. What had begun before the war as discussion about controlling drugs along the lines of professional self-regulation had now been legislated with a strong emphasis on prohibition. This was the first time that a doctor's prescription was required, by law, for the purchase of specified drugs. It was the first intervention by the Home Office into an area that had hitherto seemed to be successfully emerging as a medical prerogative. The Home Office was now to play a leading part in forming a policy of drug control.

## THE 1920 AND 1923 DANGEROUS DRUGS ACTS

The penal and criminal approach of DORA 40B influenced subsequent legislation. The regulation remained in effect until the Versailles Peace Treaty, and signatories of the Treaty were required to enact national controls on the availability of drugs in accordance with the pre-war Hague Convention. The British legislation passed in the Dangerous Drugs Act of 1920 is best seen as an extension of the philosophy of penalty and prohibition in DORA 40B. The Act covered opium, its derivatives (including morphine and heroin), and cocaine. It forbade the import of raw opium, morphine, and cocaine, and it authorized the Home Secretary to regulate the manufacture, sale, distribution, and possession of these substances. It was illegal to possess these drugs unless they had been supplied or prescribed by a doctor. A prescription could be dispensed up to three times only. Detailed records were to be kept of physicians' and chemists' supplies. The 1923 Dangerous Drugs Act imposed heavier penalties and gave the police increased powers of search.

The Home Office, then, had successfully claimed the problem as a criminal and policing one. The 1920 and 1923 Acts aimed at the prohibition of supplies to addicts, and were directed at doctors as well as drug users. The ideas behind the Acts were rooted in a criminal rather than medical model of addiction, and the 'vice' conception of drug use dominated the newspaper reports of the period, with stories of 'pedlars' and 'dope fiends'. There were rumours that blacklists of doctors and addicts would be circulated to chemists by the police, there was Home Office disapproval of those doctors who continued to write prescriptions for addicts, and a move to confirm that abrupt withdrawal, rather than maintenance or slow withdrawal, was appropriate (Departmental Committee on Morphine and Heroin Addiction 1926). It would seem that the Home Office was looking closely at the American experience where court decisions following the 1914 Harrison Act determined that prescription of opiates to addicts was not legitimate medical treatment.

Medical interests were largely unconsulted during the drafting of the legislation, but although the Home Office for the moment held the arena, some members of the medical profession strongly reacted against this penal policy, which was seen as a threat both to the autonomy of the medical profession and to the medical view of addiction. The doctors had gained by the legislation because at long last it provided them with a monopoly on prescribing, but there was a feeling that the legislation was too stringent and that it encroached on areas of medical expertise. For example, one interpretation of the 1920 Dangerous Drugs Act was that prescription of opiates to addicts was not part of medical treatment. From a medical point of view, such an interpretation was an unwarranted incursion of law into medical practice, for the medical model of addiction which had begun to emerge in the latter part of the nineteenth century saw the treatment of addiction as very much part of medical work. The issue of prescription to addicts was to be crucial for subsequent British policy.

There was, though, recognition in the Home Office that a restrictive policy could only work with the co-operation of the medical profession. The 1920 Dangerous Drugs Act allowed doctors to prescribe dangerous drugs for medical treatment, but the Home Office had been faced with a number of cases in which it was not certain whether there had been an infringement of the Act, a decision that hinged on the definition of 'medical treatment'. Medical practitioners were allowed to prescribe morphine, cocaine, and heroin, but it was unclear whether the prescription of such drugs to addicts could be regarded as 'necessary to the practice' of the medical profession. In other words, the Act had restricted the legal supply of these drugs to medical practitioners in the course of their work; but could supply to addicts be construed as medical work?

The determination of this question was crucial. If it was agreed that supply to addicts was not part of medical treatment then addiction would become a mainly criminal matter. If the reverse was the case then doctors would have a continuing part to play in handling the problems of addiction.

There were many problems for Home Office officials in the first years of the Act. They knew of cases where doctors, by their own admission, had ordered or supplied dangerous drugs not as part of medical treatment but simply to enable addicted persons 'to satisfy their craving'; there were other cases where there was no such admission, but the Home Office doubted whether supply of the drug could be regarded as *bona fide* medical treatment; some doctors had supplied prescriptions for drugs in unusually large quantities or over long periods, sometimes by post, to persons whom they saw only after long intervals, and some had supplied large quantities to persons previously unknown to them. The officials at the Home Office thought that in such cases there might have been an infringement of the Act. The crucial issue that the Home Office wished to determine was whether it was medically necessary, in any circumstances, for morphine or heroin to be supplied continuously, for long periods, to people who were not suffering from any organic disease.

## THE ROLLESTON COMMITTEE

This question could not be answered without recourse to medical opinion and in 1924 the Home Office persuaded the Ministry of Health to set up a committee:

> 'to consider and advise as to the circumstances, if any, in which the supply of morphine and heroin (including preparations containing morphine and heroin) to persons suffering from addiction to those drugs may be regarded as medically advisable, and as to the precautions which it is desirable that medical practitioners administering or prescribing morphine or heroin should adopt for the avoidance of abuse.'
>
> (Departmental Committee on Morphine and Heroin Addiction 1926: 2)

Sir Humphrey Rolleston, President of the Royal College of Physicians, chaired this Departmental Committee on Morphine and Heroin Addiction. The Rolleston Committee, as it has been known, was composed of members of medical professions. The fact that this Committee was set up by the Ministry of Health, albeit on the urging of the Home Office, and that it was a medical committee reflected a loosening of the 'vice and social problem' model of addiction pursued by the Home Office.

The Rolleston Committee's report was published on 21 January 1926 and its deliberations were to set the shape of British policy. It firmly defined addiction as a disease and as a problem for medical treatment. It heard evidence and confirmed that:

> 'there was general agreement that in most well-established cases the condition must be regarded as a manifestation of disease and not as a mere form of vicious indulgence. In other words, the drug is taken in such cases not for the purpose of obtaining positive pleasure, but in order to relieve a morbid and overpowering craving. The actual need for the drug in extreme cases is in fact so great that, if it be not administered, great physical distress, culminating in actual collapse and even death, may result, unless special precautions are taken such as can only be carried out under close medical supervision, and with careful nursing.'
> (Departmental Committee on Morphine and Heroin Addiction 1926: 11)

The Committee heard evidence that addiction was rare and had recently diminished. This it attributed to the working of the 1920 Dangerous Drugs Act which made it illegal to obtain such drugs except from doctors. This was no doubt true. Cocaine, for example, was less commonly used, even though occasional incidents created considerable public interest, as in the Billie Carleton case, when the twenty-two-year-old actress died after the Victory Ball, allegedly as a result of a cocaine overdose (Spear 1969). The Committee recognized that illegal sources of supply existed but predicted that such cases would become less frequent. It found that the majority of addicts had not started recreationally, but had been introduced to the drug in the course of medical treatment, or had occupations that gave special access to supplies. It discussed methods of treating addicts and reported that there were certain ones for whom, under the conditions of ordinary medical practice, the drugs could not be entirely withdrawn:

> 'In one class such attempted complete withdrawal produced severe distress or even risk of life; in the other, experience showed that a certain minimum dose of the drug was necessary to enable the patients to lead useful and relatively normal lives, and that if deprived of this non-progressive dose, they became incapable of work.'
> (Departmental Committee on Morphine and Heroin Addiction 1926: 7)

A third class of addict to whom drugs might be administered were those undergoing treatment for addiction by gradual withdrawal. The Committee did not consider that prescription to persons for the relief of pain was a question for its report, and said that no problem would arise unless the original condition was cured and the addiction continued. In that situation the patient would be dealt with as in those three classes outlined.

The Committee concluded that the prescription of heroin and morphine to certain addicts could be regarded as 'legitimate medical treatment' under certain conditions and for certain classes of patients, namely:

> '(a) Those who are undergoing treatment for the cure of addiction by the gradual withdrawal method;
> (b) Persons for whom, after every effort has been made for the cure of addiction, the drug cannot be completely withdrawn either because:
> (i) Complete withdrawal produces serious symptoms which cannot be satisfactorily treated under the ordinary conditions of private practice; or
> (ii) The patient, while capable of leading a useful and fairly normal life so long as he takes a certain non-progressive quantity, usually small, of the drug of addiction, ceases to be able to do so when the regular allowance is withdrawn.'

The report was an affirmation of the disease model of addiction: addicts were seen as the victims of morbid and overpowering craving, and addiction as a disease which required medical attention. The report was also an affirmation of the ideal of professional self-regulation, for it presented a case for a relatively autonomous professional body charged with policing itself. The medical profession was to take on the task of dealing with aberrant or addicted doctors; the issue was 'essentially medical' the Committee wrote, for the determination of such a case required medical expertise. It was therefore best dealt with by a special medical tribunal that would 'dispense with the necessity for police action' (Departmental Committee on Morphine and Heroin Addiction 1926: 24). against the doctor. The Committee's recommendations were accepted by the Home Office, and it was agreed that any doctor was allowed, in certain circumstances, to prescribe heroin, morphine, and other dangerous drugs to addicted patients, Maintenance doses were allowed. This agreement formed the basis of what was to become known as the British 'system' for dealing with drug addiction.

Drug policy remained in the context of penal legislation; for example, unauthorized possession – possession of dangerous drugs without a prescription – was still the subject of the criminal law. The medical profession had staked out a claim to be able to define the nature of addiction and to treat it, but policy and administration were to remain a matter for the Home Office. The Ministry of Health, established in 1919, was not to wrest dominance in this matter from the Home Office. Indeed, although for many purposes addiction was now primarily a medical matter, the different standpoints in the debate – between the views of addiction as a medical or a criminal matter, and between the disease and vice concepts of addiction – have, since the 1920s, constantly re-emerged in discussions and formulations on opiate addiction and drug control in Britain.

# 2

## *The British 'system' to 1964*

The Rolleston Committee's resolution of the ambiguities of the 1920 Dangerous Drugs Act was incorporated in the Dangerous Drugs Regulations of 1926 and established British policy for the next forty years. During that period Britain came to be described as having a distinctive 'system' for handling the problem of addiction, distinctive in that medical practitioners were allowed to prescribe heroin in the course of their work, but, more importantly, they were allowed to prescribe dangerous drugs to addicts in the treatment of addiction. Addiction had been successfully defined as a disease and hence within the remit of medical work. Subsequent commentaries on the 'system' usually favourably compared Britain with other countries, especially the US and Canada. British policy seemed benign, humane, and appropriate, whereas other countries were criticized for having 'criminalized' addiction. Some commentators, for example Edwin Schur writing in *Narcotic Addiction in Britain and America* (1963), claimed that Britain had no major drug addiction problem precisely because addiction was treated as a medical problem: addicts could get medical help, and they could get legitimate supplies of the drugs to which they were addicted. Hence there was no need for addicts to meet each other, and no 'subculture' of addiction. This seemed a reasonable analysis at the time: Britain did have a medically orientated approach, and had no problem with drugs on the scale experienced in North America.

In retrospect, though, an equally attractive interpretation might be that the British 'system' worked precisely *because* there was no major endemic drug use. Drug use did not become a major problem in Britain until the late 1950s and then, as we shall see later, the British 'system' began to break down.

THE PERIOD UP TO THE END OF THE SECOND WORLD WAR

Around the time of the passing of the Dangerous Drugs Act in 1920 there was a minor growth of recreational drug use, a drug 'scene' centred in London's artistic and theatrical circles. Accounts of this period can be found in Crowley's *Diary of a Drug Fiend* (1922a). Later in the 1920s such indigenous recreational use of opiates and cocaine became rare. Inasmuch as we can take prosecution rates for illegal possession as some, albeit crude, reflection of the scale of illegal use, we see that in 1921, the first full operative year of the Act, there were 184 concerning opium (*see Table 2(1)*). Apart from a few drug users in artistic circles, opium use was confined almost exclusively to the Chinese community and most of the offences occurred in towns with a Chinese population. From 1921 the number of offences rapidly declined: there were never more than 50 a year between 1924 and 1940, with a low of 6 in 1938. Prosecutions for cocaine numbered 58 in 1921, but these fell to 2 by 1927. In 1929 the government was able to inform the League of Nations in the report on *Opium and other Dangerous Drugs* that 'drug addiction is not prevalent in Great Britain' (Spear 1969: 249). Cannabis was not brought under international control until 1925, and legislation was not effective in Britain until 1929, but cannabis, too, attracted little attention – 3 prosecutions in 1929, 1 in 1930, a maximum of 18 in 1938. The government reported to the League of Nations

Table 2(1) *UK prosecutions and convictions for drug offences, 1921–68*

| | *Dangerous Drugs Acts* | | | *Drugs (Prevention of Misuse) Act 1964* |
|---|---|---|---|---|
| *year* | *opium* | *cannabis* | *manufactured drugs (including cocaine)* | |
| 1921 | 184 | not controlled | 67 | not applicable in these years |
| 1922 | 94 | | 110 | |
| 1923 | 167 | | 128 | |
| 1924 | 48 | | 50 | |
| 1925 | 35 | | 33 | |
| 1926 | 50 | | 45 | |
| 1927 | 27 | | 33 | |
| 1928 | 41 | | 21 | |
| 1929 | 39 | 3 | 31 | |
| 1930 | 16 | 1 | 48 | |
| 1931 | 26 | 3 | 40 | |
| 1932 | 37 | 6 | 43 | |
| 1933 | 17 | 6 | 32 | |
| 1934 | 39 | 14 | 33 | |

Table 2(1) *UK prosecutions and convictions for drug offences, 1921–68* contd

| | *Dangerous Drugs Acts* | | | *Drugs (Prevention of Misuse) Act 1964* |
|---|---|---|---|---|
| *year* | *opium* | *cannabis* | *manufactured drugs (including cocaine)* | |
| 1935 | 13 | 15 | 33 | not applicable in these years |
| 1936 | 17 | 8 | 35 | |
| 1937 | 9 | 3 | 27 | |
| 1938 | 6 | 18 | 35 | |
| 1939 | 13 | 1 | 36 | |
| 1940 | 14 | 3 | 37 | |
| 1941 | 201 | – | 25 | |
| 1942 | 199 | – | 27 | |
| 1943 | 147 | 2 | 40 | |
| 1944 | 256 | 6 | 32 | |
| 1945 | 206 | 4 | 20 | |
| 1946 | 65 | 11 | 27 | |
| 1947 | 76 | 46 | 65 | |
| 1948 | 78 | 51 | 48 | |
| 1949 | 52 | 60 | 56 | |
| 1950 | 41 | 86 | 42 | |
| 1951 | 64 | 132 | 47 | |
| 1952 | 62 | 98 | 48 | |
| 1953 | 47 | 88 | 44 | |
| 1954 | 28 | 144 | 47 | |
| 1955 | 17 | 115 | 37 | |
| 1956 | 12 | 103 | 37 | |
| 1957 | 9 | 51 | 30 | |
| 1958 | 8 | 99 | 41 | |
| 1959 | 18 | 185 | 26 | |
| 1960 | 15 | 235 | 28 | |
| 1961 | 15 | 288 | 61 | |
| 1962 | 16 | 588 | 71 | |
| 1963 | 20 | 663 | 63 | |
| 1964 | 14 | 544 | 101 | |
| 1965 | 13 | 626 | 128 | 958* |
| 1966 | 36 | 1119 | 242 | 1216 |
| 1967 | 58 | 2393 | 573 | 2486 |
| 1968 | 73 | 3071 | 1099 | 2957 |

*Note:* From 1921 to 1953 figures relate to prosecutions; from 1954 they relate to convictions. *31 October 1964 to 31 December 1965.
*Sources:* Figures derived from Spear (1969) and Johnson (1975).

in 1932 that 'the illicit use of and traffic in the drug appears to be confined to Arab and Indian seamen', and in 1935 that 'such cases of illicit import of drugs as were discovered were individual attempts on the part of seamen, mainly orientals, to bring in small quantities for the use of compatriots in the United Kingdom' (Spear 1969: 249).

So who were the drug users of the period? The Home Office was able, since the passing of the 1920 Act, to monitor the prescription of opiates by police inspection of chemist records, but a Home Office monitoring system does not appear to have been systematically implemented until a Home Office Drugs Branch was established in 1934, and it is only from 1935 that official statistics on the number of 'known' addicts are available. Addicts became known to the Home Office mainly through routine police inspection of pharmacists' records of prescriptions dispensed for dangerous drugs, and, in addition, the Home Office received information from doctors, police, prisons, and hospitals. The pharmacists' records indicated the identity of patients receiving prescriptions for dangerous drugs. The police had instructions to report to the Home Office the identity of anyone in regular receipt of supplies for six months or more, and the Home Office had an agreement with the Ministry of Health for a regional medical officer, a doctor, to visit the prescribing doctor, discuss the case, and report back on whether or not it was a case of addiction (Judson 1974).

An insightful account of the period was given by H. B. Spear (1969), now Chief Inspector at the Home Office Drugs Branch. He noted that from time to time a small number of addicts came to the attention of the Home Office, for example, in the years immediately preceding the Second World War. The numbers were so small that the Home Office knew the addicts' lives in remarkable detail. Spear wrote about three addicts who were known to make trips to Continental Europe to purchase heroin. One of these was arrested in 1937, on his way back from Paris, in possession of 360 mgs of heroin. Spear also noted that most of the pre-war heroin addicts were 'of good social standing'.

Most of the addicts who came to the notice of the Home Office used morphine, pethidine, or other opiates rather than heroin. From 1935 a major category in the Home Office statistics was 'professional' addicts – a category that referred to doctors, dentists, and pharmacists (and, from 1955, nurses) who became addicted partly through their professional access to dangerous drugs. From 1935–40 approximately 22 per cent of the known addicts were labelled 'professional' (*see Table 2(2)*). The other major group, not presented as a category in the figures until after the Second World War, comprised addicts referred to as of 'therapeutic' origin: those people who were prescribed opiates in the course of the treatment of illness and whose illness and addiction continued, or whose addiction continued after the illness has passed. Although no figures are available, it is thought that the majority of addicts in the pre-war period were of therapeutic origin.

As shown in *Table 2(1)*, prosecutions for drug offences concerning opium rose during the Second World War. There were 201 in 1941 and they remained at this level for the next five years. The government's annual reports to the League of Nations attributed the increase in part to a rise in the Chinese population, mainly seamen, in some cities; to increased police activity, especially in Liverpool; and to the diversion of traffic in opium from India and other eastern countries to the US by way of British ports (Spear 1969). Apart from opium offences, the period was much like the preceding years in terms of known drug use. The number of addicts known to the Home Office actually declined somewhat, from 505 in 1940 to 306 in 1950, and most addicts continued to be of therapeutic or professional origin.

One change that did occur in the course of the 1940s was an increase in the number of prosecutions for the possession of cannabis – or 'Indian Hemp' as it was referred to in the legislation of the time. Cannabis prosecutions had never exceeded 18 per year since the drug was first controlled in 1929, but in the immediate post-war period prosecutions relating to cannabis began to rise, from 4 in 1945 to 86 in 1950. In 1946 the government's annual report on drugs stated that 'it is known that the traffic in Indian Hemp is practically confined to two negro groups in London and those attempting to import the drugs have generally been found to be coloured seamen' (Spear 1969: 249). The late 1940s saw a gradual increase in immigration from the black Commonwealth and along with this there was an increased police awareness that cannabis smoking was to be found in all parts of the country with significant immigrant populations.

### POST-WAR YEARS

It was in the 1950s that things began to change. This was at first imperceptible though, and the decade started on an optimistic official note. Britain's report to the UN in 1949 stated that cases of heroin and cocaine addiction were rare, and thus it remained through much of the 1950s – or so it appeared at the time. Offences under the drugs legislation were low, only cannabis was an exception, and the number of addicts known to the Home Office ranged between 300 and 400. Most addicts were addicted to morphine, and a significant proportion were in medical occupations.

*The Times*, on 2 July 1955, was able to report that 'opium traffic' was still declining and that it was 'largely confined to Chinese'. The *Standard*, on 1 May 1958, compared Britain favourably with North America. *The*

Table 2(2) *Addicts known to the Home Office, 1935–68*

| *year* | *no. of known addicts* | *Sex* | | *'therapeutic' addicts* | *'professional' addicts* | *heroin addicts* | *non-therapeutic heroin addicts* | *no. of new heroin addicts in year* |
|---|---|---|---|---|---|---|---|---|
| | | *M* | *F* | | | | | |
| 1935 | 700 approx. | | | this information was not collected prior to 1958 (except for heroin addicts) | 120 | exact numbers not available but the proportion of addicts using heroin varied from 5 per cent in 1935 to 19 per cent in 1952 | not applicable in these years | |
| 1936 | 616 | 313 | 300 | | 147 | | | |
| 1937 | 620 | 300 | 320 | | 140 | | | |
| 1938 | 519 | 246 | 273 | | 143 | | | |
| 1939 | 534 | 269 | 265 | | 131 | | | |
| 1940 | 505 | 251 | 254 | | 90 | | | |
| 1941 | 503 | 252 | 251 | | 91 | | | |
| 1942 | 524 | 275 | 249 | | 98 | | | |
| 1943 | 541 | 280 | 261 | | 94 | | | |
| 1944 | 559 | 285 | 274 | | 93 | | | |
| 1945 | 367* | 144 | 223 | | 80 | | | 1 |
| 1946 | 369 | 144 | 225 | | 79 | | | 1 |
| 1947 | 383 | 164 | 219 | | 87 | | | 3 |
| 1948 | 395 | 198 | 197 | | 119 | | | 4 |
| 1949 | 326 | 164 | 162 | | 100 | | | 3 |
| 1950 | 306 | 158 | 148 | | 95 | | | 3 |

| | | | | | | | | |
|---|---|---|---|---|---|---|---|---|
| 1951 | 301 | 153 | 148 | | 77 | | | 1 |
| 1952 | 297 | 153 | 144 | | 75 | | | 8 |
| 1953 | 290 | 149 | 141 | | 71 | | | 4 |
| 1954 | 317 | 148 | 169 | | 72 | 57 | 37 | 16 |
| 1955 | 335 | 159 | 176 | | 86*** | 54 | 36 | 10 |
| 1956 | 333 | 163 | 170 | | 99 | 53 | 36 | 10 |
| 1957 | 359 | 174 | 185 | | 88 | 66 | 45 | 7 |
| 1958 | 442** | 197 | 245 | 349 | 74 | 62 | 43 | 11 |
| 1959 | 454 | 196 | 258 | 344 | 68 | 68 | 47 | 11 |
| 1960 | 437 | 195 | 242 | 309 | 63 | 94 | 72 | 24 |
| 1961 | 470 | 223 | 247 | 293 | 61 | 132 | 112 | 56 |
| 1962 | 532 | 262 | 270 | 312 | 57 | 175 | 157 | 72 |
| 1963 | 635 | 339 | 296 | 355 | 56 | 237 | 222 | 90 |
| 1964 | 753 | 409 | 344 | 368 | 58 | 342 | 329 | 162 |
| 1965 | 927 | 558 | 369 | 344 | 45 | 521 | 509 | 259 |
| 1966 | 1349 | 886 | 463 | 351 | 54 | 899 | 885 | 522 |
| 1967 | 1729 | 1262 | 467 | 313 | 56 | 1299 | 1290 | 745 |
| 1968 | 2782 | 2161 | 621 | 306 | 43 | 2240 | 2232 | 1306 |

*Note:* *Up to 1945 cases were included for ten years after the last information (except death). **From 1958, figures relate only to those persons known to have been taking drugs in the year in question. ***Nurses included from 1955.
*Source:* Figures compiled from Spear (1969).

*Times* in the same year reported that 'In the world battle against drug addiction, Great Britain holds an enviable position . . . there is abundant justification for asserting that Britain has no serious problem of addiction', and went on to reiterate Home Office statistics for 1956, published in 1958, that reported 333 addicts in the country. Of these, 77 were doctors, 2 dentists, and 20 nurses. Of the remaining 234 addicts, the Home Office noted no occupational groups of significance beyond 'a small number of dance band musicians' (*The Times* 16 April 1958).

The exception was cannabis. It was still, as *The Times* commented in 1955, 'largely confined to Africans, Asiatics and West Indians aged from twenty to forty'. Convictions gradually increased to over 100 a year and there was an increase in the number of seizures of the drug. In 1956, 114 kgs were seized, mostly at the ports of Liverpool, London, and Avonmouth. The increases in seizures and convictions were attributed to some extent to increased vigilance on the part of the customs officers and the police, 'but it was thought that there had been some increase in the traffic itself' (*The Times* 2 July 1955).

It was in the early 1950s, as Spear delicately put it, that it appeared to the Home Office Drugs Branch officials that 'cannabis was a drug with a certain amount of appeal to our own indigenous population' (Spear 1969: 249). An event of significance occurred in 1950 when the Metropolitan Police raided a jazz club in the West End of London. Spear quoted from the government report to the United Nations about this domestic raid which was raised to international significance:

> 'In January 1950 a ship's steward was arrested at Southampton after five boxes of chocolates found in his baggage proved to have Hemp concealed under the chocolates. During interrogation this man stated that in the past he had obtained Hemp from "Club Eleven" in London, where, he stated, the drug was smoked to a great extent, and this information was passed to the Metropolitan Police.
>
> Police enquiries showed that "Club Eleven" was a private dancing club frequented by both coloured and white persons, and further investigation suggested that Hemp was in fact smoked there. A search warrant was then obtained and, on 15th April 1950, the club was raided by the police, who found between 200 and 250 persons, coloured and white of both sexes, on the premises, the majority being between the ages of seventeen and thirty. These were all searched and ten men were found to be in possession of Hemp, of whom two also had a small quantity of cocaine and another man had a small quantity of cocaine only. In addition, twenty-three packets of Hemp, a number of Hemp cigarettes, a small packet of cocaine, a small quantity of prepared opium and an empty morphine ampoule

> were found on the floor of the club. All the cocaine found in this case, the origin of which could not be ascertained, had been adulterated with boric acid.
>
> Of the offenders, three of whom were seamen from the United States, all but one were between twenty-two and twenty-nine years of age, and, contrary to the normal experience in the country in cases involving Hemp, only one was a coloured man. All were later convicted and fined for being in unlawful possession of the drugs.'
>
> (Spear 1969: 249–50)

This incident indicated that young white people were now interested in cannabis, and showed the beginning of changes in the use of drugs in Britain. But such occurrences were still comparatively rare, as is highlighted by the fact that just this one raid had a marked effect in decreasing the availability of cannabis in London in the following months. Similar reports of the period are given by Ken Leech, a curate who worked among young people in London. In *Keep the Faith Baby* (1973), he recalled the 1950s in Stepney, in the East End of London, and, in particular, the Cable Street area, which had been described in the press as 'London's Harlem' and by an academic researcher as 'The Coloured Quarter' (Banton 1959). These were inaccurate descriptions, for in the 1950s only a small percentage of the area's residents were coloured immigrants, but perhaps not totally inappropriate because the number of immigrants in the country was still low, and any concentration was visible out of proportion to numbers. Leech described how he saw cannabis being used in the Cable Street area in the 1950s, mainly among merchant seamen from Sierra Leone, the Gambia, Nigeria, and Somalia.

The 1950s were witnessing an increase in the popularity of the recreational use of drugs. We have seen that cannabis smoking had been discovered by the white population, and that drugs were now available in jazz clubs. Heroin was also becoming more commonplace (though the number of users was still small). It was, indeed, only in 1954 that the Home Office began to record heroin addicts as a separate category – 57 were known to them in 1954, rising to 94 by 1960. What *The Times* (16 April 1958) article referred to as 'a small number of dance band musicians' turned out in retrospect to have been the beginning of a more extensive recreational use of heroin. There continued to be only a handful of people using opiates and Spear, at the Home Office, still knew most of their names and characteristics. But the first indications the Home Office had that young people were interested in opiates came, he said, in 1949 with the theft of 1200 grains of morphine and 14 ozs of cocaine from a wholesale chemist in the Midlands, which were sold among addicts in the West End of London. A second case occurred in 1951 when a hospital dispensary near London was broken into and morphine, heroin, and cocaine were stolen. Later, a young man referred to as 'Mark' was known by police to be selling drugs in the West End. He was in fact employed at the hospital at the time of the theft and had fallen under suspicion. Following Mark's arrest, several others came to notice. Spear detailed twenty-six people altogether who were known to the Home Office between 1947 and 1954 and who had been connected with Mark or his friends. Most of them were born between 1920 and 1930 and were twenty to thirty years old when they came to attention. Twelve of them were described as musicians (Spear 1969: 252).

The contemporary evidence showed that in the 1950s there was a small, but growing, number of people, in contact with each other, using heroin and other drugs. Spear gave this summary of the evidence:

> 'That these were not isolated events but provided the first signs of an emerging drug sub-culture in the United Kingdom was supported by the subsequent spread of heroin addiction beyond this original group . . . and by further indications of the increasing interest in cannabis being shown by young United Kingdom born persons, especially those frequenting certain jazz clubs in the West End of London, as reflected in the convictions for the unlawful possession of this drug. The first teenage cannabis smoker to come to the notice of the Home Office was arrested in August 1952 after being found in possession of 18 packets of cannabis resin. At the time he was just over 18 years of age and admitted that he had been smoking cannabis since he was 16½, having acquired the habit through frequenting "bebop" clubs and cafes where addicts congregated. He was convicted of a similar offence 3 months later after being arrested during a police raid on a cafe frequented by musicians and in 1955 appeared as a heroin addict. He was still addicted at the time of his death in 1965.'
>
> (Spear 1969: 254)

## THE REPORT OF THE FIRST BRAIN COMMITTEE

These events prompted a government review of policy, which had not been changed or critically examined since the Rolleston Committee recommendations in 1926. The key question was whether the changes in drug use required a new approach. In June 1958 the Ministry of Health convened the Interdepartmental Committee on Drug Addiction, to review:

> 'in the light of more recent developments, the advice given by the Departmental Committee on Morphine and Heroin Addiction in

1926; to consider whether any revised advice should also cover other drugs liable to produce addiction or to be habit-forming; to consider whether there is a medical need to provide special, including institutional, treatment outside the resources already available, for persons addicted to drugs; and to make recommendations.'

(Interdepartmental Committee on Drug Addiction 1961: 4)

The new Committee was chaired by Sir Russell Brain, a neurologist and former president of the Royal College of Physicians. The Committee report was published early in 1961 and noted two developments in the thirty-four years since the Rolleston Committee presentations. First, pharmaceutical research had produced a number of new analgesic drugs capable of producing addiction. Second, there were developments in the treatment of drug addiction, including the substitution of new synthetic opiate drugs and their subsequent gradual withdrawal, and the use of other new drugs, such as the tranquillizers, for the alleviation of withdrawal symptoms. The Committee therefore considered whether there were still circumstances in which the continued administration of dangerous drugs, even under the conditions strictly defined by the Rolleston Committee, could be justified.

At the end of its deliberations the Committee affirmed that addiction was still a medical matter. It said that addiction should be regarded 'as an expression of mental disorder rather than a form of criminal behaviour', and that every addict 'should be treated energetically as a medical and psychiatric problem' (Interdepartmental Committee on Drug Addiction 1961: 9). It refined the definition of what constituted addiction and considered that the compulsion to avoid withdrawal from drugs was on a par with the desire to continue using them. This formulation of addiction meant that maintenance on low amounts of drugs could be seen as positive *treatment* for addiction.

The Committee considered that the incidence of addiction to dangerous drugs – morphine, heroin, pethidine, methadone, and others – was still small. The figures provided by the Home Office, giving the number of known addicts for various years between 1936 and 1960, might, the Committee reported, suggest an extension of addiction, but also it thought they reflected an intensified activity for detection of illegal use in the post-war period and there was 'in our opinion no cause to fear that any real increase is at present occurring' (Interdepartmental Committee on Drug Addiction 1961: 9). The Committee continued:

'According to the Home Office and the police, supported by such independent evidence as we have been able to obtain, the purveying of illicit supplies of manufactured dangerous drugs for addicts in this

> country is so small as to be almost negligible. The cause for this seems to lie largely in social attitudes to the observance of the law in general and to the taking of dangerous drugs in particular, coupled with the systematic enforcement of the Dangerous Drugs Act, 1951, and its Regulations.'
>
> (Interdepartmental Committee on Drug Addiction 1961: 9)

Consequently the Committee saw no need for the establishment of any specialized institution for the treatment of addiction and thought that initial treatment could take place in the psychiatric wards of general hospitals. It saw no advantage in abrupt withdrawal and appended notes on treatment as a guide for doctors, detailing conditions for withdrawal, convalescence, physical rehabilitation, psychotherapy, occupational therapy, recreational therapy, and after-care.

The Committee believed, from the evidence before it, that there were still two predominant classes of addicts: the professional addicts, doctors and nurses, who in 1959 comprised 68 of the 454 known addicts; and second, therapeutic addicts. The Committee considered the concept of the 'stabilized' addict, which arose out of the Rolleston Committee's recommendations, and heard evidence that such persons did exist. It scrutinized the life histories of more than a hundred addicts and found that many had been taking small and regular doses of opiates for years, with little evidence of tolerance and were 'often leading reasonably satisfactory lives' (Interdepartmental Committee on Drug Addiction 1961: 11). The Committee continued:

> 'to group together all "drug addicts" on the basis of a pharmacological definition may convey an over-simplified and misleading impression. There are drug addicts who have been introduced to the practice when physically healthy with drugs procured by illicit means or in the course of their professional work. This group is a very small one in Great Britain. There are those who, having been given a drug of addiction as the appropriate treatment for a painful illness, continue to be dependent on it when the original necessity for its use has disappeared. And there is a third group of those who are unable to abandon a drug rightly or wrongly prescribed for some physical or mental ailment which itself persists.'
>
> (Interdepartmental Committee on Drug Addiction 1961: 11)

The report included six case histories to substantiate these opinions. All six addicts had been prescribed opiates by medical practitioners in the course of some painful, persistent illness or disability and would fall into the category of therapeutic addicts. For example, case number one, Mrs A., was described as follows:

> 'A housewife, well past middle age, had a radical amputation of the breast for carcinoma ten years ago. Severe pain at the site of the operation and elsewhere in associated areas had persisted ever since. For the greater part of this period she had been taking pethidine, prescribed by her general practitioner, at the steady rate of three to four tablets, each of 50 mgs, daily. On this dosage she is relatively free from symptoms and is able to undertake her own housework. There is no indication that the dose requires to be increased, but numerous attempts at withdrawal, or substitution by codeine, aspirin preparations, etc. have met with a return of her pain and incapacity. No personality changes have been detected.'
>
> (Interdepartmental Committee on Drug Addiction 1961: 22)

And Mr D., past middle age, and employed in the office of a large manufacturing firm:

> 'For many years he has suffered from generalised osteoarthritis. He has had advice and treatment from several consultants. Some years ago levorphanol was prescribed. At first there was a tendency for the dose to rise but, for about five years now it has remained at three tablets, each of 1.5 mgs, daily. Attempts have been made at withdrawal on several occasions. There has been no abstinence syndrome, but the patient's pain has returned with a severity sufficient to stop him working. So long as he is given his tablets he seems to be capable of a hard responsible full day's work.'
>
> (Interdepartmental Committee on Drug Addiction 1961: 22)

The view of the Committee appears to have been informed by the opinion that the majority of addicts were respectable citizens, addicted in the course of medical treatment, or themselves members of the medical professions. There is only passing reference to those who became addicted with drugs 'procured by illicit means'.

The evidence heard by the Committee indicated that the right of any medical practitioner to prescribe opiates in the treatment of addiction, the recommendation of the Rolleston Committee, appeared to be satisfactory. There were, from time to time, doctors who were prepared to issue prescriptions to addicts without providing adequate medical supervision, without making an effort at withdrawal, and without seeking another medical opinion, but the Committee said – 'Only two such habitual offenders during the past twenty years have been brought to our notice and it is satisfactory to note that in spite of wide-spread inquiry no doctor is known to be following this practice at present' (Interdepartmental Committee on Drug Addiction 1961: 11). The conclusion was that the right of doctors to prescribe dangerous drugs to addicts had not contributed to any increase in the total number of patients receiving regular supplies. The Brain Committee concluded that there should be no major departure from the recommendations of the Rolleston Committee. The British 'system' was unchanged.

### THE CHANGING PATTERN OF DRUG USE IN THE 1960S

The 1961 Brain Committee's assessment of the situation was, though, soon to be outdated. Indeed, from now on drugs received considerable attention in the press. On 21 April 1964 the *Guardian* reported a case in which seven people, including the daughter of a Home Office Deputy Under-Secretary of State, had been charged with the possession of cannabis. LSD was reportedly available at seven shillings (35 pence) a tablet, and cannabis from £4 to £6 an ounce. Cannabis convictions continued to rise each year, reaching 663 by 1963. But much of the concern by then centred on 'pep pills'.

'Pep pill' was the popular name given to the amphetamines, and referred to amphetamine itself (marketed as Benzedrine), dexamphetamine (Dexedrine), methylamphetamine (Methedrine), and phenmetrazine (Preludin). Amphetamine could be obtained without prescription up to 1956 when controls were first introduced (Bradshaw 1972) but even then it was not an offence to possess them, provided they had not been stolen. The best-known amphetamine was a combination of amphetamine and barbiturate called Drinamyl. This was first marketed by the pharmaceutical firm Smith, Kline and French in 1951 as distinctive, triangular-shaped, pale-blue pills which soon became known as 'Purple Hearts'. Amphetamines sold cheaply on the black market: the *British Medical Journal* (1963) reported that Preludin cost approximately £1 for twenty-four tablets. Amphetamines were popular among young people at clubs in the West End of London. Dr Phillip Connell, a psychiatrist at the Maudsley Hospital, gave his view in this account at the time:

> 'The fact of teenagers and others taking the drugs such as amphetamine, amphetamine plus barbiturate and marihuana, is not, in my submission, under dispute. I myself recently saw a boy of fifteen years who had been the round of the Soho and other clubs in London and described taking purple hearts, dexamphetamine, amphetamine and other drugs, including what might have been by his description librium (a tranquillizer), amyl nitrite (which is in a capsule and is sniffed) and cigarettes containing marihuana. He had an episode of paranoid psychosis (the horrors) and was having great difficulty in refraining from going back to the clubs and obtaining more supplies. He said that the purple hearts were 6d or sometimes 9d each, amyl nitrite capsules were 5s each and Benzedrine and

Dexedrine tablets were 6d each. He had taken 50 Drinamyl tablets (purple hearts) during one hour preceding the attack of horrors which came on an hour or two later.'

(Connell 1966: 77–8)

The reaction to these changes culminated in a burst of legislative zeal in 1964. The first initiative came at the beginning of the year when a government-supported Private Members' Bill was introduced to the House of Commons. The Bill proposed two new offences: the cultivation of cannabis, and allowing premises to be used for the purposes of smoking cannabis. The object was to ensure that owners of premises such as clubs would actively discourage cannabis smoking. *The Sunday Times*, commentating on the Bill on 12 January 1964, noted that 'until recently convictions for the possession of hemp have been mainly among coloured immigrants, but last year over a quarter were of young whites'. This Bill, passed as the Dangerous Drugs Act of 1964, also changed the legal name from Indian Hemp to cannabis.

The second legislative initiative concerned pep pills which under existing law could be possessed quite legally – although they could only be obtained on prescription. This meant that it was not an offence for legally prescribed amphetamine to be possessed by an unauthorized person. The only charge that could be brought against those who sold these drugs was unlawful sale, a charge that in most circumstances would be difficult to substantiate (Bradshaw 1972). In January 1964 the Council of the Pharmaceutical Society of Great Britain called for legal controls, as did Phillip Connell. In March the Home Secretary introduced a Bill that aimed to create a new offence of 'illegal possession' for amphetamines and give the Home Secretary powers to include other drugs under the legislation. The Drugs (Prevention of Misuse) Bill received all-party support, and its progress through Parliament was prominently monitored by the press. For example, the *Daily Telegraph* reported on the Home Secretary's investigations under the heading 'Brooke's tour of drug addicts' clubs'. Home Secretary Brooke had spent an evening in Soho accompanied by detectives. He reported his visit in the House of Commons: 'Among that sleazy stuff', he said, 'the thing that impressed itself most deeply on me was the danger to teenage boys and girls if this easy taking of pep pills grew' (*Daily Telegraph* 1 May 1964). MPs supported the Bill, but called for a distinction between the 'teenager who may be found with a few purple heart pills and the man who may be at the centre of a network of drug trafficking' (*The Times* 18 June 1964).

The Bill was criticized in some quarters: *The Times* leader on 1 April 1964 thought it was hastily conceived legislation, an unjustified addition to 'a chaotic collection of Acts and Regulations', and called it 'A Bill Too Soon'. However, such was the certainty that it would be passed that in

May the *Sunday Telegraph* reported that police drug squads were being formed in anticipation. Headlined 'Police Set Up Purple Heart Hunt Squads', it reported that 'dossiers on underground organizations making huge profits from the misuse of pills are being prepared'. It continued:

> 'Information has been collected in places where young people meet which are known to be centres of trafficking. Young detectives and policewomen have pretended to be addicts and taken sugar placebos that look like purple hearts and simulated the effects of the drug.
>
> *Coffee bar raids*
> As soon as the Bill becomes law there will be raids on certain coffee bars and jazz clubs. Pedlars will be the police target, and it is unlikely that minor users will be arrested.'
>
> (*Sunday Telegraph* 21 May 1964)

The Bill passed the House of Commons and the Drugs (Prevention of Misuse) Act came into effect on 31 October 1964. It made it an offence to be in unauthorized possession of amphetamine drugs, or to import them without a licence. It also required manufacturers and wholesalers to be registered. The Home Secretary had the power, after consulting the Poisons Board, to add or remove substances from the Schedule to the Act.

The intense activity did not stop with new legislation. In August 1964 Smith, Kline and French, the Welwyn Garden City drug manufacturers, had decided to change the shape of purple hearts to a less distinctive, round, blue tablet. They stated: 'There are numerous other round, blue tablets already on the market, and we feel this measure will confer a high degree of anonymity on the product, thereby helping materially to combat illegal trafficking and misuse' (*Guardian* 1 August 1964). Reports of other aspects of drug use continued to appear in the press – reports of thefts of prescription forms and forgeries; of the Southwark coroner who at an addict's inquest called for a drugs 'passport' to stop addicts going from one doctor to another; on the 1964 government report to the UN referring to students returning from Tangier with marijuana smuggled inside sleeping bags; and the *Daily Sketch* reported that customs officers had been asked to keep a special watch on people arriving in Britain with Moroccan or Turkish stamps in their passports (*Evening Standard* 31 October 1964; *Daily Telegraph* 25 July 1964; *Guardian* 30 July 1964; *Daily Sketch* 25 November 1964).

## NEW QUESTIONS ABOUT HEROIN

It was becoming clear that increasing numbers of people were beginning to use, and become addicted to, heroin. In 1960 there were 94 people known to the Home Office to be addicted to heroin, 132 in 1961, and 175 in 1962. Nearly all of these were 'non-therapeutic' addicts. Many were prescribed heroin by private practitioners. Isabella Lady Frankau, for example, practised in Wimpole Street and had begun to treat young addicts in 1957 (Frankau and Stanwell 1961). In 1961, writing in the *Lancet*, she detailed the treatment of 51 addicts. Only 9 of these had been originally prescribed opiates for medical reasons. The rest had started using drugs recreationally. Most used heroin and cocaine. Lady Frankau mentioned the difficulties in dealing with such patients.

> 'They lived for the immediate gratification of their desire for drugs, and were totally without concern for the welfare of others . . . they had a rigid code. They would not inform about associates from whom they borrowed or bought drugs, or to whom they lent or sold. . . . Fantastic stories were offered in efforts to obtain extra cocaine, but the most common pretexts were "accidents" which happened while they were preparing the cocaine for injection.'
>
> (Frankau and Stanwell 1961: 1377–378)

She mentioned, too, the problems of addicts using up their supplies of drugs, and how she prescribed extra amounts 'to prevent them returning to the black market, which would involve them in financial difficulties, and . . . which could mean a return to the degradation and humiliation of contacting the pedlars' (Frankau and Stanwell 1961: 1378). What Lady Frankau failed to realize was that there were no independent 'pedlars'. It was her prescribing that resulted in heroin and cocaine being relatively easily available on the black market. Some of her private patients received prescriptions for 1800 mgs of heroin a day, and while some addicts could probably inject that amount, many were selling their surplus. Addicts' motivation for asking for more than they personally required was simply financial: they could sell some to friends and other addicts and so pay the consultation fee plus provide themselves with a small income (Gillespie *et al.*, 1967).

A number of Canadian addicts were coming to this country in order to benefit from the British 'system'. Lady Frankau had herself been on a lecture tour of Canada in 1963 to describe her method of treating addicts. Some eighty Canadian addicts came to Britain in the early 1960s (Zacune 1971). In April 1964 Lady Frankau gave evidence at a St Pancras inquest into the death of a thirty-eight-year-old Canadian addict. He had called on her on his way to look for a new job and was later found dead in her bathroom with a home-made hypodermic syringe beside him. In evidence, Lady Frankau said that she had treated seventy Canadian addicts in the previous year. Not being UK residents, they had to pay for their prescriptions to be dispensed, a cost of about fifteen shillings for one hundred 10 mg tablets of heroin, and one shilling for 60 mgs of cocaine. 'But', she said, 'on the black market they fetch as much as £1 for six, five or four [tablets of heroin]' (*Daily Telegraph* 25 July 1964).

Although any doctor was entitled to prescribe for addicts, relatively few did so. Most did not want the problems of these patients. It was not surprising that those practitioners who did take on the task were soon overwhelmed with patients and their demands. Hewettson and Ollendorf, two South London GPs working in the NHS, decided in 1962 that they would take on any genuine addict who was unable to get an NHS prescription or to afford private prescriptions. Within one year they had 100 patients and their names, like those of the handful of other doctors, became household words among London addicts (Hewettson and Ollendorf 1964; Glatt 1966). Some of the 'junkies' doctors' were dedicated to helping addicts, and felt that they were taking on a task that had been seriously neglected by other members of the medical profession. Others were characterized as 'inexperienced, overgenerous, pressured, unscrupulous' (*Drug Link* 1980a: 1): the evidence was that some practitioners, especially those working single-handed, were 'disastrously incapable' of finding the correct balance between over- and under-prescribing (*Drug Link* 1980a: 2).

On 30 July 1964 the annual government report to the UN showed that in 1963 the total number of heroin addicts was 237. The figures indicated various changes in the type of addict coming to official attention. Those who started illicitly, until then a small minority, were becoming the most significant group. Of the 237 heroin addicts, 222 were neither therapeutic nor professional, they had become addicted using drugs illegally obtained. And the age level was falling: there were 9 men and 8 women addicts under the age of twenty.

These rapid changes in drug use in the 1960s were accompanied by new questions about the appropriateness and effectiveness of British policy towards drugs such as heroin, morphine, and cocaine. The situation now appeared very different from the one on which Rolleston had reported in the 1920s, or indeed from the situation of only three years previously when the Brain Committee had decided that policy changes were unnecessary. On 30 July 1964, on the same day that the new Home Office figures on heroin addiction were released, the Minister of Health announced in the House of Commons that he was reconvening the Interdepartmental Committee on Drug Addiction in order to review the situation. Lord Brain was once again to be chairman.

# 3

# *The changing response – from private doctors to drug Clinics*

The second Brain Committee met eight times. The *Observer* commented that there was 'a sense of urgency surrounding this second inquiry' because of the youthfulness of the new addicts and because 'almost all present addicts were "hooked" either through their own stupidity or free will'. Cases of heroin addiction were by then occurring outside of London and there was 'no doubt that a blackmarket [was] being created through the over-prescribing of supplies to registered addicts by doctors' (*Observer* 6 December 1964).

The Committee reported to the Minister of Health in November 1965. According to their inquiry, the *Second Report* of the Interdepartmental Committee on Drug Addiction (1965), the situation had indeed changed. The Committee heard that over the years 1959–64 the total number of addicts known to the Home Office had risen from 454 to 753, and during this period the number of addicts who were using heroin had risen from 68 to 342, thus most of the new addicts were taking heroin. Of these heroin addicts, only 15 were of therapeutic origin. There had also been an increase in the numbers known to be taking cocaine, from 30 in 1959 to 211 in 1964, and virtually all the cocaine users were also addicted to heroin.

The Committee also reported that it had heard evidence of a significant change in the age distribution of addicts. In 1959 only 50 out of 454 (under 11 per cent) were less than thirty-five years old; by 1964 the under thirty-fives numbered 297 out of 753 (nearly 40 per cent). There were forty addicts under the age of twenty, and one as young as fifteen. All of those under the age of twenty, and the majority of those under the age of thirty-five, were addicted to heroin. The picture that emerged, then, was of an increase in heroin addiction among young people. The Committee heard that much of the increase centred on London and one or two other large cities.

The report next directed itself to the crucial question of how the new addicts obtained their supplies. The evidence showed a negligible traffic in illicit (i.e. illegally produced and imported) heroin and that forgery of prescriptions did not substantially contribute to the supply of drugs. The conclusion was clear: the major source of supply was a very few doctors who had prescribed excessively for addicts. The Committee put it this way:

> 'Thus we were informed that in 1962 one doctor alone prescribed almost 600,000 tablets of heroin (i.e. 6 kilogrammes) for addicts. The same doctor, on one occasion, prescribed 900 tablets of heroin (9 grammes) to one addict and three days later prescribed for the same patient another 600 tablets, "to replace pills lost in an accident". Further prescriptions of 720 (i.e. 7.2 grammes) and 840 (8.4 grammes) tablets followed later to the same patient. Two doctors each issued a single prescription for 1,000 tablets. These are only the more startling examples. We heard of other instances of prescriptions of considerable, if less spectacular, quantities of dangerous drugs over a long period of time. Supplies on such a scale can easily provide a surplus that will attract new recruits to the ranks of the addicts.'
> (Interdepartmental Committee on Drug Addiction 1965: 6)

They accepted the evidence of witnesses that not more than six doctors had prescribed these very large amounts for individual patients. Cautiously, they commented that 'these doctors have acted within the law and according to their professional judgement' (Interdepartmental Committee on Drug Addiction 1965: 6), and they had heard that some of the doctors had embarked on the treatment of addicts out of a sense of duty, and because they felt that the treatment facilities elsewhere were inadequate. The Committee's assessment was accurate. There was a handful of doctors, most working privately, who prescribed heroin and cocaine. Many of the addicts we later interviewed were among the patients of these junkies' doctors and, as we show in the next chapter, they had little difficulty in obtaining large prescriptions. The same conclusion was reached by other observers at the time. For example, a letter published in the *Lancet* in August 1965 from Dr Ian Pierce James noted:

'A 32 year old heroin and cocaine addict in care at the present has received from four different doctors successively, prescriptions for eight–twelve grains of heroin and five–eight grains of cocaine each day. She thus had over forty grains of heroin and thirty grains of cocaine in all. The cocaine and heroin which can be easily purchased in Soho derive mainly from addicts' prescriptions. . . . A supply of ten grains of heroin and five grains of cocaine per day has a market value of over £100 per week.'

(James 1965, in the *Lancet* **ii**: 288)

The British 'system', which had allowed any practitioner to prescribe for addicts, was now seriously questioned as it appeared that far from being a policy that successfully limited the extent of addiction, it was one that, faced with a new type of heroin addict, was actually contributing to the growth of addiction by making supplies so easily available. Although the doctors involved had, as the second Brain Committee report suggested, 'acted within the law and according to their professional judgement' (Interdepartmental Committee on Drug Addiction 1965: 6) there were two ways in which some of them had departed from the recommendations of the Rolleston Committee. First, many did not attempt a cure before embarking on prescribing, and furthermore, they rarely called in a second opinion. Dr Max Glatt, who was then running an in-patient addiction unit at St Bernard's Hospital, Middlesex, pointed out that 'Instead of first attempting a "cure" before proceeding to regular prescribing, the practice of the doctors concerned consisted in turning the recommended procedure the other way round, i.e. by starting to prescribe in the first instance, in the hope of effecting a cure later on' (Glatt 1966: 38).

The report of the second Brain Committee affirmed that the system under which matters remained largely in the hands of the medical profession should be maintained, and reasserted that 'the addict should be regarded as a sick person, he should be treated as such and not as a criminal, provided he does not resort to criminal acts' (Interdepartmental Committee on Drug Addiction 1965: 8). However, this medical model of addiction, first formulated as policy by the Rolleston Committee in 1926, had now undergone some subtle but significant changes. Up to this time the model had seen addiction in terms of treatment of individual addicts. The Rolleston Committee had regarded addiction as a 'manifestation of disease' (Departmental Committee on Morphine and Heroin Addiction 1926: 11). The first Brain Committee believed that 'addiction should be regarded as an expression of mental disorder rather than a form of criminal behaviour' (Interdepartmental Committee on Drug Addiction 1961: 9). Prior to the 1960s the medical model only appears to have been pursued as treatment, but it was in the 1960s that the potential for the disease model in terms of *control* emerged. It was in the report of the second Brain

Committee that addiction came to be referred to as a 'socially infectious condition' (Interdepartmental Committee on Drug Addiction 1965: 8). Thus the medical model was reformulated to emphasize control as well as individual treatment. The second Brain Committee believed that control of the drug problem could be exercised through control of the treatment. It saw the issue this way:

> 'If there is insufficient control it may lead to the spread of addiction – as is happening at present. If, on the other hand, the restrictions are so severe as to prevent or seriously discourage the addict from obtaining any supplies from legitimate sources it may lead to the development of an organised illicit traffic. The absence hitherto of such an organised illicit traffic has been attributed largely to the fact that an addict has been able to obtain supplies of drugs legally. But this facility has now been abused with the result that addiction has increased.'
>
> (Interdepartmental Committee on Drug Addiction 1965: 7)

What were the options open to the Committee? One would have been a total ban on prescribing heroin, but this would have met with strong objections from the medical profession over such a threat to 'clinical freedom'. A complete ban would also have opened the possibility of an organized black market in illicit heroin, which had so far been avoided. The solution was to take the prescribing of heroin and cocaine out of the hands of general medical practitioners and make it the task of specialist hospital doctors, who would have more colleague-support and over whom more oversight could be exercised. The solution suggested by the Brain Committee was ingenious – it allowed any medical practitioner to continue to prescribe dangerous drugs to 'ordinary patients' but it proposed restrictions on the prescribing of heroin and cocaine to addicts. Specifically, the Committee made three linked proposals: the restriction of supplies to addicts, the provision of treatment centres, and a system of notification of addicts.

Under the first proposal doctors other than those working at the treatment centres would be prohibited from supplying, administering, and prescribing 'dangerous drugs' to addicts. The Committee emphasized that the proposals applied only to heroin and cocaine and that they were only in respect of addicts: other doctors 'should retain the right to prescribe, supply or administer any dangerous drugs required for other patients in the treatment of organic disease' (Interdepartmental Committee on Drug Addiction 1965: 10). The consequences, the Committee hoped, would be to place more controls over the availability of heroin and cocaine:

'We believe that the proposals which we have made will make it more difficult for addicts to obtain supplies of heroin and cocaine. The immediate effect may be to bring into the open a number of addicts now dependent for their supply on addicts who are receiving their drugs from doctors.'

(Interdepartmental Committee on Drug Addiction 1965: 11–12)

The second major recommendation was that there should be special centres for the treatment of addiction, at least in the London area, with medical staff, facilities for laboratory investigation, and provisions for research, these probably to be sited in psychiatric hospitals or the psychiatric wings of general hospitals. The Committee still did not accept the argument that there should be powers of compulsory treatment for addicts as this appeared to have had little success. However, the Committee thought that there should be limited powers of compulsory detention over patients who were undergoing withdrawal but wishing to break off treatment because of its discomfort.

Third, the Committee argued that there should be a system of notification of addicts that would replace the existing one whereby the Home Office relied on routine inspection of chemists and informal notifications. It argued that notification would be similar to the notification of infectious disease under the Public Health Act:

'We think the analogy to addiction is apt, for addiction is after all a socially infectious condition and its notification may offer a means for epidemiological assessment and control. We use the term deliberately to reflect certain principles which we regard as important, viz. that the addict is a sick person and that addiction is a disease which (if allowed to spread unchecked) will become a menace to the community.'

(Interdepartmental Committee on Drug Addiction 1965: 8)

The Committee proposed that it should be a statutory duty of any doctor coming into a professional relationship with an addict to notify that addict to a central authority. It foresaw that a central register might be used by doctors to check whether a particular addict had been notified or to obtain further details of an addict's history.

The proposals were, in fact, a threat to the clinical freedom of doctors (because the right to prescribe heroin to addicts was to be taken away from all doctors not specially licensed) and they attracted some objections. The Secretary of the British Medical Association, for example, said that this would be 'one more inroad into the position of the family doctors' (Stevenson 1965: 1), and a leading article in the *British Medical Journal* said it was a 'grave step to take in order – it would appear – to control the over-prescribing habits of only a handful of doctors, serious and indeed tragic though the consequences of these habits are' and that this would be 'the first time that a doctor's right to prescribe has been so restricted' (*British Medical Journal* 1965: 1259). But such protests were muted. The majority of doctors did not approve of the practices of the prescribing doctors, saw them as an embarrassment to the medical profession, and welcomed some control; the proposals of the Brain Committee were subtle, as any doctor could still prescribe heroin for medical treatment (though not for the treatment of addiction); and the proposals would remove from the majority of doctors any need to do the medical 'dirty work' of treating addicts.

## MEDICAL CARE OR SOCIAL CONTROL?

The proposals represented a shift in British thinking about addiction. Hitherto most discussions focused on the medical treatment of addicted individuals. The new element introduced in the rethinking of policy in the 1960s was the emphasis on the social control of addiction. The actions of doctors were now seen to have effects beyond individual treatment. Excessive prescribing had contributed to the spread of addiction, but moderate prescribing might be a way of controlling the development of the drug problem: doctors might be able to compete with the black market.

The second report of the Brain Committee referred to 'medical treatment' in special 'treatment centres'. It went on to say that the prescribing of heroin and cocaine would be confined to doctors on the staff of the treatment centres, and 'it would then be the duty of the doctors at the treatment centre to determine a course of treatment and, if thought necessary, to provide the addict with drugs' (Interdepartmental Committee on Drug Addiction 1965: 9). The Committee was well aware of the idea of control through limiting prescribing, but when it described the proposed work of the centres it chose to use medical (e.g. course of treatment) rather than control terms. However, when the proposals were translated into concrete policy, in the recommendations of the Ministry of Health's *Treatment and Supervision of Heroin Addiction* (1967), it was recognized that the centres would both control the drug problem and treat addicts. To quote:

> 'Some addicts will not accept withdrawal treatment, at any rate to start with, and complete refusal of supplies will not cure their addiction – it will merely throw them on the black market and encourage the development of an organised black market on a scale hitherto unknown in this country. *The aim is to contain the spread of*

*heroin addiction* by continuing to supply this drug in minimum quantities where this is necessary in the opinion of the doctor, and where possible to persuade addicts to accept withdrawal treatment.' (Our emphasis.)

(Ministry of Health 1967: 3)

The twin aims of control and treatment were later to cause problems for Clinic staff – for example, the social control of addiction might be best pursued by a maintenance-prescribing approach, but this might not be the best treatment for an individual patient, for maintenance conflicts with the therapeutic goal of abstinence. Other problems might also have been foreseen. Alexander Trocchi, himself an addict and a former patient of a 'prescribing' doctor, wrote of the troubles to be expected between Clinic doctors and addict patients:

> 'If a doctor follows the recommendations of the Brain Report and tries to get his patient to accept a prescription for the smallest possible amount of the drug, an absurd situation arises. From the first interview the user feels forced to resort to cunning, to lie, to cheat, to beg, to fawn, in order to ensure adequate supplies. Doctor and patient are involved in a battle of wits, in a destructive pseudo-problem, in which all the energies that should have been brought to bear on the real problem are wastefully dissipated'

(Trocchi, quoted in Silberman 1967: 75)

Some of the confusion between treatment and control was shown in contemporary public pronouncements when the legal changes were being formulated and implemented. For example, in March 1967, at the time when the Dangerous Drugs Bill, which was to implement many of the proposals, had just received its third reading in the House of Commons, the *British Medical Journal* published short comments on the proposed centres (*British Medical Journal* 1967). Although the article had the title 'Centres for the treatment of drug addiction', the three contributing psychiatrists concentrated primarily on the function of the Clinics in controlling the drug problem. Only one contributor, a general practitioner, chose to confine his comments to the treatment of addiction.

So just what would the Clinics be expected to do? Since prescription of heroin and cocaine would be limited to them it was clear that part of their work would be the prescribing of these drugs. But were they to become prescribing centres? The *Lancet* thought that the term 'Treatment Centre' was a euphemism for 'prescribing centre' (*Lancet* 1965: 1113), but Glatt (1966), in an extensive commentary on the proposals, felt that this was not what the Brain Committee had in mind. He thought that the Clinics should give addicts motives and incentives to come off drugs and should also be concerned with rehabilitation and after-care. He also held the view that maintenance-prescribing would succeed, if at all, only with therapeutic or medical-profession addicts. It is clear that two possible conflicting aims for the Clinics were emerging.

### THE PUBLIC REACTION AGAINST DRUG USE

The second Brain Committee report was published in 1965 but it was to be a further three years before the proposals were implemented. These three years were marked by continuous publicity about drugs and continued questioning and searching for explanations for youthful drug use. In May 1965, Joshua Macmillan, twenty-year-old grandson of the former Prime Minister, died of an overdose in Oxford. In response *The Sunday Times* on 16 May 1965 ran an article headlined 'Confessions of an Oxford Drug-taker', which had an interview with a witness at the inquest and an account of drug use at the University. The *Observer* speculated on the 'Affluence cause of drug cult' and reported an interview with a psychiatrist who said that using drugs was 'a new form of social behaviour, a cult if you like. It's a symptom of malaise in an affluent society. Fads needn't be bad in themselves, but this one must be so because drugs are addictive' (*Observer* 16 May 1965).

Drugs were always news for the press. Under the headline 'Youth Club Drugs Shock' the *Evening Standard* reported that 'a shock survey of London clubs by a vicar has revealed that more than half the young people in them were "experimenting" with drugs' (*Evening Standard* 16 December 1966). In July 1967 Mick Jagger of the Rolling Stones was sentenced to three months' imprisonment for the illegal possession of four tablets of amphetamine sulphate. The attention was so great that *The Times* even commented in a leader that the press was giving too much publicity to drugs and that 'If there were a public relations firm with a heroin account they could feel proud of the work they have been doing recently'. It considered that 'whatever may be the truth of individual articles, the total effect has been to dramatize drug-taking and almost certainly to spread rather than inhibit the habit' (*The Times* 28 February 1967).

By October *The Times* was itself under attack for having published an advertisement earlier in the year advocating the legalization of cannabis. Throughout 1967 there was a growing debate about cannabis and calls for changes in the law relating to its use. In April the government had set up a special subcommittee of the Advisory Committee on Drug Dependence, under Baroness Wootton, to examine the use of cannabis and LSD (Advisory Committee on Drug Dependence 1968). The advertisement in *The Times* had appeared in July, was signed by many well-known people, and asserted that the dangers of cannabis were exaggerated and that the law was unworkable and damaging. There followed an intensive debate on cannabis and reports of inquiries such as that by the National Council for Civil Liberties on 'Drugs and Civil Liberties'. But there was also strong reaction against liberalization of the law. Quintin Hogg, Conservative MP, called the publication of *The Times* advertisement 'a grave error of professional judgement' (*The Times* 25 October 1967) by the editor. A few days after the cannabis advertisement appeared, Professor Francis Camps, the Home Office Pathologist, speaking to Young Conservatives, called for a declaration of war on the 'permissive society'. The *Daily Telegraph* reported that 'like Mr Hogg at the Conservative Party Conference, he blamed the false prophets who lend distinguished or popular names to the advocacy of cannabis for making the task for the police in suppressing drug traffic and drug taking vastly harder than it need be' (*Daily Telegraph* 30 October 1967).

### IMPLEMENTING THE BRAIN COMMITTEE PROPOSALS

Most of the recommendations of the Brain Committee, with the exception of compulsory treatment, were accepted by the Minister of Health and the Home Secretary. In August 1966 the Minister of Health announced that there were already centres for the treatment of addicts but when a Ministry spokesman was further questioned, he revealed that the Minister was not talking about any new facilities that had been set up as a result of the Brain report. This prompted a letter to *The Times* from the Rev. Ken Leech, who was by then working with drug users in the West End of London:

> 'The Minister of Health's notorious statement of August 2nd about treatment centres was received by doctors, social workers and addicts with cynical laughter or with despair. Those who daily face the problems of the young drug-taker are finding the obstacles almost insurmountable: hours and days spent ringing round hospitals for admissions; refusals, evasions, and interminable delays; addicts whose condition deteriorates and parents whose hearts are broken; doctors who refuse to prescribe, and doctors who prescribe with almost criminal irresponsibility; and an overwhelming sense of hopelessness and despair among those who know the drug scene closest.'
>
> (*The Times* 9 November 1966)

The chaos and uncertainty that were to characterize the second half of the 1960s have been well described by Leech in *Keep the Faith Baby* (1973). He was one of several workers in the West End who saw the situation getting worse and were indignant that the government was so slow to act. The doctors who had been seeing patients, and who had faced criticism in the Brain Committee report, were withdrawing. Many of these patients now tried other practitioners, or were calling at the Home Office for help in finding a doctor. As Leech pointed out, the Ministry of Health condemned the prescribing doctors, yet at the same time hoped that they would continue to prop up the old system until the Ministry was ready with the new Clinics.

The problem for the government was two-fold. In order to put the Brain Committee proposals into effect there would have to be restrictions on the right of ordinary doctors to prescribe for addicts. These restrictions could not be introduced until alternative facilities, the new Clinics, were open. The opening of these Clinics in turn required extensive negotiation with the administrators of the NHS regions in which they were to be located. Eventually, during early 1967, the Ministry of Health did conduct discussions with Regional Hospital Boards and the Boards of Governors of teaching hospitals for the establishment of the Clinics.

There was much speculation and uncertainty as to how many Clinics would be established, where they would be located, when they would be opened and who would staff them. The situation was highly charged, questions were raised in the House of Commons, and letters were written to the press. It is likely however that even the civil servants at the Ministry of Health did not know all the answers, nor could any answers be given whilst negotiations were still taking place with hospital administrators.

In January 1967 the Home Secretary announced in the House of Commons that a Dangerous Drugs Bill would be introduced under which only licensed doctors would be able to prescribe heroin and cocaine, and which would make notification obligatory. *The Times*, on 31 January 1967, warned that the change from doctor-based to clinic-based treatment should not be rushed, that addicts would be suspicious of the new arrangements, and that the Clinics would have to win the trust 'of those in the grip of the habit'. *The Times* pointed out that the new facilities would place a strain on existing psychiatric units and that in some areas it would be necessary to build new facilities. In March 1967 the Ministry of Health issued a formal memorandum, *Treatment and Supervision of Heroin Addiction*, to Hospital Boards in the London area with psychiatric departments asking them to introduce out-patient services immediately, on a small scale, to make plans to extend these services to cope with the increased demand that would follow the implementation of legislation, to expand in-patient services, to inform the Ministry within a month of the services provided and the plans for future expansion, and to prepare lists of doctors who should need licences to prescribe. Outside London, Hospital Boards were asked to make similar provisions when warranted by the number of known addicts.

The discussions with hospitals continued to be prolonged and confused. In June 1967 the Ministry was confident enough to announce a list of hospitals in London where facilities existed, but when one West End practitioner, Dr Hawes, contacted these hospitals, only two, Westminster and Lambeth, agreed that they had Clinics. The *Daily Mail*, on 7 July 1967, reported that facilities would be inadequate for at least a year. On 16 July, Hawes' findings were published in *The Sunday Times* (1967) under the heading 'The Strange Case of the Missing Drug Centres'. The Ministry was making optimistic statements about progress in establishing Clinics: but from the point of view of many of the hospitals contacted, the proposals were still at the paper stage. To make matters worse, Lady Frankau died in May 1967, 'a factor', Leech ironically said, 'which apparently the Ministry in its planning had not anticipated' (Leech 1973: 40). But there were soon two other doctors prescribing. One was Dr Browdy, aged eighty-two, who was practising in Shaftesbury Avenue. The other was Dr Petro, who in July was prescribing heroin and cocaine from the tea buffet at Baker Street underground station (*Daily Mail* 8 July 1967), and by the end of 1967 was operating from an hotel in Bayswater. Heroin and cocaine continued to be relatively easily available even if there were temporary fluctuations caused by the departure or irregularity of prescribing doctors. *OZ* magazine in March 1967 gave an American sociologist's account: 'The Brain report', he remarked, 'is quite right in assuming that a number of so-called junkies, as yet unregistered, obtain their first supplies from registered addicts.' He went on to recount the sale of drugs around Piccadilly Circus:

> 'The most well-known method (not for the shy) is to stand outside Boots, or if tired, to sit on the baskets situated just to the left of the entrance. Most of the young junkies are willing to sell and are easily identified by their ability to sleep in an upright position.
>
> One of the most amenable pushers is a blonde well-built American girl of 22 who collects her heroin every evening between six and seven. "I think your English Health Service is wonderful!" The usual routine is to follow her until she stands by the left-luggage lockers in Piccadilly Tube after six o'clock. After a brief conversation, she will sell heroin at 3/4d a jack or £1 a grain. This has been the standard price for some time; such heroin is good unadulterated NHS heroin.
>
> Precisely how many heroin users purchase supplies in this way is difficult to assess, but on one Friday evening, thirty-four non-registered junkies were seen to purchase or attempt to purchase heroin within a period of two hours.'
>
> (*OZ* 13 March 1967)

Meanwhile, the number of addicts known to the Home Office was still increasing. The second Brain Committee reported that there were 342 known heroin addicts. By 1965 there were 521, in 1966 899, and by 1967 the number had reached 1299 (*see Table 2(2)*, p. 36–7).

The legislation required to put the Brain proposals into effect was passed in the Dangerous Drugs Act on 27 October 1967. As planned, it gave the Home Secretary powers to require doctors to notify addicts to a central authority, and to limit the prescribing of restricted drugs to those doctors who were licensed by the Home Secretary. It also gave the police powers to search people and vehicles if there were 'reasonable grounds to suspect that any person is in possession of a drug' controlled under the Dangerous Drugs legislation. But although the Act gave the Home Secretary 'powers', these were not implemented until he issued the relevant regulations, which was not until the following spring, of 1968.

In January 1968 Dr Petro appeared on the David Frost television programme and was confronted by people working with addicts (Judson 1974). After he left the television studio he was arrested by the Drug Squad and charged with failing to keep his Dangerous Drugs Register. Released on bail the next day, he left for Scotland. He was sentenced in February and struck off the Medical Register in May (but continued to practise until the end of the year, when his appeal was turned down). Along with the new Act, Dr Petro's departure in February caused panic among addicts. Volunteers set up an emergency Clinic at St Anne's, Soho, in early 1968 to cater for Dr Petro's ex-patients. Leech recalled that addicts who could not get a prescription from a doctor were 'phoning the Home Office for advice, and that all the Home Office could do was refer them to St Anne's, 'an ironic comment', he said, 'on the Ministry of Health's claims about treatment centres' (Leech 1973: 43). The Ministry continued to claim that facilities were available, while those working with addicts continued to find it difficult to get placements for addicts. *The Sunday Times*, on 18 February 1968, reported 'Ministry addict Clinics are just a myth' and gave the results of a survey of fifteen hospitals which showed long waiting lists, restrictive catchment areas, inadequate staffing and facilities, and 'general chaos'.

However, during the spring of 1968, despite uncertainty and confusion, the new arrangements became clearer. The various provisions of the 1967 Dangerous Drugs Act came into operation and these required the compulsory notification of addicts. Any medical practitioner who saw a patient considered or suspected to be addicted to certain drugs was required to notify the Chief Medical Officer at the Home Office. For the purposes of notification, a person was regarded as addicted: 'only if, as a result of repeated administration, he has become so dependent upon the drug that he has an overpowering desire for the administration of it to be continued' (Dangerous Drugs (Notification of Addicts) regulations 1968). The drugs covered were heroin, some other opiates, and cocaine. Notification was a statutory obligation whether or not the doctor prescribed these drugs for the patient.

The licensing system had to wait for the establishment of sufficient Clinics, and was finally implemented in the Dangerous Drugs (Supply to Addicts) Regulations (1968), which came into operation on 16 April 1968. From this date ordinary medical practitioners could no longer prescribe heroin and cocaine to 'addicts'. Licences to prescribe were mostly issued to consultants and senior medical staff working in NHS hospitals, and to those doctors working in the new Clinics; the licences were limited to a named place. It was not intended that general practitioners would receive licences, although a few private doctors did so. By restricting licences, and hence prescribing, to the Clinic doctors the new arrangements meant that addicts would have to attend Clinics if they wished to receive heroin and cocaine on prescription. In those areas where there were expected to be too few addict patients to warrant the establishment of a Clinic, licences were issued to appropriate hospital doctors working in psychiatric wards and departments.

A turning point in British policy towards addiction is marked by 16 April 1968. It was the end of the 'system' that had emerged from Rolleston's interpretation of the first legislation to control drugs in the 1920s; the end of the private prescribing doctor, one of whom summed up the new policy by saying that 'the sun is setting on the junkies' paradise in this country' (*The Sunday Times*, Weekly Review 20 February 1966); and the start of the new Clinic system. It was a significant date for many of the addicts we interviewed, and seven and eight years later many could still remember the day in 1968 when the changeover from private doctors to Clinics occurred. As Bill Gregor, who was still a patient at one of the Clinics in 1977, put it: 'When the Clinics started the heyday, if you can call it that, was over.'

# Part Two
## *The addicts and the Clinics*

# 4

# *Routes into addiction – addicts in the 1960s*

The heroin addicts we interviewed in this study were among those who were being discussed by doctors and legislators in the 1960s. We first interviewed them in 1969, when they were all patients at London drug Clinics. They were all receiving prescriptions for heroin, and most had come to the Clinics when they had opened in 1968. The majority started using drugs in the 1960s, and, on average, they were about sixteen-and-a-half when they first tried any illicit drugs (though we noted considerable variation, with one person claiming to have used drugs at the age of eleven and another not starting until the age of forty). On average, it was two-and-a-half years after first using drugs before people in our study used heroin, i.e. at about the age of nineteen. The majority (86 per cent) first used heroin between 1962 and 1967 (*see Appendix Figure A(2)*, p. 232). It was a further two years before they considered that they were addicted to it.

## BECOMING ADDICTED

The question 'how did you become an addict' is frequently asked of such people, and two famous addicts, Thomas De Quincey and William Burroughs, though separated by nearly a century-and-a-half both found it necessary to ask themselves this question, and to provide their readers with an answer. De Quincey, writing in the 1820s in his *Confessions of an English Opium Eater*, explained his addiction like this:

'I have often been asked – how it was, and through what series of steps, that I became an opium eater. . . . Was it on a sudden overmastering impulse derived from bodily anguish? Loudly I repeat, *Yes*; loudly and indignantly – as in answer to a wilful calumny. Simply as an anodyne it was, under the mere coercion of pain the severest, that I first resorted to opium; and precisely that same torment it is, or some variety of that torment, which drives most people to make acquaintance with that same insidious remedy.'

(De Quincey 1978 edn: 139–40)

De Quincey wrote that he first used opium to relieve pain, and went on to describe other qualities that made its use attractive:

'If in the early days I had fully understood the subtle powers lodged in this mighty drug . . . (1) to tranquillise all irritations of the nervous system; (2) to stimulate the capacities of enjoyment; and (3) under any call for extraordinary exertion (such as all men meet at times) to sustain through twenty-four consecutive hours the else dropping animal energies – most certainly, knowing or suspecting all this, I should have inaugurated my opium career in the character of one seeking *extra* power and enjoyment, rather than of one shrinking from *extra* torment.'

(De Quincey 1978 edn: 140)

The American William Burroughs, writing in *Junkie* (1969) gave a different account. You do not, he said, 'intend to become an addict. You don't wake up one morning and decide to be a drug addict.' He described the long process needed to arrive at this state:

'It takes at least three months shooting twice a day to get any habit at all. And you don't really know what junk sickness is until you have had several habits. It took me almost six months to get my first habit, and then the withdrawal symptoms were mild. I think it no exaggeration to say it takes about a year and several hundred injections to make an addict.

The question, of course, could be asked: Why did you ever try narcotics? Why did you continue using it long enough to become an addict? You become a narcotics addict because you do not have strong enough motivations in any other direction. Junk wins by default.'

(Burroughs 1969: 11)

De Quincey and Burroughs have given us inside views on addiction, De Quincey emphasizing the 'subtle powers' of opium, and Burroughs the lengthy process by which one becomes addicted. They remind us that the opiates are attractive drugs, and that one does not become addicted overnight. But such insights have often been ignored by professional workers, who have been tempted to seek explanations for addiction in the inevitability of a defective personality or an unhappy family life. They seek an understanding of addiction by asking 'what sort of people become addicts?' We found this approach had some limitations. In many ways the addicts we met had rather unremarkable backgrounds, and it would be difficult to point out any characteristics they shared that would explain why they became addicts. Certainly there were some who had led disrupted and unhappy lives before they became addicted to heroin; but there were many others whose backgrounds were quite ordinary. In seeking to understand how people become addicts, we thought we should rather look at the combination of circumstances, opportunities, and inclinations they faced: to use heroin, people have to be in the right place, at the right time, and in the right frame of mind. And, as Burroughs showed, it takes some time and effort to become an addict. This is why we have chosen to call this chapter *routes* into addiction, for this draws our attention to the passage of people into such an unusual activity as using heroin.

In seeking to understand these routes, we were faced with two difficult, methodological problems. First, there was the problem that we were discussing events that occurred some distance in the past. Most of the detailed material on how people became addicts was not collected until our follow-up study in 1976/77, ten years or more later than the events being discussed. The second problem was that addicts are frequently asked questions concerning how they became addicted. Any meeting with a doctor, social worker, probation officer, magistrate, or research worker may be turned into an occasion where the addict's biography is investigated, and addicts are perhaps more frequently than the rest of us called upon to reflect on and examine their careers. Such meetings are also occasions for professional workers to produce their own theories of addiction, explicitly, through the advice or comments they make, and implicitly, through the types of questions they ask. We noticed that many people were practised in giving accounts of how and why they became addicts, and sometimes gave stories that seemed a close fit to one or another professional theory about the nature of addiction. The accounts that we were given, then, contained not only reminiscences but also something about the subsequent experience of the individual and the particular audience being addressed. Thus, overlaying the detailed elaboration of the events, there are certain themes that bring emphasis to people's stories.

In the explanations that we were given we were able to discern two broadly different themes. Some people focused on the mood of the 1960s and the ideals of the period. They mentioned being attracted by wild tales of life in Soho and Piccadilly, of jazz clubs, and all-night dancing clubs. They mentioned hearing drugs referred to by 'Beat' poets of the late 1950s, or had read, for example, of Timothy Leary's experience with LSD. Leary was an ex-Harvard psychologist who was an active protagonist of the use of psychedelic drugs such as LSD and psylocybin (Leary 1970). Some spoke of the significance of drugs in the life of young people in places such as Richmond and Welwyn Garden City. They characterized themselves positively as young, rebellious, and bored. These were essentially *social* accounts of 'turning on' to heroin: the emphasis was on the experiences they shared with others.

The second theme was essentially *psychological*. It emphasized individual problems. In these accounts people talked of depression, of psychic pain, of mental illness, and of a hope that heroin would take the edge off these uncomfortable feelings. They emphasized their personal experiences, feelings of unhappiness and despair, and an awareness that drugs could provide a solution to personal problems. These people said they sought out drugs for private and personal reasons. The fact that heroin was chosen was at times almost incidental – there was an implication that in a different time or place they might have used something else.

A good distinction could be drawn between the two themes by seeing the psychological ones as focusing on self-therapy, and the social ones as focusing on hedonism. But the two themes overlap, and can be further subdivided. Social accounts include certain features that emphasize passive drift into groups of people using drugs, as well as the active seeking of new experiences. Psychological accounts may include a psychodynamic emphasis on childhood and family-life experiences as well as a focus on heroin in the instrumental amelioration of distress. It would be unwise, then, to imply a fixity to the accounts. After all, the same people talking about their past in other situations, to another audience, or to researchers from other disciplines or institutions, may have given a different form or focus to their stories.

### Social accounts: 'turning on' with friends

Those who gave social accounts of their first use of heroin emphasized the friends or acquaintances they were with at the time. Most were moving in a social milieu where drugs were available and widely used; most commonly, these were amphetamines, cannabis, and, occasionally, LSD. Some described mixing in Bohemian circles of artists, writers, and musicians – many of these were older and of the 1950s generation of addicts. Others portrayed themselves as 'Beatniks', travelling the roads, just as Jack Kerouac, who coined the term 'beat generation', had done in

*On The Road* (1957), and when in London congregated in pubs such as Finches and The Duke of York. Others went to all-night music clubs such as the Flamingo, the Marquee, and the Whisky-A-Gogo in Soho. For some it was the pill scene, at its height in 1963 and 1964, that was attractive. This fitted in with the style of the Mods, the clean-cut, well-dressed style popular with affluent working-class teenagers: amphetamines kept one awake if one wanted to spend a weekend dancing at the clubs. The addicts and ex-addicts we spoke to recalled that sooner or later they met someone who was actually injecting heroin.

Many addict's stories will lack the drama that non-addicts might wish to associate with self-injection. For some, the first 'fix' was a casual affair. As Greg Wheeler put it: 'Why did I think I was into it? I think I was bored really, it was just starting, a sort of craze. I did not actually realize what it was and I took it.' But Jack Daniels perhaps best summed up the nonchalance of the time: 'I was just sort of bumming around . . . from one end of the country to the next, and I came to a stop in London.' And that is where he came across heroin.

Let us look at three people's descriptions of how they came across heroin. Wayne Jennings, when he looked back on his life before heroin addiction, recalled his family as quite ordinary. He was the younger of two children in a working-class family. His father drank a bit too much and his mother was somewhat overbearing, but he remembered his childhood as a time when he was neither especially happy nor greatly unhappy. Material goods were not plentiful but he did not suffer any remarkable privation. Despite his obvious intelligence he failed his eleven-plus examination and went to the neighbourhood secondary modern school. He remembered being bored and lacking concentration. He started truanting regularly from school and first got into trouble with the police at fourteen when he was caught stealing a pair of ice skates. On another occasion he got drunk with friends and they smashed a bus shelter. He was caught and this time was put on probation. Around then he began going regularly to pubs, though under age. His parents seemed to have exerted little control over him. He left school at fifteen and seemed to settle down, fitting in well to the world of work. He worked steadily and at the age of eighteen became a roving relief manager for a chain of stores. He recalled that despite his position of responsibility he was not well-paid because he was so young. Soon after starting this job he was slightly injured in a car accident and awarded considerable compensation by the court. He recalled that the sudden windfall of money unsettled him. He found new friends and began smoking cannabis. At first he did not enjoy it: 'It was quite an experience . . . I used to buy some, smoke it, be ill and then sell the rest again . . . and really that was the start leading up to the actual heroin addiction.' Besides cannabis, he gradually used other drugs: 'Then also along came the purple hearts – those were taken quite frequently in large numbers – twenty or thirty were large numbers for me. Others took hundreds over two or three days.' And then he came across heroin, at a party in 1967, when he was nineteen. 'It all happened very quickly, there appeared on the scene half a dozen persons who seemed to be that step in front and who were using heroin, cocaine. In fact, two of them lived at the end of my road.' He continued:

> 'Although I could see what was going on to me it was rather alien because these people had an amazing amount of freedom . . . they all had girls . . . but my initial reaction was *no* – absolutely out of the question. And this went on for two or three months and of course all the time the social scene was right there. Evenings were spent there, transactions were going on . . . I was still smoking cannabis and I did have this terrible reaction against injections. . . . But eventually one day I must have wanted to try, though I feel I was a bit talked into it. By that time everyone else was injecting. . . . So I tried it.'

He remembered the effect heroin had on his friends:

> 'I saw all my other friends taking heroin and being sick and ill for about half an hour or so and then of course they would disappear somewhere to sleep it off. But it never happened to me, so in a way that in itself didn't put me off having a next one. Then the whole thing escalated. There used to be a character who lived in Highgate or Islington and this man had God knows how much of this stuff around. He was an addict and he was violent and we would go up to his place. The chosen one, who was the one who was friendliest with him at the time, would go in and buy for everyone and this could mean anything up to £50 worth. We would then all go back to Enfield and for the next four or five days the whole place would be in complete oblivion. I would say it involved at least fifteen people.'

He remembered that he kept his addiction secret from his family for a long time. He was more irritable than usual and noted that his character changed, but he did not become scruffy or slovenly and tried to maintain a normal appearance. This all happened just before the Clinics opened. He summed up his experience: 'I've reached the conclusion that I was involved without making a choice really.'

He was twenty-eight when we interviewed him in 1977. He had stopped using heroin in 1970 after using it for three years, and was working in a company in a senior position having charge of overseas trade, a job which he enjoyed. He was married and owned his house. He added: 'It's the last thing I ever thought I would do, sitting behind an office desk and running departments.'

The gradual drift into addiction was a common feature of many people's explanations of how they became addicted. In Wayne Jennings' case this all happened in the area in which he was brought up, but Raymond O'Sullivan thought that an important part of his story was that he left home. He described himself as a 'Beat', hitch-hiking around England in the early 1960s. He came from rural Ireland and his family was very poor, suffering from material shortages when he was a child. His father was a heavy drinker and sometimes violent. Raymond had little formal education: however, he had a lively mind and a 'thirst for experience'. He came to England, worked in various towns, and finally ended up in Richmond, working as a fish-fryer. He was smoking cannabis by then, and remembered:

> 'Well it was about 1966 when I was in Richmond. The doctors that were prescribing drugs were prescribing enormous amounts and it was getting all around London, people were picking up on it fast. What happened was a junkie said to me one night . . . well he wanted a place to sleep and shoot up, because you can't do it on the streets or in toilets all the time, and that's how I came by it. Well he gave me a bit of heroin . . . I think I was just curious. I took it slowly after the initial one, now and then. I wasn't really interested in it then, I was more interested in marijuana. Once I'd had some heroin and some methedrine, it opened up new things within you and you want to realize what you're taking and you want to find out more.'

He maintained that he was not too enthusiastic about heroin, viewing it simply as one of a number of drugs to choose from, and being more interested in cannabis. It was the time 'when the Beatles were making a lot of good records and LSD came onto the market in large amounts'. He liked that drug, too. However: 'What happened was I got my tracks mixed up. I started using all three . . . I had a thirst for experience as it were.'

Raymond O'Sullivan stopped using heroin in 1973 but had since used large amounts of barbiturates, amphetamines, and, more recently, alcohol. He worked occasionally, but at other times lived on Social Security benefits and begging. He had constant 'hassles' with the police because of his use of cannabis. In 1976 he still believed deeply in 'the flower generation, the hippy generation, people who realized what was happening in the world, that it was just full of hate and that love is the only answer if this world is to survive'.

Wayne Jennings and Raymond O'Sullivan emphasized the gradual way they wandered into using drugs and eventually using heroin, as if to say that they did not consciously choose what they did, but just went along with what was happening around them. This is rather like Burroughs' explanation, that one becomes addicted because 'you do not have strong enough motivations in any other direction' (Burroughs 1969: 11). Not every addict interviewed had discovered heroin in this way: some emphasized that they actively sought it out, had made a deliberate decision to use it. For example, Bennett Howell said that he tried heroin because it was one aspect of his curiosity to explore new ideas and experiences with friends. He came from a suburban South London family and when interviewed still lived, with his wife and child, in his parents' home. He was intelligent and articulate and did not regret his ten years of addiction. On the contrary, he maintained that he still enjoyed using drugs. He recalled that he started when, as a university student, he was involved with a group of people who decided to take drugs 'to see what effect they would have'. He was then twenty.

> 'In a lot of ways I was very much a leader. People used to meet round here. We were a fairly intelligent group of four or five and we had read all this stuff about drugs in the papers and we thought it can't be true, let's take some drugs and see what they are like, let's see what the fuss is about, let's see what it's all about. See if the papers are telling the truth about these "evil pushers". And we had got involved in many other things before and since, politics or doing other crazy things. We decided as a *group* that that's what we wanted to do.'

Bennett thought that drug use was misunderstood. He believed that people should be allowed to take whatever drugs they chose. At the same time, being addicted was really of no great importance: 'If it's there you take it. And it's not something you burn up your whole life worrying about. If the government slams down on it completely . . . you'll be sick for a few weeks – it's nasty but you'll get over it.'

The accounts of these addicts and ex-addicts illustrate the casualness with which some found heroin and continued using it. They all started using it when it was relatively cheap and easily available. They stress the sense of fun, excitement, adventurousness, and rebelliousness of being caught up in a new style of life, and the novelty of being with a group of strange and interesting friends. Few expressed regret about the way their lives turned out, nor did they see themselves as having, then or previously, any serious problems.

### Psychological accounts: 'turning on' alone

In contrast, some people who became addicted described themselves as essentially lonely people. They perceived their early drug experience as primarily a personal one, rather than a shared experience with others. They referred to serious emotional difficulties, unhappiness, or suicidal feelings. Some felt as though life had no great meanings, so their actions were of no consequence.

One person's experiences, though unusual, emphasize the solitariness of some addicts' drug use. He ascribed his interest in drugs not to meeting other drug users but to reading *Junkie,* in which Burroughs described how to extract the amphetamine from a plastic nasal inhaler: 'I remember how he described how you crack it open and swallow the paper. So I took out a couple of strips of paper and that just knocked you clean out. It was just unbelievable, and I really started from then on.' From amphetamines he went on to injecting methedrine, and finally used heroin, obtaining it from a friend at work who had connections with jazz musicians. He took heroin whenever he could buy it: 'It was very cheap . . . six or seven tablets to a pound.' He never became closely involved with other addicts, relying at the beginning on his friend at work, and later going to a Clinic. He used heroin from 1967 through to 1970.

Others were more explicit about their emotional difficulties. Nick Humphreys, for example, used heroin as a way of coping with long-standing depression. He had worked in industry for about ten years, in his home town of Middlesbrough. The way he described it, his family life had been difficult, with his parents always quarrelling, and an atmosphere at home that was unhappy. A relationship with a girl broke up, and he felt lonely and depressed and was drinking a lot. He recalled his drinking days prior to heroin: 'I used to drink with friends and I used to drink on my own as well and maybe I'd be out with a group of friends and I'd think, "Oh hell", and go away and drink somewhere else on my own. I was getting less and less sociable.'

When he was twenty-five he left for London and soon after arriving met people who smoked cannabis. He continued his description of what happened:

> 'I've always been pretty heavily into drugs of some kind . . . alcohol first – I used an incredible amount of alcohol prior to my using drugs and then I came into contact with people who smoked hashish and I started to smoke it. It was ideal really because I was getting pretty depressed at the time and of course alcohol doesn't help depression. And so I was quite happy for two years, or one year, and then I had the opportunity, if you can call it that, of using heroin, so I used that. I suppose there were lots of little reasons, perhaps a little bit of despair, a bit of curiosity, not really caring, knowing it's dangerous but inclined to think of suicide at times. Kept thinking, "What the hell", I mean I knew the dangers of addiction before I started, it wasn't as though I didn't. Just prepared to take that chance.'

He started using heroin in 1966. When we interviewed him ten years later he was thirty-seven and still addicted to heroin. He did not work, saw few friends, and spent most of his time at his parents' home, listening to records and watching the clock until the time for his next fix or visit to the Clinic. He used a small amount of heroin and yet his entire existence was bound up with his two daily injections. He summed up the reasons why he started: 'Well personality defects I suppose. I just feel as if I've got to have these props. Yes, and I think it just becomes a ritual, like a religious ritual really.'

David Milford was another man who stressed his personal difficulties, but for him it was not a long-standing emotional problem but a sudden crisis. He remembered that he made a calculated decision to take heroin, choosing it, he said, because he wanted instant relief from unhappy feelings and thoughts. Heroin was unrivalled in dulling the mind and removing his sense of anxiety – at least for a while. He experienced the crisis when he was at the end of his second year at university, in 1965, and was twenty years old. He felt then that he did not have the time 'to sit about and mope about things', so he made his 'cold-blooded decision' to take heroin for six to nine months to get him through the final exams. He told us:

> 'I bought it for about three months and then switched over to getting it from a GP and carried on like that for three years. I consciously decided at the time I started only to take it for a fixed length of time. Everything worked out as intended, the only thing that didn't work out was I didn't stop.'

When we interviewed him in 1977, he was working as an engineer, and still a patient at a Clinic.

Finally, there was Elizabeth Collinson, who also stressed her mood at the time she started. This was in 1966, when she was nineteen. She recalled beginning to use heroin regularly at a time when she was unhappy and confused. She was an art-school model and the idea of using drugs was 'not for kicks or anything' but a means of getting through the day. She had tried heroin at a party and did not use it again for six months. Then, when she 'was in a right state' and was 'slightly screwed up', she had an unexpected chance to use heroin, believed that it might help her, and it did. 'I don't know what I'd be like if I hadn't gone on it. I didn't trust people then. If things started hassling one, you could always turn on to heroin, and it was always there, you could rely on it.' She used heroin for seven years until she stopped in 1973.

These, then, are some of the people who gave essentially psychological explanations of their first experiences with heroin. They used it as a means to combat their unhappy feelings, talking primarily of looking for answers to their inner conflicts and of the alleviation of emotional pain, or a sense of purposelessness and depression. They did not characterize themselves as mixing with other drug users, nor sharing any topical ideology of drug use, saying that, mostly, their drug-taking was a private and personal activity. Like De Quincey, they emphasized the power of the opiates to 'tranquillise all irritations of the nervous system' (De Quincey 1978 edn: 140). Using heroin was something necessary at the time, which they might stop should circumstances render that possible. They were not out to change the world but to change themselves.

### FROM CASUAL TO REGULAR USE

As we have already noted, heroin is not instantaneously addictive. There are people who can use it and never become addicted; others use it occasionally in small quantities for quite prolonged periods without addiction resulting. We have even found ex-addicts who reported being able to use heroin occasionally, without becoming re-addicted, provided they were careful to space its use. All the people we interviewed, though, had become addicted eventually, for we selected them by virtue of that fact and they were addict patients attending drug Clinics.

This group of people identified the occurrence of a crucial change when a casual use turned into a 'habit'. This came with the realization that instead of choosing to use heroin at will, they needed it every day. The reader can refer to Kevin Cummings' biography in Chapter 8, where he recalled that he repeatedly tested himself to see if he was addicted, and how one day he realized that he was, because all he wanted was 'a fix'. Raymond O'Sullivan also recalled that realization of needing heroin every day: 'Then I got more and more into it and I was using it every day, it went up to three pills a day, half a grain, and then I said "I'll have to stop this" and I tried.' But he found that he could not stop. When casual use became daily use, or a habit, he had to ensure a regular supply. He had been buying heroin from a friend. But then:

> 'the guy I was getting it off got nicked and you know I found that it was getting a bit harder to get – so I could have gone over to Piccadilly to get it very easy – but I didn't know the Piccadilly scene. So I went to Dr Orpheus in Kingston and he gave me two-and-a-half grains of heroin a day.'

This was not the immediate response of all the sample to the question of availability. It was easy to obtain supplies of heroin and cocaine in the 1960s. We heard many stories of those doctors who were unable to withstand the pressures and persuasiveness of addict patients. There was a steady supply of surplus-prescribed heroin and cocaine being sold on the black market. Prices were low. For Bill Gregor the financial drain caused by his addiction was zero. He came from a middle-class family and was a runaway from public school. He started using heroin early in 1968, spent about two years as an addict, living in Soho and the West End and working in sex-film cinemas. His habit was never a big one, even though drugs were extremely cheap. He said:

> 'You've got to remember the economics of the situation. Before the Clinics came you had a situation where a grain of heroin cost you, what was it, six jacks [pills of heroin] to one pound, eight to a pound if you were lucky. You were talking about peanuts. . . . The level at which I was using I could sustain out of "pocket money" without any fear of running out of either junk or cash.'

Buying heroin was exciting and sometimes dangerous. Unless one had a regular contact one needed to know how to meet people around the all-night chemists – Boots in Piccadilly Circus and John Bell and Croydon in Wigmore Street – where many addicts obtained their prescribed drugs. It was possible to sustain an occasional use of heroin, or even a moderate habit, without too much worry about money or the need to obtain a legal prescription from a doctor. Rita Hemmings, by 1976 in her forties and still attending a Clinic, was married to an addict in the late 1960s and she and her musician husband could somehow find enough money to sustain their addictions 'scoring' heroin. For £60 a week they bought 60 grains (3600 mgs). It would have been easy to 'register' with a private doctor and receive a legal prescription for heroin, but they did not want to. 'We preferred to pay for it and keep it dark, as it were . . . we lived in fairyland half the time.' Both kept this up for ten years: she could buy as much as she wanted and ended up using eighteen grains of heroin a day.

Most of the addicts we talked to eventually obtained a prescription for heroin and cocaine from a private doctor. Louise Wrighton gave one of the most startling accounts of her first meeting with such a doctor. Although bizarre, her story illustrates the ease with which drugs were obtained. At twenty, she was 'young and confused' and her friends thought she needed psychiatric help. She was brought up in Chelsea and her friends included members of London's criminal underworld. She had some aquaintance with drug users but only had one injection of heroin before going to a doctor. It was a coincidence that the Wimpole Street doctor recommended to her for psychiatric assistance by well-meaning friends was one of the doctors who was willing to liberally prescribe heroin and cocaine. This is how Louise Wrighton described what happened:

> 'So I went there and the people in the waiting room said "Oh ask for four and four" and I didn't know what "four and four" meant. So I

> went in and she said "Sit down, oh yes, you are Miss Wrighton. I don't usually take girls on, they are usually prostitutes, but I've been over your case". She said "I do hope you are not injecting cocaine. I do hope you are sniffing it, because you'll get an orgasm if you inject it". My goodness I was only very young. I didn't know what she was talking about.'

Instead of getting psychiatric help Louise came out of the surgery with a prescription for a daily dose of four grains of both heroin and cocaine. With this sudden windfall of drugs she went to see a girlfriend and they both injected. It was only her second injection of heroin, and the first of cocaine. She said that she remained unconscious for eight hours. Despite this experience, she discovered she liked heroin and cocaine and the glamour attached to their use. She continued to use drugs, from about 1964 to the time the Clinics opened, obtaining plentiful supplies from her private doctor. At one time she attempted to stop by going away from London and recalled that her doctor, concerned for her well-being, posted unsolicited prescriptions to her. She mentioned Christmas 1965, when the doctor gave her 65 grains (3900 mgs) of heroin and 65 grains (3900 mgs) of cocaine for Christmas Eve, Christmas Day, and Boxing Day. On Boxing Day she went back to her doctor's house, having run out of cocaine, and was given 720 mgs of both heroin and cocaine. She remembered: 'I was in love with cocaine, it sounds crazy but it was the love of my life, nothing ever has meant anything to me.' She still attends a Clinic.

Most stories were not as extraordinary as this. We expected that people would tell us that the first visit to a doctor, 'medicalizing' their drug use, would be a traumatic experience, or at least a memorable one. But, it turned out this was not so. Going to see a doctor was just another step in what by then had become the attempt to obtain daily supplies.

Becoming 'registered' with a doctor was generally financially motivated. As the need for money to buy drugs became greater with increased drug use, so a person's ability to find the necessary money lessened. Marty Rose, for example, first used heroin in 1967. He was sixteen and a 'Skinhead' with short hair, short jeans held up by braces, tee-shirt, and Doctor Marten boots. He had left school in the East End and 'hung about' with a number of other unemployed friends in cafes around Brick Lane. He wanted to do all the things his friends did. He recalled: 'Well, there were a lot of us, a lot of people who used to go out drinking and things like that and used to see each other and it just happened from there really.' He quickly became addicted to heroin without much awareness of what was happening. He came from a respectable working-class family, was living at home, but his parents remained unaware of his addiction. He sold his personal valuables – clothes, rings, and other things collected over the years – in order to purchase drugs. He went to London's

West End to buy drugs for friends and was rewarded by receiving his own drugs free. He remembered that he took enormous risks. At first he went to the West End only once in a while, but as his habit grew together with those of his friends, he went several times a day or just stayed overnight in the West End. At the end he was equally 'terrified' of looking for drugs and 'too ill' to return home. Finally, in early 1968, he decided that he needed a regular source of supply. He was unaware that the Clinics had opened, and went to see a general practitioner who in turn referred him to a Clinic.

Some people went to a doctor for a prescription because they were worried that they were slipping into a criminal way of life which they did not like. Andrew Wright, by 1976 aged forty-two and still receiving a small prescription for heroin, remembered disliking the idea of breaking the law to buy drugs: 'For the first time in my life', he said, 'I was drifting from society, from convention, from being an honest person to being dishonest. . . . This was a world which I did not enjoy . . . it was not the way I was brought up, not the way I wanted to carry on.' Trevor Buckton was also worried at the prospect of thieving to buy drugs. He and a few friends used to shop-lift:

> 'We used to nick jumpers most of the time at Marks and Spencers. Two of us would go in and nick the jumpers and two of them would go back, say they'd bought it and get the money back on it. Then go out and score – that £5 was more or less enough. I didn't like doing that, I don't know, it's the feeling of having to go out and thieve in the morning.'

Finally he was arrested for shop-lifting. This gave him a double motivation for seeking a legitimate prescription. It meant that he would no longer have to steal, and he could also show the court that he was under medical treatment.

### THE END OF THE 'JUNKIES' PARADISE'

The people we followed obtained heroin and cocaine quite easily in the mid-1960s. Virtually all of them started on the overspill of medicinal heroin which was legitimately prescribed to addicts. As they became addicted they found, first, that they could obtain sufficient supplies from addict friends and, later, could themselves go to one of the handful of doctors willing to prescribe. If one doctor did not supply enough there was nothing to prevent an addict going to a second or a third. Many people gave vivid accounts of the times when they were able to go from one doctor to another and obtain unlimited supplies of heroin and cocaine. Andrew Wright nostalgically recalled these days:

'Until the time that the Clinics came into being I spent six months of the year out of England . . . I could go abroad and take 3000 or 4000 tabs of H with me, easily that. Very easily. I mean let's face it, I broke the law in those days. I had five doctors working for me. I mean I just had five different names, five different addresses, and five chemists. I used a lot of stuff and it was easy to pick up 1000 tabs at a time . . . I used to have a box full of it. No trouble at all . . . and going abroad, I mean they only started searching for drugs in the middle 60s and then they weren't really experienced in this, only picked up the sort of hippy type person which I've never really been inclined to be anyway. Before, I could . . . fly around the doctors and get stuff. I didn't see them regularly, only saw them when I thought that I needed it. You paid the money and they gave you the gear and the money was very little. A couple of quid a visit, for which you'd get by today's values £5–6000 worth of drugs.'

This period did not last long and the 'heyday' for addicts ended in April 1968 when ordinary medical practitioners were replaced by the specially licensed doctors working in the new Clinics. The change to the new 'system' was approached with trepidation and uncertainty by the addicts. It had been easy to deal with the prescribing doctors. What would the Clinic doctors be like?

# 5

# *Going to the Clinics*

The publicity surrounding the establishment of the Clinics meant that few addicts could have remained unaware of what was intended, even if they were less than certain of the actual mechanics of the new system. Word of mouth, which so efficiently informed addicts of the whereabouts of junkies' doctors, spread news of the Clinics. Addicts found that chemists could no longer honour prescriptions from unlicensed doctors. Those who were known by the Home Office Drugs Branch and had been receiving prescriptions from private doctors were sent a letter, through that doctor, informing them of the need to go to a Clinic. Voluntary agencies in the West End, such as the Association for the Prevention of Addiction, in Covent Garden, also helped addicts to find Clinics.

By April 1968, there were, in Britain, approximately 600 doctors licensed by the Home Secretary to prescribe heroin and cocaine, and by the autumn there were 39 Clinics providing treatment, 15 in London and 24 in other parts of England and Wales (although the term Clinic might not be so appropriate for some of the facilities outside London, as these were often small and not organized as a separate hospital facility).The Clinics had, by October, a total of 1139 patients and the majority of these (nearly 80 per cent) were attending Clinics serving the London area. The average caseload for London Clinics was 60 patients, but there was a wide range – from 26 up to 121 (and one Clinic with 2 patients only, *see Table 5(1)*).

The new London Clinics were located, for the most part, in teaching hospitals. Some shared general out-patient facilities in the hospital, others had their own separate locations and entrances. For example, the Clinic at the Maudsley Hospital occupied several rooms above the main waiting room for psychiatric out-patients. At Hackney Hospital, the Clinic occupied the basement of one of the psychiatric ward blocks and had its own entrance. Charing Cross Hospital Clinic had its rooms in a building across the street, at the back of the main hospital. Some were given clear names such as 'Drug Dependence Clinic', while others were more euphemistically called 'Psychiatric Unit Annexe', or 'Special Psychiatric Clinic'. The facilities, the quality of the accommodation, and the staffing varied from Clinic to Clinic. Generally, the staff consisted of a doctor or two, a social worker, nurses, and secretarial staff. Some Clinics had more nurses than others, some more social workers, and some had very few of either.

Table 5(1) *Number of patients on the books at London Clinics in October 1968*

| *Clinic* | *A* | *B* | *C* | *D* | *E* | *F* | *G* | *H* | *I* | *J* | *K* | *L* | *M* | *N* | *O* | *total* |
|---|---|---|---|---|---|---|---|---|---|---|---|---|---|---|---|---|
| no. of patients | 33 | 98 | 121 | 87 | 26 | 41 | 103 | 38 | 42 | 92 | 63 | 37 | 44 | 77 | 2 | 904 |

*Source:* Personal communication, Department of Health and Social Security.

When the new regulations were finally implemented, not everyone felt an immediate necessity to 'get on' at a Clinic. Some stayed away at first because they thought that doctors would force them to come off heroin. There were others, especially those who had not been using heroin for long, who saw no immediate reason to attend a Clinic because they were able to obtain adequate supplies on the black market. Mick Hollis, for example, had only started to use heroin in the autumn of 1967, when he was seventeen; when the Clinics opened he was not addicted and did not want to attend. In the winter of 1967/68 he bought heroin from other addicts in the East End who were receiving large prescriptions from private doctors. It was several months before he had 'a daily habit . . . I might have took it one week a couple of times in that week and then left it out for a fortnight or a month.' He continued to use heroin sporadically and had little trouble buying from friends, some of whom were getting '12 grain of H, 12 grain of coke, 12 amps of meth.' And it was cheap. He recalled that 'things were so easy that if you bought a grain, they'd give you 2 or 3 jacks on top.' But after a while his friends found that they received much smaller doses from Clinic than they had from the private doctors, 'they were maybe getting 6 of each [heroin and cocaine], or 6 of H . . . [and] 6 of meth..' So by the summer of 1968 it was harder for him to buy heroin because his friends 'never had the stuff to sell'. This was just at the time when he was beginning to use drugs more frequently. He continued to score for the first three months after the Clinics opened, but when more of his friends started going to Clinics 'then there was no stuff available'. His developing addiction, coupled with this shortage of heroin, persuaded him to go to a Clinic himself.

The majority of people we talked to were already well-established addicts when the Clinics opened, with an average of four years of addiction behind them. Undoubtedly there were some who were barely, if at all, addicted when they first came for a prescription, but on the other hand there were, too, people who had been addicted on-and-off for twenty years or more. All had some experience of the life of the addict under the 'old' British 'system', which had meant spending time chasing doctors for a prescription or experiencing the uncertainty of scoring from a well-supplied addict. The new Clinics did not change things overnight. There were still uncertainties for addicts, but of a different sort. Now that the government was actively involved, people wondered what sort of regime to expect. Many, like Susan Hughes, an ex-addict (*see* Chapter 10), were well-practised in persuading doctors to write prescriptions. She was eighteen at the time the Clinics opened, had been using heroin on-and-off since she was fifteen, and during 1967 and 1968 she sometimes received prescriptions from private doctors. She was one of the first Clinic patients and featured in a television documentary about the changes. She had a boyfriend who was a television camera operator.

> 'My boyfriend said to me "We hear there's a new Clinic opening up. We'd like to find out what it's all about. Would you care to come down with us and see if you can get registered there?" And I said "Fine, I think that's a great idea". Because I thought I won't have to go through all this business of finding the money to pay the doctor so I could get my 'script' [prescription] and I wouldn't have to sell my script because it would only cost me a token amount, four shillings or something like that. So I went down and I got dressed up for the part in a little black chiffon dress and fish-net stockings. And I walked into the Clinic and the doctor said "What are you doing here?" I said 'I've come down to seduce you so that I can have a script.'

The addicts' talents for persuasion, developed in dealing with private doctors, were now applied to their dealings with the Clinic doctors. Take, for example, the problem of being accepted as a patient. What guarantee would there be that the doctor would accept an addict as a patient? The astute addict realized the need to convince the doctor that he or she was indeed addicted and deserved a prescription. Trevor Platt came from the East End of London and had quite a gift for talking. He had been using heroin and methedrine for about a year but he claimed that he was not addicted when he first went to the Clinic, 'I just made out to be addicted'. He took advantage of the difficulties facing the doctors in the early days. At first he was not asked to provide a urine sample and thought that the doctor believed it was possible to diagnose addiction by 'talking and looking' and it was 'quite easy to con'. He was prescribed 2 grains of heroin – 12 pills – much more than the 4 to 6 pills a day he was actually using. He gave a friend 1 pill in exchange for 2 ampoules of methedrine, and sold the rest 'for cigarettes'. In those first few months, in the summer of 1968, he 'skin-popped' – injected under the skin – but to convince the doctor that he was injecting into a vein he would, after injecting under the skin, push the needle into a vein and move it about to cause a swelling, 'so that when I went to the Clinic it looked like I'd been main-lining. At that time I was much more a convincing liar than I am now because I had a better memory . . . I could look at him and give him the little-boy look and really get my own way.' It was not only the doctors who were naive and easily manipulable. Trevor Platt recalled how he and his friends pressurized the local chemist to give them more drugs than the prescription allowed. He and seven East End friends had their heroin dispensed from the same chemist's shop, which was run by an elderly pharmacist who 'was terrified of us'. They went to the shop when it opened at eight in the morning and collected their drugs for the day. Later: 'When nine o'clock came we used to walk back in and say he hadn't given us any . . . Donald used to go in there and sit on the floor and cry, and he [the chemist] used to feel so sorry he used to give him more and more.' Eventually the police and the Home Office found out what was happening. By then, Trevor Platt had been dispensed an extra 200 tablets of heroin. The Clinic doctor wrote a prescription to cover the extra heroin which had already been dispensed – 'to pay the chemist back' as Trevor Platt put it. Trevor was not allowed to collect his drugs for a week and the pharmacist was able to balance his records before being moved to another shop.

In general, the Clinic doctors were relatively unprepared for what to expect, many having had little experience of addicts. They were, and addict patients recognized this, 'novices' who were 'new to the game', they lacked knowledge about addiction and how to deal with addicts, and had to 'feel their way'. Crucially, as we have seen, they were uncertain about determining whether a person was addicted, what they were addicted to, and how much to prescribe. People were questioned about their use of drugs, checked for needle marks, and urine samples were examined for the presence of various drugs, if such testing facilities were available. The most reliable method of assessing intake levels is to admit the person to hospital, where reactions to different amounts of opiates can be monitored – but this was, and still is, costly and time-consuming, and many Clinics lacked the use of in-patient facilities for this purpose. Faced with the prospect of so many new addict patients, such precise clinical assessment of each individual was not possible. The doctor was usually forced to rely on a physical examination and on the patient's own report of drug-taking and dosages. Even if more reliable tests had been used there would still have been room for doubt and discretion. After all, as Edwards (1969) has asked, what is the 'correct dose' for an addict patient? As he argued, there are several doses that are 'correct'. There is a dose that will prevent the occurrence of gross withdrawal symptoms but still leave the addict anxious and uncomfortable; there is a higher dose that will relieve the anxiety and make the addict comfortable; and there is a yet higher one on which the addict can experience some euphoria.

Some doctors found it hard to believe that people were actually using extraordinarily high doses, some of twenty grains of heroin a day or more, which had been prescribed by private doctors. Many suspected that their patients were exaggerating. One addict recalled that when she told the Clinic doctor what she had been using, 'he literally threw me out of his consulting room'. Thereupon she went to the Home Office and obtained a letter verifying that she had in the past received prescriptions for the vast amount of heroin she requested. Often, though, suspicions on the part of the staff of the Clinic were verified: one patient recalled that on the first visit to the Clinic it was 'standard practice to double what you first thought of [asking for] and pray you got half of it'. The doctors, faced with an uncertain diagnosis and treatment decision, where there could be little reliable assessment of the patient's claims, and faced with a form of medical consultation quite unlike any experienced elsewhere in medicine, were often reduced to using a simple rule of thumb. The routine, as one doctor recalled, was to 'divide what was asked for by two' and prescribe this smaller amount.

### SETTLING DOWN TO THE NEW SYSTEM

A picture emerges, from people's reminiscences about the first year of the Clinics, of overworked staff and harassed chemists faced with demanding and manipulating patients. Many Clinics were overwhelmed by the number of patients seeking prescriptions in the first few months and staff had few guidelines or routines for handling such difficult work situations. One social worker said this about her early days at a new Clinic in 1968:

> 'It was a general shambles. The waiting room seemed to be constantly full of waiting patients, and I was endlessly on the 'phone to patients who had problems with their prescriptions, and to chemists to sort out those problems. I was also expected to be on the

> look-out for intoxicated patients. There was little social work in what I was doing.'

Most patients soon learnt to view their relationship with the doctor and other staff as a game in which the two sides had opposing aims – the doctor hoping to reduce the amount of drugs prescribed and the patient trying to maintain or increase it. It was a game that could be played according to certain strategies. Two contrasting approaches were to keep a low profile, or to be a nuisance. An ex-addict, Bill Gregor, recalled at length how he used to deal with staff:

> 'I was probably remembered as a nice, polite guy. "You're too intelligent to be on drugs" I think I was told on a couple of occasions, but from an addict's point of view that's totally irrelevant. I would have done, probably without limit, whatever was necessary to remain in good books at the Clinic, mainly because I work from that side of the fence. There were other addicts who had to be as difficult as possible on the theory, quite correctly at times, that if you were violent and annoying all the time you would get what you want, and you usually did, mainly because it was the easiest way. Or you could be like me, nice, logical, intelligent, and still get what you want, mainly because I wouldn't allow myself to be talked out of it.'

Waiting rooms were a good source of gossip abour drug prices and supplies, and, of more immediate relevance, what to expect from the doctor – what sort of mood he was in, what earlier patients had asked him for, how successful they had been – all relevant for the decision about how best to deal with the doctor. Susan Hughes recalled what it was like when she visited the Clinic in the early days:

> 'You'd get there and there would be half a dozen other people in front of you waiting to see the doctor and you would work it out who was going to ask for "extras" and who wasn't. If somebody wasn't going to ask you would say "will you go in front of me so that he is in a good mood by the time I come in to ask for my extras?"'

Conflict and confrontation are more common in consultations between addicts and Clinic doctors than in other medical settings, but it is difficult to sustain an adversarial approach for a long time. As staff and addicts settled down to some routine after the initial chaos, overt conflict between them probably became less frequent, though not uncommon. Eventually, most patients realized that they would not be able to secure increases in their prescriptions and observed that all were subject to the general policy of reduced doses. Joe Henrick who remained addicted until his death in 1977, recalled how every patient was affected by such a policy:

> 'Well they were cutting you down, you see the trouble was, they were treating everybody as a case . . . they don't treat you as individuals, what's good for one is good for the other one. Dr Patel was sitting there and he said, "I'll cut everybody down half a grain this week". So everybody is losing half a grain.'

In such circumstances, addicts felt successful if they maintained a prescription at a certain level, let alone increased it, so confrontation became a less appropriate tactic than being inconspicuous or trying to please the doctor – 'avoiding hassles' is how addict patients described it. Eventually there might be some sort of truce, where the doctor ceased attempting major cuts or changes in the prescription, and where the patient no longer asked for an increase. One addict, who had achieved a truce in the early days and had maintained it through to the mid-1970s, looked back on it this way:

> 'As far as I myself am concerned, I really have no complaints. It's sort of like a *status quo* situation there. They don't hassle me and I don't hassle them. I don't get into that lark so they don't bother so much. It's now got into a maintenance thing, they're prepared to give me "x" amount of stuff if they can see that I'm making out reasonably okay, that I've got somewhere to live and a job.'

A truce could be perpetuated by being polite to the staff and the doctor, by being co-operative, and by avoiding serious discussions with the latter. A truce could be interrupted when the patient came to the doctor's attention for some reason or another, such as for getting arrested, for overdosing and being taken to casualty, for missing appointments, or for being reported by the chemist for bad behaviour. Such things gave the doctor a reason to change the prescription and 'if you give the doctor an opening he will take it'. If a satisfactory truce had been reached, then it was unwise to upset the doctor, after all 'he is the guy with the magic pad, so I don't want any hassles'. It was better to just 'plod along' and 'let them worry about the more urgent cases'. One patient summed up his view of the Clinic: 'That Clinic is ideal for me because I just go up when the nurse is there, once a fortnight, just go in and say hello, chat for about a quarter-of-an-hour, get some works [syringes] and needles and come home. Which is all I want really.'

Some patients regularly asked for increases in their prescriptions, really doubting whether their request would be successful, and asking almost as if it was part of their role as addicts to keep the pressure on the doctor. Changes of doctors often provided openings for patients, for new doctors were seen as easily 'conned'. One woman, who had been at the same Clinic since 1968, described how a new doctor reacted to the demands of his patients. When he first came he was 'green as grass', she said, and could not resist those demands: 'you could always get "extras"' from a new doctor. Then one day 'you would come to the Clinic on the day when the doctor is disillusioned':

> 'They finally see through it and nobody gets an extra for at least a month. Then they come round again. They start to think, "Well they are out for what they can get, aren't they, you can't blame them, they are addicts and they want dope, you can't blame them really". And then everybody for a week gets massive extras, then you don't, then you do, then you don't, and then you don't at all. But it's funny, every new doctor without fail has gone through that, believing what people tell him and then finding out that it's all been a load of lies, and then deciding that everybody is lying, no matter what they say, and then deciding "well, perhaps everybody can't be lying all the time".'

But such games did not last for long. Doctors reacted to the obvious pressures coming from patients, and developed strategies for handling them. The tendency on both sides of the consultation was to settle for some routine.

### PATIENTS' PERCEPTIONS OF THE NEW POLICIES

Addicts are unlike the majority of patients a doctor might see in ordinary medical practice in the NHS. In our sample deference or passivity were rarely found in addict patients. On the contrary, when they came to the Clinics, addicts knew what treatment they wanted and were vocal, forceful, and astute in trying to get it. Attendance at a Clinic was, after 1968, the only way to get a prescription, but such attendance did not, for many, commit them to seeing that they needed 'treatment' in the sense of medical help, a 'cure', and eventual abstinence. In most cases, the motivation for attendance was that this was the source of a 'legal' and 'regular' supply of drugs. It follows that addicts saw the doctors' main task as one of writing prescriptions. Some patients took the logic of this a step further to argue that they had a legal and moral 'right' to be prescribed the drugs they were addicted to: Clinics were 'there to be used' and to provide a 'service' to addicts. It also followed from the addicts' point of view, that the Clinics that supplied larger prescriptions soon gained reputations as the 'best' ones.

Would the patients get what they wanted? It was clear to many that they were faced with a situation that could, and was intended to, change the nature of addiction treatment and of the drug scene as a whole. People who attended the Clinics quite accurately saw that now 'the government was involved' their dealings with doctors would become more difficult.

They knew that the treatment they received would emerge not only from the policies and medical decisions of the Clinic staff, but also from pressures from 'the higher up ones who are running the thing'. Addict patients were aware that there was a government policy on addiction and that 'this policy influences and limits what the Clinics are able to do'. The relationship between doctors, the Home Office Drugs Branch, and the Department of Health and Social Security (or Ministry of Health as it then was) was, and is, more complex than the accounts suggest; however, what the addicts said is a fair summary of the rather subtle ways in which doctors' prescribing practices have been influenced.

One fear soon realized was that doctors would reduce the amounts prescribed. Bennett Howell's initial reaction was typical. Clinics were, for him, 'the beginning of the end'. He thought that the doctors 'were going to jab people into hospital under compulsory orders' and force addicts to stop using heroin. He managed to keep away from Clinics in their first few months, but by August 1968 'although I was still digging it, I could see the end was in sight, you know, now that the government had taken a hand'. So he went to a Clinic and asked to be taken on as a patient.

> 'I thought well I'd better show willing and I started on 4 and 2 [4 grains of heroin and 2 of cocaine]. I mean before it was the private doctor, he could write whatever drugs he considered necessary for his patient, anything. So I thought well it's not going to be easy to get loads of drugs through these [new] guys . . . I mean it was just the way it seemed to me.'

And so it turned out – it was not so easy to get drugs, and the amounts prescribed were smaller. Some addicts told us that the Home Office influence had continued over the years, and that various treatment changes had come about because 'there was pressure from the top'. One doctor told Pete Rossi that he was 'the only one getting a big dosage of heroin and it doesn't look good', he took this to mean that it was not acceptable to the Home Office. Another addict commented that 'perhaps the Home Office is on their backs all the time, wanting to know why they're giving such big amounts', and Pete Rossi summed up the situation by saying that 'they were given rules and they tried to implement those rules without really understanding the problem'.

### HOW THE CLINICS CHANGED PEOPLE'S LIVES

Looking back on the events of 1968 from the vantage point of the 1970s, most addicts and ex-addicts agreed that the Clinics made an impact on their lives. Their main effect was to reduce the quantities of drugs available: prescriptions were reduced, and people were persuaded to accept methadone in place of heroin. The amount of overspill NHS heroin on the black market was reduced and changed the economics of buying and selling drugs. Heroin had been at a steady price of about one pound for a grain through much of the 1960s, but increased in price, to three pounds a grain by the end of 1968. A few people said that the opposite occurred, that Clinics actually increased the drugs available at the very beginning (probably because the staff were naive – 'they were giving them out like sweets'), and a few patients, as we have seen, did not consider themselves addicted to heroin when they first became patients. However, any increased availability of drugs was a short-term phenomenon experienced by a minority of patients.

When NHS heroin and cocaine became scarce, other drugs became more popular. This dilemma of drug substitution, that as soon as one drug is controlled and becomes harder to obtain others take its place, was argued by Bennett Howell:

> 'From the government's point of view, they were faced with a situation where general practitioners were writing big scripts for a few people and stuff was being sold on the black market. They wanted to stop that and so they stopped general practitioners, so they brought in the Clinic system. To a certain extent it succeeded, although there has been a very large market in Chinese heroin, and the number of deaths has gone up. Because the amount of heroin, and opiates, and cocaine has dried up, people have gone on to barbiturates, which are a far worse and more dangerous drug than opiates. I think the policy has been a failure from the junkies' point of view because they're dying now. More of them are dying. I think there's a better way of doing it. I don't know what it is, but I'm sure there's a better way of doing it.'

There were only a few people who claimed that the Clinics had little effect on them. Those who made this claim usually argued that it was not possible for doctors to help addicts or even to influence their behaviour. Bill Gregor thought that the effect of the Clinics had been over-rated, though acknowledged that they made drugs harder to obtain:

> 'The influence of the Clinic was fairly small despite what they might like to think, they have little bearing on the case. In the case of most addicts, it's not the end of the world; if they cut your script down you just found other ways of providing it. It's if you run out of other ways that you get problems.'

Most people agreed that the Clinics heralded major changes in their lives. Some pointed out that the system helped them to stabilize their lives because the amounts of drugs prescribed were controlled and they had to bring some order into their lives if they were to collect their drugs on time and attend for appointments. Without this control they might have continued to escalate their drug use, or use erratically, and thus increase the chance of death by overdose or infection. On the whole, a regular and reliable supply of opiates meant there was less need to spend time scoring, and more time to settle down, have children, and work. Besides, a Clinic supply of drugs was a *legal* supply and so the patient did not, if using only Clinic drugs, face legal prosecution for possession of drugs. Clinics also made possible a cleaner style of drug use. With NHS heroin or methadone the addict knew the exact strength and quantity of the drug, whereas with illegally manufactured drugs this was often unknown. Many Clinics provided 'fixing' rooms, sterile syringes, needles, swabs, and distilled water which helped to reduce the risk of infection, and in addition offered physical health care for their patients.

The Clinics were soon to take some of the glamour and excitement out of being an addict. Christina Boyd, who had stopped using heroin by 1971, summed up the impact of the new system and reflected what many addicts felt about the Clinics soon after they opened:

> 'The setting up of the Clinics was on one hand an absolute bore. Because it focused your entire life, because you had to go every morning to the chemist to get your script. So before you'd had weekly scripts and at least you could do things, you could get about, but then suddenly you had to go every single day to the chemist and once a week to the Clinic. So you got this focusing of your attention which has been on junk anyway.'

Many addicts and ex-addicts spoke nostalgically of the days before the Clinics opened, when to get a prescription one had to 'chase Dr Petro round in a taxi or go and find him in some sleazy bar in the West End or something'. With the Clinic system there was less excitement and increasing restriction on their lives.

# 6

# *Developing treatment policies – care versus control*

'Sir,

In your article regarding the investigation of drug addiction, I was interested to read that no addict has apparently been interviewed during the preparation of the Brain Report. . . . If help is expected of them in the running of these treatment centres, the authorities are making a big mistake in neglecting the wealth of information available from addicts. . . . As an addict with a great deal of experience of other addicts, I cannot claim that they know all the answers but they should be given the opportunity of giving what information they can. I feel that the "experts" cannot have had much personal contact with addicts and, perhaps, not enough knowledge of the drug itself. . . . This letter has been written on behalf of the heroin and cocaine addicts in the addiction unit of St Bernard's Hospital.

Stevie F.M. (and Yuri W., Brian W.D., Brian D., Shirley A.)

Southall, Middlesex.'

(*The Sunday Times* 6 March 1966)

The staff of the new Clinics were uncertain of their role. There were few medical workers with extensive experience of working with addicts, and for the most part the Clinics were staffed with newcomers to this area of medical work. True, there was a wealth of experience that could have been drawn upon. There were the experiences of the general medical practitioners who had prescribed heroin and cocaine, there were the voluntary workers in the West End, and there were the addicts themselves. In the main, however, the staff had to find out for themselves what the work would entail. There were two sorts of problems to be worked out: first, the day-to-day running of the Clinic; for example, how should consultations be organized and how should prescriptions actually be written and dispensed – in other words all the administrative details that have to be arranged in any medical facility, and the additional arrangements necessitated by the peculiar clientele of the Clinics. Second were the aims of the Clinics: what would they be and how would they be implemented? As we have suggested earlier, the change in policy suggested by the Brain Committee presented two jobs for the Clinics, that of treatment and that of the control of the drug problem, and it soon became apparent that these two aims may sometimes conflict. In this chapter we look at how treatment policies developed up to the mid-1970s, a period in which the numbers of Clinic patients in England and Wales gradually rose to about 1500 (*see Table 6(1)*).

Table 6(1) *Annual average numbers of out-patients attending NHS hospitals for narcotic drug addiction in England and Wales, 1968–78*

| *year* | *out-patients* | | *total* |
|---|---|---|---|
| | *London* | *elsewhere* | |
| 1968* | 871 | 220 | 1091 |
| 1969 | 918 | 236 | 1154 |
| 1970 | 955 | 200 | 1155 |
| 1971 | 830 | 206 | 1036 |
| 1972 | 953 | 299 | 1252 |
| 1973 | 1045 | 335 | 1380 |
| 1974 | 1125 | 371 | 1496 |
| 1975 | 1145 | 401 | 1546 |
| 1976 | 1062 | 391 | 1453 |
| 1977 | 1023 | 409 | 1432 |
| 1978 | 1023 | 468 | 1491 |

*Note:* *From May.
*Sources:* Central Office of Information (1979) *Prevention and Treatment of Drug Misuse in Britain*; Johnson (1975); Institute for the Study of Drug Dependence (1980).

THE CLINIC SETTING

In order to understand how policies developed in the context of Clinic work it will help to summarize the setting in which the doctors, other staff, and addicts came together. The facilities, quality of accommodation, and staffing varied from Clinic to Clinic, but a description of University College Hospital Drug Dependency Clinic will give an idea of what they were, and are, like. The U.C.H. Clinic, situated a few minutes walk north of Tottenham Court Road, where London's West End fades away to be replaced by small businesses, workshops, and residential housing, had its own rooms in the National Temperance Hospital, with a separate street entrance for patients. Staff entered through the main hospital. Entering the Clinic from the street there were a few steps up to a waiting area, which had wooden seating on three sides. The visitor may have found six or seven waiting patients. Just opposite the street door was a cubicle for the porter, who took details of arriving patients. To the right of the entrance, and in view of the porter, were male and female toilets. Beside the porter was a corridor leading to the consulting rooms, and a door into the secretaries' office. The corridor led off to several small rooms, which were used for consultations, and a larger one, used for staff meetings. Further round the corridor there were double doors leading into the main part of the National Temperance Hospital. The busiest part of the Clinic was the secretaries' room, a large room with side windows looking out on to the street. There were several desks, telephones, filing cabinets with patients' records, and, in one corner, a kettle and cups for coffee and tea. This room was occupied by two secretaries, but was also used by social workers and doctors. The door to the waiting room was usually open, but the secretaries' room was staff territory. A patient wanting the attention of a staff member would usually wait at the doorway. In 1975, this Clinic was under the charge of a part-time consultant, helped by another senior psychiatrist, working a total of six half-day sessions a week. There were two full-time secretaries, a part-time nursing Sister, two full-time social workers, and a part-time clinical psychologist. There was also a social work adviser appointed by the area Social Services Department to liaise with local services and, unusually for many Clinics, to develop a service for intermittent drug users. The Clinic opened for three half-days a week, and one evening. During 1974, a total of 328 addict patients were treated by the Clinic, of whom 102 were new referrals. In addition, and this was unusual for many Clinics, twenty-eight non-opiate-using patients were seen. The effective caseload in any month would be smaller than the overall total number of patients seen in the year. Most of the patients seen were aged in their twenties and three out of four were men.

Other Clinics may have slightly different facilities. For example, St Clement's in the East End had a large room which was used as a day centre for patients; this was equipped with tables and chairs, and staff provided hot lunches. It also, like some other Clinics, had a room where patients were allowed to inject. All Clinics were, and are, run as out-patient units, with variable access to in-patient facilities. At U.C.H. detoxification took time to arrange but some patients could be admitted to a general medical ward. Patients with medical, surgical, or obstetric problems were admitted to appropriate general wards. In London and adjacent areas, specialist in-patient units are located in St Bernard's Hospital in Southall, Bexley Hospital and the Royal Bethlem Hospital in Kent, and Tooting Bec Hospital.

### STAFF VIEWS OF TREATING ADDICTS

Many doctors view treating addicts as unattractive. When the Clinics were first established there was a marked reluctance among potential recruits to accept the invitation to work in them. Treating addicts is sometimes seen as a low-status occupation within psychiatry. It is an area of medicine with few of the rewards found in other medical jobs: one doctor, writing in *World Medicine*, put a view that is probably shared by many doctors looking, as outsiders, at the addiction field:

> 'Treating drug addicts in Britain is now a full-time job. You either do it or you don't. As I have a choice, I do not because the therapeutic rewards are so small. From the acquaintance I have had with addicts in our adolescent unit, I have found heroin addicts to be dull, proletarian and not particularly gifted or intelligent.'
>
> (Beard 1970)

This doctor assessed work with addicts from the point of view of 'therapeutic' rewards, or success in treating addicts. But what is meant by 'treatment' in the context of the Clinics? A major aspect of Clinic treatment was the prescription of opiate drugs. Nearly all the patients who attended London Clinics received prescriptions for drugs; in the sample we followed, it was extremely unusual for a person to attend a Clinic and not receive a prescription. There was considerable variation in practice around the country. In Bristol, Crawley, and other towns away from London, some doctors refused to prescribe injectable drugs. In Birmingham, and in many London Clinics in the first years, there were some doctors who preferred to prescribe heroin rather than other drugs. There were others who preferred to prescribe injectable methadone, and those who would attempt to get patients quickly on to oral methadone. There were also variations within Clinics, with some patients receiving heroin, some receiving heroin with methadone, and some receiving only methadone. Other treatment was also offered in the Clinics: group therapy, individual therapy, in-patient detoxification, referral to therapeutic communities, and a wide range of social-work help.

'Treatment' is a word that conjures up the image of individual therapy, involving either curing or caring. In the context of addiction, treatment might thus be construed as helping the addicted individual to become abstinent from drugs, or helping the individual to lead as trouble-free a life as possible whilst still being addicted. But in the context of the drug Clinic treatment was often a euphemism for other goals and we have to look not just at what was done to or for patients, but also at the clinicians' motivations in so acting.

To outsiders, the fact that the Clinics are staffed by medical people and are located in hospitals might suggest that the main aim for staff is to cure people of their addiction, to help them with their problems, or, very broadly, to provide some sort of therapy. But staff to whom we spoke in 1976 talked a great deal about 'control' and 'containment' of the drug problem as a major aspect of their work. Many described their work primarily in terms of social control, or talked about 'benefits to society', seeing themselves as working 'on behalf of society' to control the drug problem. For example, a psychiatrist at one Clinic had this to say:

> 'I was a bit worried last year because I felt that there were a lot of social workers working in addiction units, who were trying to deny that we as Clinic staff should have any concern for the social control of addiction, and were trying to deny that it was one of the aims of the Clinics.'

A similar point was made in a one-page handout from another Clinic, which described the impact of their work:

> 'The Clinic opened in 1967 as one of the facilities proposed as an urgent measure under the second Brain Committee Report. . . . The more controlled prescribing policy initiated in 1967 would seem to be a qualified success from society's viewpoint. The number of opiate addicts known to the Home Office, particularly young addicts, has only increased slowly over the past four years. There is little evidence of wide-scale illegal importation of heroin into this country and whilst the majority of addicts coming to this Clinic have criminal records, the extent of their criminal activity nowhere reaches that reported of American addicts.'

This is not to say that the staff saw their work only as social control; the people who made these statements also talked of therapy. Nevertheless, it is unusual in medicine for doctors to refer to their work as social control. Even in areas of medicine in which we can see that doctors' work is more to do with social control than treatment – for example, in issuing sickness certificates, or the detention of the mentally ill – doctors are rarely so consciously explicit about their work.

The emergence of this social control orientation can be traced to the reformulation of British policy in the second Brain Committee report of 1965. The Committee recognized that it was necessary in some circumstances to prescribe opiates to addicts, but also saw that over-prescribing could itself contribute to the increase in addiction by making supplies readily available: as the Committee put it 'if there is insufficient control it may lead to the spread of addiction – as is happening at present' (Interdepartmental Committee on Drug Addiction 1965: 7). But the dilemma was that a complete ban on heroin and cocaine, or severe restrictions on availability, might 'prevent or seriously discourage the addict from obtaining any supplies from legitimate sources' and might 'lead to the development of an organised illicit traffic' (Interdepartmental Committee on Drug Addiction 1965: 7). Following this analysis it was expected that Clinics should prescribe opiates in competition with, or to prevent, the development of a black market. Such a policy was often described as 'competitive prescribing' or 'keeping the Mafia out'. Let us see the implications of this policy for staff. The Clinic would be a legal source of drugs and it was hoped that this would undercut or prevent a black market. After all, if addicts could get drugs legally, the attraction of a black market should decrease. The main aim of treatment then was not necessarily individual therapy, but an attempt to affect the drug scene, mainly the supply of drugs, by the way in which individual patients were handled. Such a policy required staff to attract patients to the Clinics, to keep them there, and prescribe conservatively and accurately.

## THE POLICY OF SOCIAL CONTROL

How did this policy affect the doctors in the Clinics? First, they saw that their job was mainly to deal with the heroin problem, rather than deal with drug problems in general. So, with a few exceptions, they restricted their caseloads to people who were addicted to heroin or other opiates. Wary of turning on a person who was not addicted, and wishing to confine the caseload to opiate addicts, their work required an elaborate and extended process of diagnosis and acceptance. A new patient was usually expected to prove that he or she was addicted to an opiate, and a procedure developed whereby people were expected to give at least one, and usually two or three, samples of urine, which were then tested for the presence of opiates. The evidence from the specimens was checked against a detailed history of drug use, and a physical examination was conducted, which looked for signs of self-injection (the extent, site, and age of injection marks, scars, or abscesses) and for the presence of withdrawal symptoms. It was usually necessary for a patient to attend the Clinic two or three times before a diagnosis was reached and a prescription decided upon (or not). The yearly numbers of new attenders at Clinics in England and Wales from 1969 to 1973 varied between 500 and 800, but not all patients were accepted (Johnson 1975: 50–1). One study, conducted in 1971, looked at new patients approaching Clinics and found that about a third of them did not receive any prescription, at least initially. Those who were not prescribed were those whose urine was found to contain no traces of opiates (Blumberg *et al.* 1974).

Second, as the policy required Clinic workers to control the drug problem through controlling drug supplies, much of the work in the Clinics centred around questions of how much and what should be prescribed. The task was difficult for staff. The problem was to prescribe enough drugs so that these patients did not turn to the black market for supplies, yet at the same time not to prescribe *too much* in case the patients sold their supplies and fed the black market. To do this, staff felt that they needed an effective intelligence system, to gauge what was going on 'out there', in order to make decisions about individual patients. They sought to know what drugs were available on the black market, and whether the ones being sold were legally prescribed, stolen, or illegally imported. Hence the perennial attempts by doctors to establish how many addicts there are 'out there' who do not come to the Clinics but who survive on black market supplies.

The prescribing 'tightrope' was difficult to walk. A basic problem was that there were often alternative drugs available on the black market. After the Clinics were established many other drugs became popular. In the first few months doctors made a concerted effort to reduce or eliminate the prescribing of cocaine, reasoning that it was not a drug of dependence and was, therefore, one that patients could forego. Many addicts were soon obtaining supplies of methedrine ampoules instead, an injectable amphetamine with stimulant effects, and two private doctors, Petro and Swan, switched many patients to methedrine when they were no longer allowed to prescribe heroin and cocaine. Underground newspapers campaigned against its use under the slogan 'Speed Kills' and *International Times* (9 August 1968) described it as 'one of the most dangerous drugs around at the moment'. Methedrine was eventually restricted in October 1968 when the Ministry of Health persuaded the makers, Burroughs Wellcome, to supply it only to hospitals. Ritalin, another stimulant, was popular for a short time in 1973, and from 1975 onwards illicitly manufactured amphetamine sulphate was available. Towards the end of 1968 and the beginning of 1969, just as the Clinics were beginning to drastically reduce the amount of heroin prescribed, illicitly produced heroin appeared on the black market. Until this time nearly all the heroin available in Britain had been obtained on prescription and then sold. This new, illicit heroin was imported from Hong Kong where it was manufactured from morphine or heroin obtained from the Golden Triangle in South-East Asia. It was sold by Chinese in Soho – hence its name, 'Chinese heroin'. It has continued to be available, with sporadic changes in availability, ever since. The other popular alternatives to heroin have been sleeping pills, such as Mandrax (methaqualone), and barbiturates, such as Tuinal, Seconal, Nembutal, and Sodium Amytal, all of which can be injected after they have been dissolved in water.

In the early days at the Clinics, the majority of patients, between 60 and 80 per cent, received prescriptions for heroin. The peak months for prescribing the drug, in terms of total quantities, were July and August 1968 when a total of 5889 grams of heroin were supplied to addicts. In the early years of the Clinics, doctors attempted to reduce the quantity prescribed by reducing average doses per patient and by transferring people to methadone: the total quantity of heroin prescribed had fallen to 3685 grams for July and August 1969, and in that year only 34 per cent of patients received heroin (*see also Tables 6(2)* and *6(3)*). Transfers were often achieved by a straight exchange of methadone ampoules for heroin pills, the 'rate' being one 10 mg ampoule of methadone for a 10 mg heroin pill. Methadone as a drug of choice has a peculiar history in British

Table 6(2) *Amounts of heroin and methadone prescribed to addicts attending NHS hospitals in England and Wales (in grams)*

| *year* | *heroin* | *methadone* | |
|---|---|---|---|
| | | *ampoules* | *linctus and tablets* |
| 1968 | 16895* | ** | ** |
| 1969 | 22778 | 4371* | 1432* |
| 1970 | 17392 | 11344 | 3488 |
| 1971 | 14201 | 11548 | 3742 |
| 1972 | 14322 | 14227 | 8227 |
| 1973 | 14287 | 19099 | 9072 |
| 1974 | 15332 | 21454 | 8295 |
| 1975 | 15474 | 20937 | 9563 |
| 1976 | 13178 | 17297 | 11682 |
| 1977 | 10924 | 14668 | 14022 |
| 1978 | 8501 | 14003 | 17498 |

*Note:* *This total is for the 6 months from July to December. **Figures not available, but totals are less than in subsequent years.
*Sources:* Johnson (1975); Institute for the Study of Drug Dependence (1980).

addiction treatment. Originally promoted in the US by Dole and Nyswander (1965) as a substitute for heroin, it was preferred by the medical profession because it 'blocked' the effects of the small doses of illicit heroin taken by American patients and because it could be taken in an oral (not injectable) form. When it was introduced in Britain it was not for its blockading effects, which do not occur with the larger doses of heroin used in Clinics here. It was introduced to addicts in injectable form because of its longer lasting effects, which meant that addicts would have to inject less frequently than with heroin. In addition, it could be dispensed in ampoule form ready for injection, thus reducing risks of infection, and did not produce the immediate, exciting 'buzz' associated with heroin. It was hoped, then, that addicts would be persuaded to accept methadone as a small step towards eventual abstinence. Taking the addicts in our sample as an example, in 1969 they were all initially prescribed heroin, but four out of five of them additionally received some form of methadone within six months of the Clinics opening (*see* Appendix, *Table A(1)*, p. 233).

By the end of 1969, nearly 50 per cent of Clinic patients in England and Wales were receiving solely methadone, and only a third were still receiving prescriptions for heroin (*see Table 6(3)*). (It is worth noting that since our sample of patients were those who were receiving heroin in 1969, they were already part of a rapidly declining proportion of Clinic patients). Since 1970, the proportion of patients receiving heroin has continued to decline, until by 1978 less than 10 per cent of them received it. It would now be exceptional for a new Clinic patient to be given heroin. Since 1970 there has been a corresponding increase in the percentage of patients being prescribed only methadone, from approximately 50 per cent at the beginning of the decade to over 70 per cent by 1978 (*see Table 6(3)*).

### INTERACTION BETWEEN STAFF AND PATIENTS

The Clinics are an unusual medical setting in which there is a higher level of overt conflict between patients and staff than is found elsewhere in medicine, with the possible exception of Accident and Emergency departments. In most medical work settings there is the appearance of calm and order, with the views of patients often being ignored or prevented from emerging. But it is not like this in the drug Clinics. Patients' views are vociferously expressed and are difficult to ignore or suppress. Our fieldnotes written after our visits give some flavour of the atmosphere at the Clinics in 1976, and we believe are illustrative of their first few years. One of us wrote the following:

'The Clinic was teeming with people – a great deal of activity. At

Table 6(3) *Addict patients receiving prescriptions for different types of drugs*

| *year* | *total* | *heroin only* | *heroin plus methadone* | *methadone only or with drugs other than heroin* | *other drugs only*** |
|---|---|---|---|---|---|
| | | % | % | % | % |
| 1968 | — | *estimated 60–80 per cent heroin with or without methadone | | — | — |
| 1969 | 1466 | 14 | 20 | 49 | 17 |
| 1970 | 1430 | 13 | 18 | 51 | 18 |
| 1971 | 1555 | 10 | 15 | 60 | 15 |
| 1972 | 1615 | 9 | 12 | 67 | 12 |
| 1973 | 1815 | 9 | 12 | 67 | 12 |
| 1974 | 1969 | 8 | 12 | 66 | 14 |
| 1975 | 1951 | 5 | 11 | 68 | 16 |
| 1976 | 1876 | 4 | 9 | 70 | 17 |
| 1977 | 2018 | 3 | 8 | 69 | 20 |
| 1978 | 2406 | 3 | 6 | 71 | 20 |

*Note:* The numbers on which these percentages are based derive from Home Office notifications and are not directly comparable to the other tables, which are based on Department of Health returns from Clinics. The base figures refer to the UK (rather than England and Wales), include in-patients, and are as of year end (rather than annual averages). *Personal communication, Department of Health and Social Security. **Mainly opiates.
*Sources:* as for *Table 6(1)*, p. 94.

least twenty-seven addicts attended today and more were expected. The 'phone rang continuously. The secretaries were busy writing out all the prescriptions and handing these and the notes to Dr T. to sign. Everyone seemed to be in a tremendous hurry. Constantly clients were coming up to the office door asking how much longer they had to wait.

All the addicts seem to know each other and there were little groups in the waiting room talking together.

My prospective interviewee arrived late and was in a bit of a state today. She was immediately approached by the social worker and agreed to be interviewed, but only after going to the toilet. She stayed there for a very long time. Staff were very suspicious because fixing is not allowed in the toilet.

Meanwhile M., who was hovering about listlessly at the door of the office, had been telling the staff that he wanted to get off drugs but he didn't think he could manage it at F. hospital. He wanted admission elsewhere. The secretaries suggested that he talk to the doctor about this – but not before telling him that as he is after all a junkie, why does he think he should get special treatment?

Incidentally, J., who is in our sample, turned up at the Clinic. He came out of prison this morning. I gather that he wrote to Dr U. from prison asking for an early appointment. He was offered one for tomorrow. He was already very drugged because he had been to Piccadilly and scored on the way to the Clinic. He could hardly stand up. He asked for syringes from the staff nurse and there was a bit of discussion about this. The social worker warned him that if he were found with drugs and syringes today he would be in 'illegal possession'' as the Clinic was not yet officially prescribing for him. He didn't seem to care and said that he wrote to Dr U. in order to avoid such a situation. He couldn't wait till tomorrow for his drugs. Finally, he was supplied with syringes and sent off with warnings to be careful.'

We noted the following observations a few days later, at a staff meeting at the same Clinic:

> 'Earlier in the week there had been some trouble at the Clinic when a patient had become violent. There was a discussion on how to handle such situations in future and a ''post mortem'' on events of this week. Apparently the hospital security man was not available, so the police were called (after the patient attacked the doctor). By the time the police came, the patient was calmer and with the social worker so the police left without waiting. Later, when the patient still refused to go, the police were called again but refused to come. It was decided that in future, if the police are called, the patient should be escorted out of the premises. There was some discussion about security for the staff and alarm systems but Dr U. thought that the 'phone was the best way, or simply a loud shout to alert others in the Clinic. It was suggested that, as a sanction against violence, patients could be required, if disruptive, to attend the in-patient unit and/or collect their scripts once or twice daily.'

Similar incidents were observed on a visit to another Clinic at about the same time:

> 'The door was locked at 5.00 p.m. and a couple of minutes later the doorbell rang. Somehow the staff knew (by looking out of the window?) that it was a patient who was due up for an appointment. The patient lives outside of London and comes up to the Clinic monthly for his prescription. The doorbell rang several times. Dr P. refused to allow him to be let in. The secretary had to go to the door,

the door was kept on the chain. The office window was closed, and Dr P. told us to sit down – in order to keep out of sight from the street. The porter was told to lock the back door. Apparently when the patient came up he liked to stay over in London in order to score in the Dilly. Dr P. likes to get him back to where he lives as soon as possible. Last time they gave him a one-day rail warrant so that he had to return the same day; he kicked up a fuss and wouldn't leave the Clinic. This time I think the secretary gave him his prescription through the door. Patient then hung around in the street for a while.

At 5.10 a friend of M.K. 'phoned saying there had been a bomb scare on the tube and that M.K. was in a taxi on the way to the Clinic. The secretary explained that it was too late as the Clinic was closed. Some doubt about whether M.K. had actually left home. The Sister spoke to the friend and said that M.K. would have to come in for an appointment to get her prescription. The Sister challenged the friend by saying that she suspected that they had both been taking too many sleeping tablets (and had overslept). She said to us it sounded like M.K. was in the background. It was agreed to leave the prescription for one day's supply at the porter's lodge.'

Finally, from the notes of the next visit to the Clinic:

'All in all quite a difficult afternoon for the staff and they had my sympathy. There was a patient who was in with his parents, arguing with staff that he should be put on injectable drugs. This person had been involved in some sort of armed robbery and had spent some time in prison. Staff told me he was suggesting that if he was not put on injectable drugs he would get a gun and shoot someone or himself. Seemed quite extraordinary to me that a bank robber should be at the Clinic with his mum and dad! He must have been there for at least an hour-and-a-half and was seen by Dr P., the Sister, and the social worker. The staff saw this [his threats] as an attempt to blackmail them and refused to put him on injectable drugs.

I was in the office and the staff mentioned that a patient was in the waiting room crying because his prescription had been reduced by one pill on a previous occasion, and how he had thought he might get it back but now realized he wouldn't. Later there was a problem between him and the secretary over his fares. The discussion over the fares went on for three-quarters of an hour, on-and-off, with the patient trying different approaches. Then a twenty-minute discussion between him and the Sister. He had been complaining that he didn't even have money for cigarettes, so the social worker gave him one from her pack, "on the NHS" as she said. The Sister, getting a bit tough with him, suggesting that if he really wanted some money he should get a job. The patient complained that he was too busy at the moment moving into ROMA (a hostel). He had been seen by Dr P. that afternoon but wanted to see him again for "two minutes"; he tried to corner Dr P. as he came into the office but Dr P. kept moving and said that he was already running an hour late. The patient asked if he could wait until the end of the Clinic to see Dr P. Dr P. said it was unlikely as he had to be at another hospital.'

### DEVELOPING WORK ROUTINES

As is obvious from these reports, a major concern for staff in this medical setting, as in any other, was to keep sufficient order in their work-place to allow them to pursue their work in their chosen way, with minimum interruption. It is clear from other research work on encounters between doctors and patients that patient behaviour that is perceived by staff as disruptive and manipulative is met by staff strategies that aim to maintain staff dominance (Roth 1963; Stimson and Webb 1975). The drug Clinics are no exception – a wide range of staff strategies emerged that were used to keep some sense of order.

The task of prescribing drugs would be easier if the addict patients agreed with the aims of doctors. However, many do not. Addict patients know what they want and are not reluctant to convey this to staff. Furthermore, what they want is often not what the staff are prepared to give. Where staff and patients differ is in their ideas about the nature and meaning of drug use, the purpose of the Clinic, rights to prescription, and the place of therapy. The central conflict is that addict patients maintain that they have a need for the drugs they are addicted to and that it is the function of the Clinic to help them by providing them with a legal and regular supply, whilst the staff see that prescribing is not a right of patients but at their discretion.

A common view among the staff we met was that 'most addicts are liars'. Indeed, in a situation where one group wants something over which another group has a monopoly, and where that second group wishes to restrict the supply, the situation is one that will generate lying on both sides. As we have observed, the upshot is that staff distrust patients, are supicious of them, and are ever on the lookout against being conned by them. To drive this point home, staff would calculate how much a patient's prescription would be worth if sold on the street. One consultant pointed out that a patient selling a daily prescription for fifty pills of heroin would have a daily, untaxed income of around £100 (in 1976). On the other hand, patients often told staff they were using illegal drugs, hoping to persuade staff to increase the prescription of opiates. We have already seen that Clinics instituted procedures for testing urine each time the patient attended and sanctions might be imposed if illegal drugs were found to be present. In one set of case notes, the doctor referred to a 'disciplinary reduction' in dosage because illegal drugs were found in a patient's urine.

Many other procedures and rules grew up around the issue of prescriptions and the dispensing of drugs. Before the Clinics opened there were no restrictions on the quantities prescribed nor on the period the prescription was to cover. In July 1967, the Ministry of Health, following discussion with doctors working in the field, and with the Pharmaceutical Society and the NHS Chemist Contractors Committee representing dispensing chemists, circularized doctors working with addicts with guidance on precautions to prevent the misuse of prescriptions; the Memorandum in question was entitled *Treatment and Supervision of Heroin Addiction: Precautions Against Misuse of Prescriptions* (Ministry of Health 1967 and 1968). The aim was to ensure that heroin-addict patients would receive no more than one or two days' supply at a time. Since it was thought impracticable to require addicts to attend Clinics at intervals of one or two days, the measures enabled doctors to write prescriptions for longer periods, which could be dispensed daily or at other short intervals. Clinic doctors were recommended to restrict the total quantity prescribed to one week's supply (this was later extended to two weeks), with the prescription showing the amounts to be dispensed each day. For days when retail chemists or hospital pharmacies did not open, for example on Sundays and public holidays, multiple quantities were to be dispensed on preceding days. The prescription form indicated the day from which dispensing was to begin. To avoid the concentration of addicts at chemists' shops at opening times, some prescriptions were endorsed with a time, agreed between the retail chemists, before which the drugs would not be dispensed (usually 10.00 a.m.). In general medical practice in the NHS, prescriptions are handed to patients who then take them to the retail pharmacist. Clinic doctors were advised not to give prescriptions to addict patients but to post them direct to the chemist. A new patient for whom heroin or methadone was to be prescribed should be introduced in person by a member of the hospital staff to the chemist, or, where this was not possible, the doctor should provide the patient with a letter of introduction. In the case of illness or other incapacity that prevented the patient from collecting the drugs, special alternative arrangements were to be made with the Clinic. Retail chemists were not allowed to dispense heroin to anyone other than the addict in person, unless under an arrangement with the authority of the prescribing doctor at the Clinic. The chemists, for their part, were entitled to refuse to enter into arrangements to dispense heroin, or to restrict the number of such patients they received. When each daily quantity was distributed, the chemist endorsed the reverse of the prescription with the date and quantity dispensed, and entered each separate dispensation into the chemists' Dangerous Drugs Register. Heroin, along with other dangerous drugs, was to be kept under special secure conditions at the chemists' shops.

Most other rules concerning prescriptions were not formalized as they were in this Memorandum but emerged in response to problems that staff faced in dealing with patients. For example, staff thought that addicts would try to con extra drugs using the excuse that their drugs were lost or stolen. Most Clinics had a policy that there would be no variation in a prescription during the time for which it was issued. This problem was discussed at the staff meeting in one of the Clinics that we visited in 1976:

> 'Re-affirmation of policy that "no rises" or replacements for lost drugs shall be given. The doctor felt that this policy, now adopted by most Clinics, makes sense as it avoids long discussion and arguments about dosages. In fact someone at the Clinic today had just received a rise. . . . He was told by staff not to tell anyone about this rise and said that he wouldn't.'

There are two interesting points here: first, having a rule makes life easier for staff – they can refer to the rule as limiting their options, so avoiding individualized discussion with patients. Second, deviations from the rule must not be disclosed to patients – if they find out one person has had a 'rise', 'they will all want one'. The 'no tomorrows today' rule, also known as the 'no advances' rule, was part of the same policy – it prevented patients getting some of the next day's prescription in advance. Advances would have had to be authorized by a 'pick-up slip' presented to the chemist, allowing him or her to vary the prescription. A policy of 'no pick-up slips' backed-up the 'no tomorrows today' rule. In some Clinics there were notices informing patients of these regulations, and *Figure 6(1)* reproduces a letter to patients outlining such rules.

A major consequence of a drug-control policy that put the responsibility for control in the hands of Clinic staff was that much of their time was taken up in administrative tasks concerning the issue of prescriptions. But there were many other problems that arose in Clinics that staff sought to prevent, such as buying and selling of drugs, faking urine tests, disruptions, and disrespect for staff territory. In some Clinics a staff 'bouncer' role developed – played by a person who had the respect of patients and who could keep order. It was not a fixed staff role but was adopted in different Clinics by a nurse, porter, or receptionist. The physical location of such a person in the Clinic was important. If, for example, injecting in the toilets was not allowed, the staff member had to be able to observe who entered the toilet and how long they stayed.

Sanctions imposed on patients who misbehaved included dosage

Figure 6(1) *Letter sent to patients by a Clinic consultant in 1977*

Dear Patient,

I understand that since I have temporarily replaced Dr. D. at this clinic, rumours have arisen that I intend to make drastic changes.

This letter is to reassure you that this is NOT so.

It is my intention to enable you to lead as normal a life as possible and so interfere with your present prescription as little as possible. However, this means not only not reducing your script but also not increasing your script.

Extras and Advances. The policy of the clinic of strict control over issuing of extras and/or advances will continue.

Requests for Extra Issues or Replacements will be refused and you must accept full responsibility for your medication and take special care of it so that it is not lost, mislaid, destroyed, stolen, mis-injected or misused. Very rarely, and only in exceptional circumstances, Mist. Methadone D.T.F. may be issued.

Requests for Advances, such as for picking up drugs a day early at short notice, put a great strain on the clinic staff and telephoning the clinic for special arrangements to be made with your chemist is very time-consuming and involves much extra work. This will have to be discontinued.

You are, therefore, asked to inform us a full week in advance if you intend to go on holiday, away for a weekend, on a course or any other reason for early issue so that an alternative chemist can dispense and arrangements made for this.

Voluntary Withdrawal. As you may know the in-patient treatment unit at J. Hospital (B Ward) is being renovated and redecorated and so will not be open until March 1977.

Whilst I believe that withdrawal from drugs is best effected by in-patient treatment, I am very willing to co-operate with any patient who voluntarily wishes to try an out-patient basis reduction of medication with a view to withdrawal.

Any patient who wishes to try to manage on a lower dosage of drugs need only mention this to the doctor and an agreed reduction will be made. I wish to assure you that should such reduction fail, that is, that you find yourself unable to cope on the reduced dosage, the doctor will change your medication and if need be increase the reduced dosage up to the amount you were receiving at the time you volunteered to reduce (but no higher).

Do not worry about failure, you can always try again.

Appointments. I am trying to arrange the appointments system on a time basis and ask your co-operation in attending on the day and time given you.

I hope, too, in the very near future to allocate patients to one particular doctor so that you see 'your own doctor' each visit. Poor time-keeping only leads to confusion in the clinic and a long wait to see the doctor. Your co-operation in respect of appointments is earnestly requested so that the clinic can function smoothly and mistakes, tensions and frustrations minimised.

Finally I would be very pleased to receive constructive suggestions or criticism which you consider may help the smooth running of this clinic.

reductions, switches from heroin to injectable methadone or oral methadone, or temporary cancellation of the prescription. Such sanctions might be imposed for failure to attend an appointment, if the patient was arrested, or if the patient did not work – as in this doctor's notes of a consultation:

> 'I made the following bargain (my offer, not his). I will supply heroin 5 × 10 mg pills daily from 14.2.75 if he can tell me of a job arranged when he comes on March 5 (with starting date) and can show me pay slips the following visit. If unemployed we shall use time for a transfer to methadone.'

Similar constraints over patient behaviour were exercised in in-patient drug units. At some, patients were asked to sign 'good behaviour' contracts; an example of these is given in *Figure 6(2)*. Addicts cannot be compulsorily detained under the Mental Health Act on the grounds of their addiction alone, but they may be 'encouraged' to stay in hospital by, as one consultant reported, the doctor's 'simple manoeuvre of refusing to supply drugs if they discharge themselves before completion of their withdrawal programme'. This coercive aspect of the doctor–addict relationship is so taken for granted that doctors do not hesitate to publicly write about this policy.

The ability of staff to pursue such coercive strategies was enhanced by limitations on patient mobility. Clients can exert more influence over professionals when they are able to pick and choose who to consult; conversely, the power of the doctor is increased when the patient has no choice about consultation. Administrative encumbrances limit patient choice of doctor within the NHS, but patient choice was even more restricted in the Clinics. Clinics agreed among themselves not to accept patients seeking transfers from other Clinics, except in special circumstances. The Home Office notification system was used by Clinic staff to assist in preventing client movement – to check if a prospective patient was at another Clinic all that was necessary was a telephone call to the Home Office Drugs Branch. The experience of the patients in the sample of addicts we followed may be typical: in the years from 1969 to 1979, 86 per cent stayed with their original Clinic and only 14 per cent transferred to a different one.

How did staff rationalize strategies that in other medical settings would be frowned upon and that could even be seen as ethically dubious? First, addicts are well known as being difficult patients. Clinic staff felt therefore, that they were only doing what other reasonable people would do if faced with the same situation. Second, addicts, like other patients such as the mentally ill, the handicapped, or the old, are looked upon as being, in a sense, disfranchised: they might have interactive power but

Figure 6(2) *'Good behaviour' contract for an addict in-patient admission at a London teaching hospital in 1976*

Conditions applying to Drug Clinic patients during in-patient treatment in hospitals.

1. Visitors must be discussed with the clinic staff prior to admission. Nobody other than those agreed upon will be allowed to visit.

2. You will be expected to remain on the ward throughout your stay in the hospital.

3. You will be expected to remain dressed in pyjamas and dressing-gown while in the hospital.

4. The staff reserve the right to inspect parcels.

5. You are free to leave the hospital at any time. BUT if you leave without the agreement of the staff you will not be readmitted.

6. You are expected to use NO DRUGS other than those prescribed by the hospital staff.

I have read these conditions and accept them.

SIGNED ....................

Date ....................

they have little economic or political power; they are marginal and have no effective protest. Third, staff did not see addicts as really being like other hospital patients. We found that, in their eyes, many addicts did not fit the patient role: they did not seem to want to get better (or change), they were incorrigible, they seemed to enjoy their 'illness', they behaved as though they were absolved of social obligations (in fact, staff thought that they were malingerers and should get jobs), they did not seek 'advice' or 'help' from doctors, and did not co-operate in getting 'better'. Fourth, staff could explain patient misbehaviour in terms of psychopathology: the aggravation of patients was seen as due to their 'immaturity', 'low thresholds of aggression', 'high levels of hostility', and so on; in other words it was seen as emanating in the person's psyche and not in the social situation.

Why did staff and patients endure such conflicting relationships? One solution to a difficult relationship is to terminate it; and this was certainly an option in the Clinic, but it was a limited option. From the patient's point of view, attendance would not be terminated until he or she was ready to give up drugs, or as long as the Clinic was the easiest source of their supply – the 'hassle' of the Clinic was weighed against the hassle of the black market. Clinic staff seemed to temper their termination option because it ran counter to what they saw as their broader function of social control, which could not be pursued if a patient no longer attended; therefore staff were not usually willing to terminate the relationship.

### CONTROL OVER THE PRESCRIBING DOCTOR

It was not only the addicts who became subject to more control, for the 1968 policy changes also introduced more governmental control over doctors. The individual GP, isolated from colleagues, was always in a potentially weak position *vis-à-vis* addicts, and the history of GP prescribing in the 1960s shows how vulnerable these doctors were. The transfer of addiction treatment to the hospital system, and exclusion of the ordinary practitioner, made the activities of doctors involved much more visible, and provided them with possibilities for seeking advice and moral backing.

In a sense, the setting up of the Clinics made possible increased state control over both the addicts and the doctors. While both groups may at times have been confused about the policy aims, the situation could be seen more clearly by outsiders (and is easier to see now, with hindsight). A particularly perceptive comment on the policy aims was made by Roy Jenkins, who was Labour Home Secretary under the Wilson government in 1967 when the details for the Clinics were being negotiated. He recalled the position that was adopted:

> 'Throughout, I was firmly against criminalising addiction, as I think we all were. What was wanted was other kinds of social controls, for the addicts under medical care and also – very importantly – for the

doctors themselves. We thought that a chief objective had to be to institutionalise the care of addicts through the Clinic setting, in which nobody would be acting alone, but, instead, as part of a group with checks and supports for the doctors as well as more visible controls supporting the addicts.'

(Judson 1974: 91)

Practising medicine in this area became a relatively 'public' endeavour with the doctors' activities monitored by colleagues and government agencies. For example, the Clinics sent details of their patients to the Department of Health and these were then compiled to give data on the average doses prescribed at each Clinic. These data were available to Clinic consultants. The consultants met every three months at the Department of Health where they discussed their activities. There were similar meetings for social workers. Perhaps because the clinician group was small,approximately fifteen consultants and thirty junior doctors in London, the doctors were peculiarly sensitive to the comments of their colleagues. The Home Office and the Department of Health were also in a position to monitor the activities of the Clinics. It would not be accurate to think of clear-cut policy directives emanating from the government. Again, the influence was subtle. Indeed the very fact of being monitored may have exerted some influence over the doctors.

Such monitoring, though, was not unwanted or disliked by Clinic consultants; indeed, they were on friendly, first-name terms with the civil servants at the Home Office and the Department of Health. They met at conferences and seminars, they exchanged information, and were often in contact by telephone. The close involvement of these non-medical people was not seen by the doctors as a threat to their clinical freedom or professional autonomy, or as an interference in their decisions about the treatment of patients. We have seen how the primary task of the Clinics was defined as the social control of addiction, and if medical work is seen as control rather than treatment then outside involvement is no danger to the position of doctors, indeed it is welcome. The doctors, then, did not see outsiders as enemies, but as allies in the fight against the 'drug problem'.

# 7

# *A decade of attending a Clinic – patients' perspectives*

'The whole thing is that your life revolves around the Clinics and the chemists.'

'I think the more "normal" you try to lead your life and the more inroads you're going to make into normal society, the more likely you are to have to tell lies at certain times . . . ducking into toilets, even though it's only a few times a day, especially if you keep to a schedule like I do, someone might say "How come when he's out here on Saturday night he always goes to the toilet at 9 o'clock?"'

'Since I've been on with the Clinics my life has never been my own, it more or less belongs to them. I mean I can't put a foot wrong or say anything wrong because I'm under their thumb. They can turn round and say "Right we're cutting this off you", "We're cutting that of". I mean it's like cutting chunks off my body.'

The three people who made these statements were still patients at Clinics in 1977, and had been for nine years, since 1968. They found it difficult to forget that they were addicts and patients. No matter what arrangements they made for their lives they were constantly reminded of the fact that they used drugs regularly, and that to ensure a regular supply they had to attend Clinics.

## THE IMPACT OF THE CLINICS

The Clinics did not change the drug scene overnight, though eventually they took much of the excitement out of being a junkie. As we have seen,

Clinic doctors exerted general pressure on patients to reduce dosages and to switch from injectable heroin to injectable methadone, then to oral methadone, and finally to abstinence. In 1968 about 60 to 80 per cent of all Clinic patients in the UK were prescribed heroin, but by 1978 only 9 per cent were receiving prescriptions for it (*see Table 6(3)*, p. 102). These changes are reflected in what happened to the people we followed. In 1969 all 128 were receiving prescriptions for heroin. When interviewed in 1976/77 only 55 were still patients; of these there were 35 who were receiving prescriptions for heroin, and 22 cases also getting methadone; the remaining 20 were receiving only methadone (see Appendix, p. 240). If anything, the people in our group were more 'successful' than the rest of the addict patients in England and Wales in continuing to receive heroin on prescription. Home Office statistics indicate that in the whole of England and Wales in 1977 there were only 232 such people (Central Office of Information 1979).

The fifty-five people in our sample who were still receiving prescriptions for opiates in 1977 had been patients since 1968. If we total the time they spent as addicts prior to 1968, they reach an average of thirteen years of addiction. Among them are many who have achieved considerable stability in their daily lives, such as Robert Jones about whom we write in the next chapter. Some have led rather chaotic lives, risking death from frequent overdoses and risking imprisonment by frequent brushes with the law; Gillian Morris, whose life, up to her death by overdose, is described in Chapter 10, is one. Others have had a mixture of periods of stability and chaos.

How did people live their lives on drugs for thirteen years or more? How and why did they continue addicted despite pressure from Clinic staff, families, and others to 'come off', despite warnings about the risks of addiction, despite knowing people who had died, despite the restrictions that the Clinics imposed? 'Why', as Jack Daniels mused, 'am I still a dope addict after all this time?' We have looked at these questions in three ways. First we considered the reasons people gave for their continued use of drugs, and what they expected from Clinics. Second we examined the problems, troubles, and hazards associated with addiction. Third we examined the way in which people organized their lives in order to avoid many of the hazards – in a sense, we found that some people were successful addicts because they continued addicted. We looked at how they managed this.

The material we use here is based mainly on interviews with those fifty-five people who were still addicts at Clinics in 1977, along with some comments from those who had stopped using heroin. Some characteristics of both those who continued and those who stopped will be found throughout the Appendix.

### REASONS FOR USING DRUGS: 'GETTING A BUZZ' OR 'KEEPING STRAIGHT'?

Many people lack a sophisticated vocabulary for describing internal states, and words like 'buzz' and 'stoned', although meaningful to those who have shared drug experiences, may fail to convey the effects of heroin to outsiders. Many addicts are ready to admit that drug effects are hard to explain and cannot get much beyond saying that when you inject heroin 'you just feel it'.

Many people's accounts of their early days on heroin emphasized the enjoyment they got from the drug. They could get a buzz on relatively small quantities. Heroin 'made you feel on top of the world', 'you felt happy', as if 'you wanted to talk to everybody', or 'just want to sit there and fall right asleep'. Mick Hollis was twenty-six in 1977, had been an addict since he was seventeen, and still attended a Clinic. He was one of the few who claimed that he still got a buzz, and described it as 'a sort of flash', with 'a taste at the back of the throat', lasting, by then, only for a couple of minutes. Any feelings of withdrawal sickness, such as your 'guts rumbling and churning' soon go away as 'you sort of feel it flow over you'. When he first started using heroin in the East End in 1967 Mick Hollis could get a buzz that 'used to last for a couple of hours. You could have a fix at nine o'clock if you bought some stuff . . . you'd be buzzing until about eleven or twelve. Then have another fix . . . I used to be stoned all through the day.'

With the growing level of tolerance that accompanies increased use, there is a necessary build-up in the amount of heroin needed to produce these euphoric effects. This change has been described in experiments and clinical observations (Wikler 1952; 1965). At the same time, physiological changes take place in the body's response to heroin such that when the drug is not taken the person begins to feel uncomfortable. This is the characteristic withdrawal syndrome, which may be nothing more than a few aches, sweating, and edginess, or mean feeling 'strung out' and 'sick'. For one man, feeling sick was when 'your head feels like a typewriter that's all rusted up' so that the words just do not come out properly. He continued: 'Physically you're so lethargic, if that's the word, so sluggish and you can't sit down or lie down and rest because your body won't relax. At the same time you feel so weak when you get up to move. It's such an effort to go on living.'

Sooner or later people talked less about getting buzzes and more about using heroin 'to keep me straight', 'to keep me normal', 'to stop me being sick', 'to be able to talk and do normal things that people do without thought'. By this stage continued use less often brings positive pleasure, but rather alleviates discomfort – 'It's just bringing yourself up to normal from that few degrees lower and you think "Oh that's better"'. Using heroin to feel normal is not only described in physical terms – if it were then all that would be needed to cure someone of addiction would be to help them through the bodily changes experienced on withdrawal. 'Feeling normal' means feeling well, feeling in the right frame of mind. Hence it is not just 'that I have a habit in my body, I have it in my mind, which is far worse'.

Heroin is, in a neuro-physiological sense, a depressant. It is an effective tranquillizer, and can work by 'keeping the lid on'. One man, interviewed while he was serving a prison sentence for a violent offence, was convinced that he would have been a more violent person if he had not been addicted, for when using heroin 'all was well with the world' – not so when he was abstinent. (Incidentally, violent crimes are unusual for users of opiates in Britain.) Using heroin can 'simplify life' because the many problems of living in the world are compressed into one – obtaining and using heroin. Others saw it as controlling anxiety and enabling them to get on with their life – this was the explanation given by Robert Jones who figures in the next chapter.

Though for most addicts the main reason given for continuing to use heroin is to keep straight there are a few who, despite prolonged use, can still get some positive gratification from the drug. Bennett Howell said simply that 'having started I found I enjoyed it and carried on, that's all'. He still attended a Clinic in South London and could still get a buzz if on some days he used a lot of his prescription, staving off withdrawal by drinking alcohol on the others. 'If you've gone a day without, or if you get a weekend script and you have it all on Saturday, and Monday morning you pick up your script, that first fix on Monday morning is probably the best of the week.'

## WHAT PATIENTS EXPECT FROM CLINICS

The addicts' main reason for attending a Clinic was to ensure a regular prescription for heroin or methadone, thus the ideal Clinic was one where the doctor would agree to prescribe heroin in reasonable quantities, and where the staff did not hassle patients by changing and reducing prescriptions, or hassle them to change their way of life. Many agreed with the view that 'with luck, you go in, you're in a minute or two minutes with them, it's hello and goodbye'. The ideal arrangement was seen as a brief visit once a fortnight or less to ensure the prescription would be posted and to collect a supply of needles and syringes. Treatment was generally regarded with suspicion, for all therapy involves changes. At best, it was something that should be offered when the patient felt it was time for a change; at worst, it was seen as an interference in the addict's life, without the addict's consent. The majority of the long-term addict patients told us they believed that treatment would not be successful without their co-operation. Doctors who tried to 'force people' to change were blamed for turning them to the black market and for pushing people into a life of crime. One ex-addict complained of a doctor who 'sort ot tried to analyse you all the time' using terms 'straight out of Freudian or Jungian dictionaries or whatever was popular at the time' but 'all I wanted was my prescription'. One woman felt that most people 'wanted a prescription, they didn't want a psychiatrist'. Bennett Howell remembered with some amusement the failure of group therapy at his Clinic:

> 'When the doctor formed the group therapy he said, "I'm forming a group, I want to get together four or five of the most intelligent married junkies that we've got on this Clinic and meet once a week just to talk and see what happens". He did that and we met about once a week for about six or seven weeks. I don't think it turned out quite the way he wanted. Instead of everybody saying how much they hated taking drugs and how they wanted to get off and that they were going to help each other get off, instead everybody said how much they liked taking drugs, how much they didn't want to get off, and they reinforced each other's opinions.'

Of course there were patients who did welcome the idea of therapy, the development of a good relationship with their doctor or social worker, or some other helping action. A woman ex-addict recalled her experiences at a Clinic when she was trying to come off drugs. She felt that it was largely due to her doctor's support and understanding that she succeeded in coming off:

> 'I was very fond of Dr Allen, I got on with him very well. . . . It was a case of you sit there and you talk about anything, and every now and then he'd say "what do you think" and I'd say "you're acting like a psychiatrist" and things like that. . . . But I suppose that's psychotherapy in a way, I don't know really. We just used to talk. He was one person I could talk to, which does help.'

Staff turnover is relatively high among junior doctors and this hardly allows for the development of therapy. Though many addicts claimed that they did not desire a therapeutic relationship with a doctor or social worker, they complained when they left partly because 'it's better the devil you know'. They were wary of the enthusiastic new doctor who wanted to get everybody off drugs or introduce drastic therapeutic innovations.

The usual complaints made by patients about doctors were expressed in a somewhat heightened manner by the addicts. They said that the doctors did not have enough time to see patients, that they were too busy dealing with their 'Harley Street practices', that they treated a patient as a 'statistic' or a 'number' rather than as an individual, that they were 'arrogant' and 'authoritarian'. But drug Clinics differ from many other medical settings because the patients consult frequently, over long periods of time, and have little opportunity to change doctors. Of the 128 people we followed 110 remained at their original Clinic throughout their time as patients. Consequently they had the opportunity of getting to know all the quirks and characteristics of the doctors and staff.

Some addicts had so much experience of the medical profession that they regarded doctors rather cynically and had a wide repertoire of 'atrocity stories' about how they had suffered at their hands. Let us look at some of the more commonly expressed sentiments. Bennett Howell, who had had eight different Clinic doctors, had this to say:

> 'The medical profession tends to build up a kind of mystique about itself, a kind of untouchability. The general population regards doctors as absolute, "doctors are always right". When you come across as many doctors as junkies do, you tend to regard doctors just as other human beings – they are good or bad and nothing special. And certainly psychiatrists . . . I think psychiatry as a discipline is about on the level of the witchdoctor. It's not a science for a start. It's got no basis, they don't use the scientific method. Everybody chucks in an idea here, there, and everywhere, and people don't know what they are doing. They don't know how to treat mental illness, they don't know how to treat junkies, they don't know how to treat anybody. I have got no respect for psychiatrists, some I like as people, but as a body I've got no respect for them. I think they're a sham.'

Joe Henrick criticized the Clinic doctor for giving him the wrong sort of prescription:

> 'I've always had my heroin, I've never been off heroin since I came to this Clinic in '68. And suddenly I came out of prison and he decides that I should go on Physeptone [methadone], which he knows is no use to me now. He knows that I'm going to sell this, and it's putting me at risk. Then he's giving me a miserable eight amps . . . and there're people here who have only been here about a year and they're getting more than me, so again he's putting me at risk. He knows that eight amps is no use to me whatsoever.'

Bennett Howell summed up what many addicts felt:

> 'Clinics? I think in terms of doctors. I mean Clinics are only what the

doctors are like. Since I've been on this Clinic, and I've been on it for five years now, it's varied according to the doctor I've been under. They tend not to last very long, some are very, very good, some are bloody awful. How you decide whether they're good or not is: how sympathetic they are, how often they'll let you get your script out early if you want it, if you want to go away or something like that; how sympathetic they are if you get sick and you need extra stuff, all that sort of thing. That's how I determine if the doctor's good or not. And how interested they seem in you. Some of them, you go in and they talk to you; they say "How are you", and you say "All right". They say "All right, here's your script" that's it, bang, out you go. Others you can talk to for half an hour and they're interested in what's going on. Others try all the time. Why don't you give up? Why don't you stop? Others say "Well, you know, I don't think it's a good idea for you to stop. I think that you're on a maintenance script, that's all right. You've got a good job". You know, each doctor's different and, you know, you just judge each doctor according to how you get on with them. My present doctor's all right. He's very sympathetic and understanding and he lets me get my stuff out early if I want it. There's no hassles with him, so that's all right. The worst doctors are the ones who cause you hassles and all the time cutting your script down and that sort of thing.'

The forcefulness of the accounts illustrates how the patients saw themselves as dependent on the decisions of the Clinic doctors. The way in which addicts' lives were interwoven with the doctors' policies is illustrated in the autobiography of Kevin Cummings, whose nine years with the same doctor is discussed in the next chapter. For addict patients the relationship with the doctor is one of conflict, suspicion, and mistrust. The successful addict has to convince the doctor that he or she can manage as an addict and avoid giving the doctor any opportunity or reason to change the treatment. Addict patients do not want any hassles; therefore a major part of their problem of managing daily life on drugs is to learn to manage the Clinic staff.

### HAZARDS OF ADDICTION

We have argued that one of the hazards for those who wanted to continue addicted was the risk that Clinic staff would intervene to change the prescription and thus upset a carefully achieved *status quo*. But there were many other hazards that could accompany addiction. There were dangers linked to injecting drugs: by 1969 40 per cent of the people we interviewed had had one or more overdoses, 40 per cent had already suffered from hepatitis, 46 per cent had had abcesses, and 16 per cent had

had septicaemia. There were the hazards of being known as an addict: in a limited housing and labour market, landlords and employers do not welcome junkies as tenants and employees. There were hazards from other addicts: of being 'ripped off' when buying illicit drugs, and the occasional brush with a violent character. There were risks of being stopped and searched by the police and the possibility of arrest and imprisonment: by 1969, 79 per cent of our sample had been convicted of an offence. Successful addicts organized their lives to avoid these difficulties. But there were others who had been less successful in finding a balance between their drug use and life style and who were caught up in many difficulties that were associated with the way they managed, or failed to manage, their addiction. Let us firstly look in more detail at some of the hazards and problems that are associated with using drugs, before going on to examine how people can successfully avoid them.

### Hazards from using drugs

People take risks when they first begin using drugs. The novice is entering into unexplored areas and activities that can be perilous until they discover their own reactions and limits. Kevin Cummings, who remained addicted to methadone, damaged the nerves of his arm when he injected a grain of heroin in 'the biggest fix I'd had when I first started', back in 1967, when he was twenty. He related how his girlfriend had given him the injection in a telephone box. Being a new user, he was 'too fussy to go down Camberwell bogs' to inject. 'It's only as time goes on, then you'll go down, but in those days that was too dirty for me.' His girlfriend told him what to expect from the injection:

> 'She said "don't worry if you start to feel a tingling, prickling in the back of your head and your neck, it's just a small OD". So she went off down the Ladies and I'm in the telephone box and on it comes and it's prickling at the back of my neck and I'm thinking "ah terrific, it's just a small OD" and I'm feeling really nice. I looked down at my arm, and I took another look and it was coming up, it was getting bigger, and I was taking my watch off and my rings off, and it came up and my arm was that big all the way down, my hand, the lot . . . I freaked out, I honestly believed I was going to die. . . . Well it went down in forty-eight hours. But I mean that killed the nerve right there . . . even now if I ever put a needle in there it's incredibly painful.'

Losing consciousness after an injection because an excessive dose of drugs had been administered could be seen as just another part of life. It was not uncommon if one was living a chaotic life. Lew Tunstall put it this way: 'It depends what you mean by an overdose. I mean doctors call it an overdose when you just drop out, you know, asleep. That happens all the time . . . I've been taken to a casualty department because I've been found asleep somewhere.' There were many people who went through phases when they overdosed several times a day for weeks on end. Some had periods of chaotic drug use, with frequent hospitalizations for overdoses, and yet managed to pull out from that life style. Others continued and their chaos ended in death. Frequent overdosing increases the chance that one day a fatal dose will be taken.

'Street' (illicit) drugs bring greater health risks than drugs prescribed by a Clinic. Street heroin is often 'cut' (diluted) with potentially damaging substances, and it is difficult to gauge its strength. Barbiturates are particularly harmful drugs, for they are both highly intoxicant and are not intended for injection. Indeed, many addicts associated their chaotic periods with the excessive use of barbiturates. In the early 1970s there was an increase in their use, which some addicts blamed on the restrictive prescribing policies of the Clinics: they argued that they used barbiturates because they were no longer getting enough opiates. Some, of course, were simply no longer enjoying opiates (not getting a buzz) and so turning to barbiturates as an alternative. The chief attraction of barbiturates was that they were readily available from GPs, and sold on the black market at a lower price than heroin. Dave Godfrey recalled that in the early 1970s the price of Chinese heroin began to 'start flying' and 'everybody started taking "barbs" because you could inject them and they would knock you silly, so when you were really bad it was the best thing in the world for you'. Barbiturates should not be injected but 'junkies get around everything, don't they'. There are ways of preparing them for injection, for example: 'if you put them in a bottle and slung a lump of cotton wool on top you could drain the sleeper out and then leave the chalk at the bottom.' Not everybody took the trouble, though, to prepare barbiturates for sterile and safe injections. Those who did not do so often suffered from abscesses, septicaemia, and damage to nerves, veins, and muscles. In some cases such damage led to the permanent loss of a limb.

Dave Godfrey thought that his Clinic did not give him a big enough prescription and so he relied on Chinese heroin and when this ran short, in 1970, he started injecting a barbiturate, Tuinal 'which was where I really came unstuck'. The drug had such an effect that you did 'not know what you were doing', had a 'total lack of knowledge', and felt 'very violent' so that you 'just started fighting people' or 'fighting with ambulance drivers'. A barbiturate user might wake up in the morning 'in hospital with stitches round my eyes' and not be able to 'remember a thing about it'. A further problem with barbiturates was that the intoxicating effect made it hard to remember how much had been taken. Dave Godfrey explained how: 'You couldn't score enough H to get high so you would just score on Tuinal, and you would knock yourself out with them, and then after your first three or four you feel great, but then you don't remember anything but you still took the other six.' Lew Tunstall, who was still using drugs when we talked to him, recalled his worst periods. He had three years of chaos when he just 'gave up hope completely' and was 'more or less waiting to die'. When he took barbiturates he was 'taking a chance that he would take one too many'.

> 'When you've taken the first lot in the morning, you take them just to get stoned – but when you're stoned you don't know what you're doing, you go out and get more and take them without realizing . . . I didn't feel there was anything in life for me. Everything was just getting up and getting barbs – being stoned, that's all I wanted.'

Exploits of 'barb freaks', as avid users are called, are part of the everyday talk among addicts. For example, we were once sitting in a Clinic waiting room where there were three patients waiting to see Dr Allen. The tone of the conversation was matter-of-fact. One man began talking about his friend 'Smiler' who had been found drowned in a canal a few days earlier. The man had been fishing with Smiler who was 'all barbed up'. Smiler fell into the canal; his friend pulled him out and took him home. Later he called round to Smiler's house only to be told that he had gone fishing again. Returning to the canal bank to look for Smiler, he found the fishing rod on the path and Smiler's body floating in the canal.

We were relying on people's memories of their periods of drug-taking, but the excessive use of barbiturates adversely affects memory. These times seemed 'all a bit of a blur' and dates became virtually impossible to remember. Incidents, though, were recollected more easily; for example, an addict's husband recalled the time he had gone with her to the ABC cinema in Bayswater. She went to the toilet 'and she was in there three hours and missed two films'. She chipped in 'and I swore blind I'd only been in there five minutes'. Another incident was recalled by Louise Wrighton. She had permanently damaged her leg through injecting barbiturates, and was very conscious of her appearance, trying hard to find plausible ways to explain her limp. She recalled one time when she was unconscious on barbiturates and someone had stolen her purse and stripped her of the white suit she was wearing: 'I came back with a towel round me . . . that's what barbiturates do to you.' She continued her condemnation of barbiturates by describing an accident that happened to Frank, who became her husband:

> 'He almost killed his niece, didn't he? His sister's baby, only eight months old, she was in hospital for ten months. They took her to specialists, they've spent hundreds on her . . . he said that he'd lit a

> match and he had a nylon shirt and it blew up on him. Really what happened was he went into his bedroom, he had a smoke, but he was stoned you see, so he lit this cigarette and he's probably holding it, so while he's holding it, it drops to the floor. He pulled the whole pelmet and curtains on top of him. I mean, you should ask him, his body is not a body. Full of burns, but not ordinary burns – real great big red things.'

Louise and Frank married in 1975. At the wedding reception they made a public commitment about their drug use: 'We made a vow in front of his parents and said "the day I take amphetamines and the day you take barbiturates, it's finished". And it's right isn't it really? I mean he's proved to be so much better.'

The ultimate hazard of addiction is death. Over the ten-year period of the follow-up, from 1969 to 1979, 19 people died (i.e. just under 15 per cent of the sample). Fourteen of the people who died were men and 5 were women. The age at which they died varied between 20 and 55, with an average of 31. Hospital case notes, coroners' inquests, and Home Office records indicated that all were using drugs at the time of their deaths. The commonest cause of death, for eight people, was an overdose of opiates and/or barbiturates. For three more the coroners' verdicts were 'addiction to drugs'. One person died at home from burns, one died from carbon monoxide poisoning from the fumes given out by a faulty oil heater. He was intoxicated at the time. One was found dead with cut wrists. One died from bronchial pneumonia, four from renal diseases, including the eldest of those who died, a fifty-five-year-old woman. She had used heroin and other drugs for thirty years and in her doctor's opinion the numerous injections she had over the years eventually led to kidney failure. The Clinic Sister had arranged for us to interview her and on the day in question she was brought into the Clinic by a friend. She was staggering and her friend helped her stand. She was haggard and emaciated with the skin on her face drawn tight. She was admitted to hospital and died the following week.

### Hazards of arrest

A life that involves scoring street drugs brings a further hazard in addition to likely infection. Being 'known' and visiting places like Piccadilly Circus brings the risk of being 'busted'. Being busted is accepted as one of the risks of life. One woman, who bought most of her drugs on the black market because she received only methadone linctus from the Clinic, explained, 'you know there is a chance you are going to get nicked but you don't think about it'. The 'Old Bill' may be around, but 'when you've got to go out and buy that's it'. She continued:

> 'There's no thinking, "oh I might get nicked today". Everybody knows that they are taking a risk but everybody still does it and when you hear that somebody's got three years [in prison] that doesn't put you off going to buy that day. You don't say "I won't take today, I'll stay at home", because you can't.'

Joe Henrick explained that he still went to Piccadilly despite the fact that he was well known by the police, because it was the one place where he could be reasonably certain of scoring, 'you can go down there anytime'. It was central, and easy to get away from if things went wrong. Not that it was always a simple matter to score. It could be 'a hit and miss affair'.

> 'You can go down there looking for heroin and you can be there for hours and hours. Another time you'll be down there and just get it all right. Gerrard Street is still thriving but you know what it is now, everybody's got their own certain contact you know and although you go down to Piccadilly it's always just to meet people and that.'

Addicts were not fond of the police and told numerous stories of encounters with them, in which there was a sense of being singled out and persecuted, a feeling of being punished more for being addicts than for the offence committed. There was no denial by those quoted that they had broken the law in a variety of ways, in particular with respect to the illegal possession and the sale of drugs, but a general feeling persisted about the arbitrary enforcement of the law. Joe Henrick, who went to Piccadilly every day to sell his Clinic methadone and buy heroin in its place, reported bitterly on his experience with the police: 'They know you are doing wrong but they just can't put their finger on you so what they do is they go and stitch you up. That creates a great deal of bad blood between a lot of people and the police.' He felt that he had never been arrested for a 'genuine case' and that he was not treated fairly in court.

> 'You walk into court and the minute they hear that you're a drug addict, you are condemned straight away. When I went to court last time there was no drugs in my case but because I was a drug addict he told me "I'm going to put you somewhere where you can't touch drugs for a long time". What's that got to do with it? I got two-and-a-half years for nothing.'

Joe Henrick was suffering from a kidney disorder when he was interviewed in 1977 and died a few months later.

### Continuing chaos

Some people pursued a chaotic life for many years. Their lives were punctuated by overdoses, hospitalizations, and imprisonments. Finding them and trying to interview them was difficult. One such person was Benny Ackroyd, who after ten years of using heroin still consumed a wide range of drugs. We talked to him in 1977, when he was in hospital undergoing detoxification from barbiturates because he had suffered fits when using them. The doctor described him as the most difficult patient at his Clinic, frequently overdosing and being taken to casualty departments each time he was discharged from the in-patient unit of the hospital. In recent months he had lasted only a few days in the community before being readmitted to the in-patient unit. When we saw him again he had been discharged from hospital and was on a daily prescription of 480 mgs of heroin, five ampoules and sixteen tablets of methadone, and 320 mgs of cocaine. (He was one of the few still being prescribed cocaine.) He also used barbiturates and other hypnotics, mainly Mogadon, Tuinal, and Nembutal, which he received from GPs; and most days he also took Chinese heroin, Ritalin, Dexedrine, and Largactil. He had nowhere to live and had no contact with his family.

He started using heroin at the age of nineteen, in 1966, and used it occasionally for three or four months, and then became addicted. In 1968 he received a Clinic prescription for four grains (240 mgs) of heroin daily. Almost every year he had spent some time in prison and had frequently been in hospital for treatment of infections or for withdrawal from barbiturates. Most years he had not worked. One exception to this pattern was a period of eighteen months during 1974/75 when he married a German woman who did not use drugs. They lived in Ladbroke Grove and after three months with her he got a job with Westminster Council. He stopped using barbiturates and most other drugs, except heroin and cocaine prescribed by the Clinic. It was, as he put it, a 'happy year'. In the spring of the following one he was arrested for breaking and entering, and although he received a conditional discharge the details of the conviction were sent to his employers and he was sacked from his job. Benny started using barbiturates again. Around that time his wife went to Germany to visit her parents. He then went into hospital for a 'barb. detox.' and withdrew from heroin and barbiturates. For the first time since 1966 he was voluntarily free of all drugs. He went abroad to join his wife and spent four months with her. He used a little Valium and methedrine and, by his own standards, did some heavy drinking. He was unable to obtain employment abroad, though, and as his wife was unwilling to leave Germany he returned alone to London at the end of the year. After three weeks in London he went back to the Clinic asking for a prescription. A few days before we talked to him he had been taken to a casualty department after overdosing on thirty Tuinal and an unknown quantity of Largactil.

Another chaotic addict was Glaswegian ex-amateur boxer Eddie Cox who was brought up by his grandparents and finally drifted down to London in the early 1960s. He married another addict and together they lived in a bedsitter off the Portobello Road, a life that seemed to be wholly centred on drugs. In an effort to regularize their lives they moved down to Somerset (though he continued to attend a London Clinic) but even in the country they remained involved with other drug users. He lost count of the drugs he was using and could not even remember what he had used the day we spoke to him. He was interviewed on a freezing January evening in an unheated room. The interview lasted two hours, during which the interviewer shivered from the cold and Eddie shivered from withdrawal. He was one of the few addicts who injected during the interview, putting the needle through his jeans into his thigh. He resisted any effort made to help him, with the exception of the offer of more drugs. He had no illusions about the possible consequences of his way of life and believed that he might die from his incautious use of drugs.

> 'Cocaine – if I couldn't get it legally I would get it by any way I could – even by killing. I can say from the bottom of my heart this is the life I want to live and I'm living it. . . . It doesn't frighten me, death, because I'd rather be dead than be without drugs. . . . Because I am a chronic addict, I mean *chronic*. I've got a "cancer" and I know it . . . I have done nine cures, and I've been on a Section (under the Mental Health Act) for one year and I've still broken into three chemists during that Section.'

The last time we saw him he was in a frightful state of health – thin, toothless, nose running, with recent scars from a knife fight, legs bandaged, intoxicated, and crying. He left the office where he had been interviewed and staggered across Denmark Hill to walk down to Camberwell Green to buy drugs. He looked as though he would soon be dead. A year later we heard that he had died.

### The Clinic response to chaos

Few people were able to continue a chaotic life style over many years. First, this life style increased the risk that they might die. Second, their chaotic behaviour led to interruptions in their addiction, for example it increased the likelihood of arrest. Perhaps more important was that they came to the attention of Clinic staff. One of the consequences of a chaotic life style was that doctors attempted various types of intervention in order to reduce the chaos. They might require patients to attend daily and to inject drugs under staff supervision; they might reduce or cancel the prescription; they might persuade patients to enter hospital for treatment. Clinic doctors tended to mix persuasion, treatment, and coercion. Thus the outcome for chaotic patients tended to be that their addiction was interrupted. Those who were most chaotic when we first interviewed them in 1969, whom we called the 'junkies', were, ten years later, less likely than any others to be in receipt of prescriptions. By 1979 they tended to be either abstinent, in prison, or dead. (*See Tables A(5)* and *A(12)* in Appendix). In a sense then, one of the 'hazards' for the chaotic addict was that the Clinic staff might intervene to reduce the prescription and begin therapy.

### From chaos to a managed life

Most people eventually moved out of periods of major chaos. Lew Tunstall remembered how he moved into a controlled and managed life style. In his recollection of the events, he said it needed a 'shock of realization' to jolt him from some sort of inner 'rock bottom'. He was in hospital for a 'barb. cure' and thought it was time he was allowed to leave. He asked Dr Amsden if he could be discharged: 'I asked him if I could go and he said "you only want to go out and get stoned". He said, "all right you can go, but you are not coming back in this ward". . . . I think it was just the look on his face.' Lew believed that Dr Amsden expected him to die. 'They really did think I was lost.' Others talked about the change as a more gradual realization that their lives were pointless and dreary, and that there was no glamour in overdosing and spending much time in a locked hospital ward. Brenda Martini, who when last interviewed still used heroin, but in a more controlled fashion, remembered how eventually she became rather tired of it all, but not before she was arrested in Carnaby Street and had spent a month in Holloway Prison charged with supplying drugs. This chaotic period resulted in her return to hospital, detained under the Mental Health Act. Dr Amsden would no longer prescribe heroin and instead gave her ampoules of methadone. She recalled how she felt:

> 'The constant being locked up there just being completely hopeless. I don't know really, the staff were so pissed off with all of us I think, just being treated as a hopeless case I suppose – just to hang around was very depressing, people stoned all the time, being forced to be with others. The only thing I had in common with everyone else was just drugs, nothing else. Didn't make many friends really, in fact people were always bringing drugs and I never got into any of the scene. I didn't want to.'

By 1972 she was discharged from the ward and went to live in a hostel associated with the hospital. While there she found a job which she held for the following two years. During this time her use of barbiturates declined and while still staying on methadone, she gradually gave up barbiturates and was able to leave the hostel.

### AVOIDING THE HAZARDS: HOW TO BE A SUCCESSFUL ADDICT

We have emphasized the problems that can be associated with a life on heroin. It would be misleading however to suggest that all addicts lead chaotic lives all of the time. Many of the addicts we followed led quiet, stable lives for the whole of the period we were in contact with them. Many who had a regular supply of drugs from a Clinic led lives that were characterized by their use of drugs, but that were otherwise remarkably uneventful and inconspicuous. Robert Jones, who we write about in the next chapter, was one such addict, leading, in his own words, a relatively normal life. Others had had chaotic periods but relatively few continued to lead such life styles for a long time – basically because it is difficult to do so without meeting ever-increasing problems, or dying. How then did some addicts manage to continue addicted and avoid problems? We think it is useful to ask why some addicts were *successful*, in that despite the hazards of addiction, and despite the efforts of others to get them to stop using drugs, they managed to continue as addicts. Success, though, should not here be equated with contentment: it refers to the avoidance of trouble, in addicts' terms the avoidance of hassles. Successful addicts seemed to arrange their lives so that they avoided trouble. They developed strategies to avoid putting their regular drug use at risk, were careful about the amount of drugs they used and about the cleanliness of their injections, and shunned the company of other addicts and their meeting-places. They also avoided the police and the hazards of arrest and imprisonment, and, finally, the difficulties that the Clinic could bring – an alteration in the prescription and an unwelcome change in the *status quo* – by keeping a relatively low profile as far as the Clinic staff were concerned. The successful developed a highly structured and routinized life, and learned to cater for unavoidable changes in routine. They avoided chaos by keeping a balance between their drug use and their life style.

In 1969 we described one type of addict as 'stable'. Addicts of this type worked, avoided other addicts, and avoided crime. They led a life that, we predicted at the time, would avoid many of the problems of addiction and prevent giving Clinic staff a reason to intervene to change or curtail their prescriptions. These addicts were more successful than any other patients in continuing addicted. In 1979, ten years later, they were more likely than others to still be patients. Indeed, a third of them had received heroin prescriptions without interruption since 1969, a feat few of the other addict patients achieved (*see Tables A(5)* and *A(12)* in Appendix).

### Routines for using drugs

As we have mentioned, successful addicts developed a *routine* for using drugs – they injected the same quantity at the same time day-in and day-out. Some went to the trouble of ensuring that the drugs only served to 'keep them normal' and did not use them to get a buzz for this would have interfered with other things they wanted to do in their lives. A parallel might be drawn with the use of alcohol: few people wish to drink alcohol to the point where they are intoxicated every day and, similarly, many addicts avoid intoxication on the drugs they use. However, one immediate problem for addicts was that it is characteristic of addiction that they needed to use opiates at frequent intervals if they were to avoid physical discomfort from withdrawal or marked mood swings. A second problem for addict patients was that their supplies of drugs were limited and controlled: they were required to visit the Clinic weekly, fortnightly, or, more rarely, monthly. Most had to visit their dispensing chemist daily to collect their drugs. Thus both the nature of addiction and the social policy applied to it placed constraints within which addict patients led their lives. Using up drugs too quickly, missing a Clinic appointment, or failing to make it on time to the chemist could have disrupted the addict's life. Jack Daniels, who wondered why he was still an addict, gave the solution to these problems when describing how he led his life: 'I guess I stick pretty much to a routine, don't worry too much, because in my situation I can't worry too much because then I'm going to come unstuck. My tolerance and so on . . . it means I've got to stick to a routine as best I can.' Carefully arranging the timing of injections and using a determined amount of drugs on each occasion reduced the risk of running out before the next day's supply could be collected from the chemist. Someone with a prescription for 80 mgs of heroin for example, which is eight pills, might fix 'two threes and one two', in other words two injections of 30 mgs and one of 20 mgs. A routine also reduced the risk of overdose and the problems of intoxication and marked changes of alertness and mood.

Early morning was a difficult time for most addicts as this followed a long period without an injection. Most liked to inject on waking and planning was needed to make sure some drugs were set aside for this first fix of the day. One woman who lived with her son and parents in Kent made arrangements to pick up her drugs from the chemist every day: she explained 'out of this I always save two [pills] for the morning'. She had learned to do this because she didn't 'like having to wake up and feel grotty . . . and to struggle up to the chemist just before nine o'clock in the morning'. She kept those two pills in a bottle, which she put out of sight to reduce the temptation of using the pills before scheduled. She, like many others, worried that the prescription might not turn up on time at the chemist. Most chemists, even though they knew a person had a regular prescription, would not dispense until that prescription had arrived. In this case, though, the woman had a good relationship with the chemist and he dispensed for her even in the absence of a prescription. This is illegal and a risk most chemists would not take.

Any activity that might have upset routines could have been problematic. An addict who wanted to go out for the evening had to consider how this might interfere with the routine – 'Do I have my fix before I go out, or do I wait 'till I get back, or do I take it with me?' – an obvious problem, as we see below, for anyone who had a job. A daily routine could be upset by a change in prescription. Some said that just staying on the same dosage may be equivalent to a reduction because increasing tolerance requires larger doses for the same effects. Any change in the prescription required a change in the daily routine and a new balance to be struck between drug use, feeling of well-being, and life style. If the dose was too low, the addict risked running out too early in the day:

> 'I feel that half a grain for me is not enough – really, but I know that's common. Every drug addict thinks that his script isn't enough – but it *is* a low script . . . I fix two pills and then one pill – it's not really enough you know . . . I usually have my last fix at about three o'clock and it's only half a fix any way – so I feel pretty rotten during the night.'

As we have argued, addicts carefully considered the strategies they would use with their doctor. A major tactic of those who had struck a balance between their drug use and their life style was the avoidance of giving the doctor a reason to make any changes. Many would agree to almost anything for 'peace and quiet' and to avoid hassles.

### Managing daily life: work

In 1977 there were thirty-eight Clinic patients in our sample who were using heroin or methadone and who were working. The range of jobs was wide. Many, understandably, feared disclosure of their drug use. They preferred jobs that allowed them to pick up their drugs from the chemist in the morning, or jobs where employers tolerated their arriving late, or slipping out from work during the morning. Otherwise quite complicated arrangements had to be made with the Clinic and the chemist about dispensing the daily prescription. One woman complained that:

> 'The way you have to pick up your script every day, I find it very difficult. When I wasn't working it just didn't matter, but now I find it really difficult because that means that when I was starting [work] I had to buy stuff so I could save a day's drugs. Now I always have to take "tomorrows" . . . because I go out to work so early that I can't get it [from the chemist] until on the way home.'

This woman was unable to collect her drugs in the morning because this would have made her late for work and, therefore, had to make sure she had one day's supply of drugs in hand. In addition, working addicts had to organize their injections outside of working hours or find somewhere to inject, not taking too long about it for fear of raising suspicion. On the other hand, a job without regular hours or a place of work could jeopardize the daily routine of drug use. Pete Rossi is a good example of how someone handled these problems. He was over forty years old and lived in his own house in West London with his wife and children. He became addicted to heroin in Canada when he was eighteen. He was then a musician and said that nearly everyone he knew at the time was taking drugs. He found the effects of heroin were very inspirational and helped him play with fewer inhibitions. In his home country his addiction led him to break the law on numerous occasions and he served prison sentences for drug offences. He was one of the addicts who came to Britain in the early 1960s when he found that heroin could be obtained on prescription here. Since then he had had no problems with the law and spent no time in hospital. Before the Clinics opened he had been receiving large prescriptions for heroin. The Clinic doctor tried to reduce the prescription. However, Pete fought hard to persuade the doctor to give him the dosage of heroin that he felt he required, and remembered how he once spent four hours in a momentous argument with his doctor. However, he failed to persuade the doctor and his dosage was greatly reduced. He accepted the constraints of the Clinic policy and tried to live within its confines. He did not turn to black market opiates or to barbiturates. He did however drink quite heavily, though this had only started about four years previously. He saw himself as someone who was inclined towards addiction, who would also tend to 'over use' any drug once started on it. He did not mix with other addicts and had gradually drifted away from the music scene. He kept his addiction a secret from everyone except his closest family, and took precautions not to run short of drugs or to have to stay away from home for too many hours at a time. Pete Rossi said that any activity that might disrupt his routine had to be carefully considered. He had, for example, to weigh up carefully how long he could stay away from home and his drugs.

> 'If I've got work – like say I'm doing a job like we did the other day down the coast near Brighton – I don't like carrying any drugs with

me, it's only as a last resort I'll take something with me. Maybe I plan to stay away eight hours or something, so I use enough stuff early [in the morning] so that I figure I will last and I'll be able to work comfortably for eight hours. If something goes wrong and I've got to stay twelve, then I start falling apart, the sweat is pouring off me and I'm completely weak, can hardly walk about, let alone do work.'

Work brought the addict into contact with 'straight' people and a major fear was that employers and fellow workers would not accept them if the addiction became known. Andrew Wright, like many of the addicts who attempted to lead a relatively straight life, decided to keep his addiction a secret rather than risk losing his job. After fifteen years of addiction, many of them chaotic and difficult, he had settled happily in his own house and had many interests outside the world of addiction. He could only maintain this satisfactory life style if he kept his job, which he had had for five years. He spoke about the difficulties of keeping his addiction secret. For example, when he was on his way home from work with a colleague he had been stopped and searched by the police near the chemist where he picked up his drugs. The police did not find any drugs on him, but the incident was embarrassing.

'In a pin-striped suit with my briefcase in my hand and somebody from the office with me, I've been stopped and searched. Fortunately I wasn't carrying anything. The policeman was very nasty, had he been nice I would have been pleasant, but he wasn't so I took his number and reported him.'

Like many people who successfully live with drugs he liked to be 'as unobtrusive as possible' to the extent that he didn't 'want people to even notice that I exist'. He had a repertoire of excuses to maintain his front. He resisted being sent on business trips abroad by inventing a fictitious girlfriend who supposedly would not allow him to travel. He was careful not to draw attention to himself. He would not refuse a drink after work, for fear of being 'looked upon as a freak', though quite often he might not feel like one.

### Managing daily life: addict friends

All the addicts we talked to had bought drugs on the black market at some time in their lives. Much buying and selling was restricted to the safety of close friends, but there were occasions when an addict would risk the open market in places like Piccadilly Circus or Gerrard Street. Much depended on the balance a person had achieved between the Clinic prescription, the drugs needed, and the life style adopted. Addicts who tried to lead relatively ordinary lives though would no longer go near places where drugs were traded. They tended to have broken contact with other addicts and avoided the risks such friendships could bring. One example was Marty Rose, an addict from London's East End. He was seventeen when he first attended the Clinic and the doctor put pressure on him to reduce his drug intake and get a job. He recalled that things were difficult and that for a while he used more drugs than ever. However, within two years he had 'settled down'. Some of his friends began to 'leave the scene' and drift away, then got married, and stopped using drugs. For him addiction continued, though he had not scored for 'years and years'. 'I just settled for my prescription, it was quite a bit of bother you know – you just don't get heroin in Piccadilly these days.' He worked, lived at home with his parents, and had just bought a new car. Thus for seven years he had successfully avoided problems by cutting himself off from his former addict friends. He led a rather uneventful life.

For some addicts, getting older, perhaps getting married and having a family involved losing their contacts in the drug world and simply having to rely on their prescription for supplies. Many found that they no longer knew where to buy heroin: 'I wish I did' said one middle-aged addict wistfully, even though she had heard in the Clinic that it was now £6 a pill. She had once been part of the Bohemian circles of the 1950s, but no longer knew other addicts. She could not score even if she wanted to because she did not know how to do it: 'I don't know these Chinese people, I don't want to get involved with all that.' It was much the same story for Jack Daniels who had lost contact with his old friends because 'that scene bores me you know'. In the old days, 'when I needed to score', those friends were useful and 'it was a social thing. But now I wouldn't give a hoot about them.' His contacts with addicts were confined to occasional fleeting meetings in Clinic waiting rooms.

When addict friends were no longer needed they could become an embarrassment for those drug users leading a straight life. One woman used to mix with addicts 'all the time', at Piccadilly Circus, before she got married, but had then moved out of London and was bringing up her family. She recalled, with some alarm, a recent incident:

> 'I walked through Piccadilly with my daughter last year after taking her to the cinema up in town and I mean, we were both dressed up fairly nicely, we'd been to see a film. I got stopped three times and was absolutely appalled that people actually had the nerve to stop and ask for drugs off me . . . and I had my daughter with me at the time and I didn't think I looked like an addict.'

Having a family, working, and adopting a more steady pattern of drug use meant that buying illicit drugs brought with it great risks. Also, older addicts often felt different from younger ones; they just did not see themselves as being part of what is really a young person's world. Buying and selling drugs does not fit well into a life where drug use has become an incidental, but of course significant, part of a daily routine.

### An uneasy balance

The stable, or 'maintained', addict has figured prominently in the literature on addiction. The concept was an important basis to the conclusions of the Rolleston Committee in 1926 and the first Brain Committee. Maintenance is also an important concept in the thinking behind the methadone programmes in the US. For the most part 'stabilization', or 'maintenance', has been conceived of and discussed in terms of drug effects, in that the stable or maintained addict is said to have achieved a balance between drug intake, drug metabolization, physiological state, and psychological mood. But the accounts of the addicts we spoke to, and an examination of their lives over several years, showed that there is no simple relationship between the ingestion of a drug with powerful psycho-active and physical effects and the life that an addicted person leads. The physical and psychological effects of the drug set some parameters to the sort of life that can be led, but within these boundaries there is scope for tremendous variation in individual response. Some of the addicts had led chaotic lives, where harmony between drug use and life style was elusive. Others had achieved a balance between drug effects and the life they led, a balance requiring considerable routine and planning. The stable addicts we met may have been stable for reasons other than, or additional to, the pharmacology of drug use.

We earlier suggested that the Clinic system, with its special requirements for the behaviour of patients, took much of the excitement out of using drugs. We would go further and suggest that these constraints, the socially organized policies, treatments, and controls, enabled some people to lead stable lives. Stabilization is, then, not just about drugs, but is about being integrated into a socially engineered system for obtaining them.

# 8

# *Two biographies – Robert Jones and Kevin Cummings*

We have shown, in the last chapter, that being an addict involves more than just using drugs. The lives of those who are long-term Clinic patients are interwoven with the treatment policies and the rules and regulations that make up the institutional fabric of the Clinics. Within this context we found that a range of solutions had been adopted to the problems of living as an addict for ten years or more. In this chapter, in order to look at the relationship between the individual patient and the Clinic staff, we consider in detail the lives of two people who attended the same Clinic.

We should point out that our style of analysis is rather different from what has preceded, taking here a biographical stance towards the data. In doing this we are able to illuminate the way in which the addicts' lives were related to institutional constraints. We also, by virtue of the way biographical data are collected, emphasize what things looked like from the point of view of the patient at the drug Clinic. There are four biographies in this book. The ones concerning Robert Jones and Kevin Cummings, in this chapter, and Susan Hughes, in Chapter 10, rely heavily on their recollection of past events, and perhaps should be read as autobiographies, presenting as they do the person's own perspective on what has passed. The biography of Gillian Morris, who is dead, relies mainly on other sources.

The two biographies presented in this chapter differ in many ways. Robert Jones, described himself, in 1977, as leading 'a perfectly normal life'. Like the others we talked to, he started using heroin for fun. Over the years he drifted away from other drug users and no longer sought enjoyment from drugs, having no time 'to enjoy a buzz' because this would interfere with other things he wanted to do. He described how he had struck a balance between his addiction, his work, his leisure, and the Clinic. From his description he was an example of how some addicts lead relatively stable lives. He did not see himself as a junkie.

Kevin Cummings, on the other hand, was, in 1976, still involved with other drug users and at one point referred to himself, rather sarcastically, as 'a dirty junkie'. He by no means led the quiet life of Robert Jones. His account of the previous eight years stressed how his life had been dominated by Clinic requirements. He had been with the same doctor since 1968, had experienced the various policies and treatment ideas pursued by him, and saw the doctor as holding a position of power. 'His pen', said Kevin, 'is mightier than the sword: he writes the script.'

Kevin Cummings' account was essentially a list of complaints. Subsequent to our interview with him in 1976 we heard from his doctor that he and his wife continued to have problems with the Clinic, and had problems with the police which resulted in him being sent to prison. We have given Kevin Cummings' view of his position, in which he emphasized that he was dependent on the Clinic. There was another perspective which we have not explored here: that of his doctor. Dr Stratton appreciated that much of what Kevin said was fair comment from the patient's point of view, which was, he agreed, 'an unenviable and dependent situation'. But from the doctor's point of view, Kevin himself contributed to this state of affairs. 'Prior to this [regular attendance at the Clinics]', Dr Stratton argued,

> 'his life had always been dominated by an inability to accept responsibility to parents, Clinics, wives, etc. Time and again . . . where he had a choice he chose a course of action which involved him in further drug use and inevitably, since the Clinics are charged with the job of providing legal drugs, he did indeed have to conform to bureaucratic requirements.'

## *A normal life for Robert Jones*

> 'I manage to live, you know, a perfectly normal life. Now, okay, people wouldn't call you normal I suppose would they? Couple of injections a day . . . but to me it's perfectly normal because I can manage to cope with work, social life, and even manage to save some money.'

Robert Jones was thirty years old in 1977 and had been using heroin for fourteen years. He was interviewed one early winter's evening in a public library in Paddington. We sat in a quiet corner. He was of medium height, well-built, had a moustache and fair, balding, short hair. He was wearing a jacket, cardigan, and cord trousers, all rather drab. He had back trouble and walked with a slight stoop. He was single, had his own flat, his own business, drove his own car, and had yearly holidays with friends. He had a girlfriend and drank to be sociable. He attended a drug Clinic once a month for group meetings, collected his drugs from the chemist twice a week, and injected himself three times a day with a mixture of heroin and methadone. By his own account he led a quiet, unremarkable life.

### The route to addiction

How did Robert Jones come across heroin? He said that he came from a fairly conventional, middle-class background and was brought up in a family where academic achievements were highly valued. He felt that he was a disappointment to his family and more especially to his father for, unlike his brothers, who went to university, he was not very interested in learning. He failed his 'O' level examinations and left school at sixteen.

> 'My teachers were always complaining that I couldn't concentrate, that my IQ test was good but why the hell couldn't I get it right, just because I couldn't concentrate? I would be gazing up at the sky or looking round noting other people's reactions instead of concentrating on my work. My father got really upset. I didn't care for academic things. I was always looking for a way to change my consciousness. I don't know, but I certainly wasn't happy as a child.'

He could remember many tensions in the home, and when he reached his teens things became very difficult. He remembered this time in his life: 'I often think if it weren't for drugs – I was going through a kind of traumatic period, I've always had a very strained relationship with my parents – I often feel that if it weren't for drugs I could have had a nervous breakdown.'

After leaving school in 1963 he decided, after all, to go to college and retake his 'O' level examinations. However, after the first year his father withdrew financial support, presumably because his son was not making much progress. So Robert left his London home and went 'on the road'. For nine months he travelled about Britain, sometimes sleeping rough, sometimes going to hostels or reception centres, and sometimes working, when short of money. It was when he was travelling that he first came across heroin. He lived in various towns on the south coast and was first offered, and took, heroin at a party in Bournemouth. He was then seventeen years old. He remembered the occasion and the feelings he experienced at the time:

> 'Yes, I was drunk, but not that drunk – I knew about it, I'd read about it. Funnily enough I had sniffed an inhaler you know, but it hadn't done anything to me – not much anyway – I didn't consider it that great. I was still kind of looking for something, what it was I was looking for I don't know. I thought perhaps I had this kind of inner shaking, I thought perhaps the further I went away from home I might settle. I thought I would calm down inside. I was very upset, I was very shaky – I would sleep and yet not sleep. I was always tired yet my brain was always racing and doing stupid things.'

After the party Robert took heroin whenever he could get it. At first this was intermittently, but over the months it eventually became daily. He realized that he was addicted after about a year, when he found that he needed to take heroin every day. It was, he recalled, around Easter, 1964, when the pirate radio station Radio Caroline started broadcasting. At that time he made the discovery that he was able to function more effectively when he was using heroin and that in doing so his relationships with people had improved. He went to a private doctor who gave him a prescription for 360 mgs of heroin and 640 mgs of cocaine each day. By now he had moved back to London and, although his dosage of heroin and cocaine was fairly high, he started working as a warehouse clerk. Apart from periods spent in hospital, he had worked all the time since.

### An unsuccessful cure

Early in 1968, just before the Clinics opened, he went into hospital for a cure for his addiction. There was family pressure to come off drugs, but he found life without them intolerable. This was to be the only time he stopped using drugs since he first became addicted.

> 'When I was taken off, I felt very disorganized. When I first went into hospital, I can still remember very vividly the state of complete remoteness and very intense feelings, which were extremely disagreeable. I found everything was much more intense, my head was extremely painful, I couldn't cut my brain off, I couldn't sleep because my brain was so active, I couldn't switch off, and it wasn't just for a small time. I had quite a long time off, about six months before I started using at the Clinics, and in that time everything was totally disagreeable, I couldn't concentrate.'

For ten months after his discharge from hospital he persevered, still hoping to get by without drugs. He used heroin occasionally but resisted going back to the doctor for a prescription. After about five months he began to share a prescription with a girlfriend who was a patient at one of the newly opened Clinics. He recalled:

> 'I'd spent most of my savings by then and I'd decided that it wasn't any good, I might as well go back, at least be under medical supervision. I never liked the idea of scoring at all because of the danger, plus the fact that it might get you put in prison. So I went to see Dr Neville and explained my predicament, and we sat down and had a chat about it and at the time I would probably have agreed to anything, just to get back on. I was rather worried about the amount of money I was spending, plus the people I was having to go around with – you can't choose your friends then. So it was affecting my work, I was having so much time off away from the office.'

### Going to the Clinic

So in March 1969 he became a patient at one of the London Clinics and was given a prescription for 360 mgs of heroin daily. Eighteen months later, Dr Neville had reduced this to 90 mgs of heroin plus 70 mgs of methadone. Robert welcomed the idea of the Clinics and thought them an improvement on attendance at private doctors' surgeries. Before going to the Clinic he had already spent most of his savings on drugs. He said:

> 'I didn't like the idea of the private doctors – they were so impersonal and it was just fee, then prescription. They weren't at all bothered. Okay, some of them might have been but there were too many patients for them to be bothered for a start, and eventually they were all corrupted anyway. Their patients were so corrupt that it was inevitable the doctors were going to be corrupted.'

With his middle-class family background and upbringing, Robert had a distaste for the sorts of activities that might have led to brushes with the law. He had a 'real horror' of going to prison, and realized that if he continued buying drugs on the black market, he might well be drawn into a criminal career.

> 'I don't like the idea of having to do things which normally I wouldn't do. Now I've worked it out that my fear of being without drugs . . . would dissipate any fear I had about doing something slightly illegal. Although normally that would be totally against my normal character. I don't like the idea because I always worry about consequences.'

For him, it was a relief, and a stabilizing influence upon his life, to *know* that he had a regular supply of drugs from the Clinic.

In the years that elapsed since Robert Jones first went to the Clinic his attitude to his drugs and the way in which he used them changed very little. They were an integral part of his life – something he felt he needed in order to get on with other aspects of life. He reflected:

> 'Life has been varied – although it's had one central factor for the last fourteen years. You see, whereas with some people it [using drugs] would be considered a great event – I've tried to keep it on a low key. I've tried to keep it just one facet out of many that make up my life. I've always been very careful to keep it in perspective and keep everything else correct around my life.'

For a while Robert lived with a girlfriend but when they were unable to agree on the future of their relationship they broke up and he lived alone for a while – they had decided to go their own ways to see how they felt about each other. Around 1971 he went back to live at his parents' home in Ealing because his mother had been ill and the family needed his help in looking after her. Throughout this period he worked as a clerk in an office. In 1972 Robert himself fell ill. It was suspected that he had an infection relating to his drug addiction. However, he recalled that he had always been careful with injections and had never had abscesses or hepatitis.

> 'I've always been careful. I've known about the death rate, but I've also known that most people that die, they die from associated diseases, malnutrition, septicaemia, or overdose. But it's by letting themselves get run down, getting in such a state their body can't withstand it. They were convinced that because I was on drugs it had to be jaundice – so they gave me all the tests in the book.'

Finally, it was his cousin, who was a doctor, who helped diagnose a stomach disease. Robert had an operation for this condition in 1972 and spent six months in hospital. His heroin intake increased in hospital because, unbeknown to him at the time, he was given additional heroin in his drip, presumably to reduce the pain. For convalescence, Robert returned to his parents' home. In the following two years he had two further operations – this time for a fracture resulting from a car accident.

In April 1974 Robert decided to move. He had lost the clerical job, which he had held for two-and-a-half years, because of the amount of time he had spent in hospital. He decided to try his luck in a different town, in the Midlands, away from his family. After a few months, Robert became a partner in a painting and decorating business and was, in 1977, busy building up this enterprise.

### Daily life and routine

Life, by 1977, was quiet and uneventful. On a typical day he injected himself three times:

> 'Morning when I get up, midday, and when I come home in the

> evening. . . . I used to collect my prescription a week at a time but when I moved I was a bit worried about it so I decided to collect twice a week, which I do at the moment. It's just that I do always trust myself, but I wasn't quite sure in the new circumstances what I might do. So I was a bit wary in those first few weeks and I've left it as it is so I shall pick up twice a week. I haven't gone back to picking up weekly. Daily would be too interfering with work.'

Robert went on to explain that he had managed to sustain himself in regular employment throughout most of his addiction, deciding to keep his drug dependence secret:

> 'There is one thing in common in all the jobs I've had – nobody has ever known that I was on drugs. I've always had references and I've always managed. Ever since I really started working, I've always had more or less the same problem and it's never really affected my work. I've never let drugs affect my "nine-to-five" existence.'

In some ways his illnesses were convenient for him because he was able to use them to hide his addiction. His occasional ups and downs on heroin he attributed to the lasting effects of his stomach disease and car accident. The only time that his drug use interfered with his working life was during his early days at the Clinic when he used to arrive at work half-an-hour late after collecting his drugs from the chemist. He made up this time by working late in the evenings. He felt that the Clinic had helped him stabilize his drug-taking. He had always earned enough money to supplement his prescription with illegal supplies if he wanted to do so, but it was his decision to keep to the amounts prescribed.

Robert had some suggestions about how the Clinics could be improved. He said he would like a twenty-four-hour advisory service for addicts in crises and more immediate help if prescriptions did not arrive promptly at the chemist. He was a little apprehensive about the future because he had heard that Clinic doctors intended to offer patients methadone linctus instead of injectable opiates.

> 'All they seem to want is to take you off injectables, put you on to linctus, so I agreed to change 10 mgs of my methadone pills for 10 mgs of methadone linctus . . . I've had to change everything. It's become rather awkward, still no doubt I can settle down to it. It's rather annoying because I was doing very well and I was quite happy and I don't see how this silly change can help. However, for peace and quiet, I'll do most things.'

He explained in more detail how this recent change had upset the routine he had built up over the years:

> 'Because the main thing is, as you know, I have three fixes a day. I use one amp. of methadone and 50 mgs of heroin; later, one amp. and 40 mgs, and last of all 30 mgs of methadone. Well, now its down to 20 mgs in the evening and unfortunately I can't keep that linctus down, it's so sickly. I don't know if it's anything to do with my insides, but I get nauseated ever so easily and I was bringing it up – which is a waste – but I just can't help wasting the damn stuff. Still I'll do my best.'

Robert had been on opiates for so long that he found it difficult to remember what he was like before using them, and what sort of a person he would be like should he withdraw.

> 'It takes somebody else to tell you, but people that I've known who have seen me "on" and "off", they say that I'm much more curt. I get a much more uncomfortable person when I'm not on drugs and I can be rather hurtful apparently. And then I couldn't hold a conversation, like somebody would sort of look me in the eye, I would get very embarrassed and try to get away from the person's presence as soon as I could.'

He had given much thought to the obvious question – why stay on drugs? Not getting any special pleasure from heroin, he explained:

> 'I'm not really into buzzes anyway, they only affect you. Most people want to enjoy a buzz so they lie back down, I haven't got time to do that so that's not the point of taking it for me now. I know it doesn't increase my awareness or anything like that, but it just continues the state that I like or need to be in. I mean, drugs must have an effect. Now the only effect is the one that I desire, which is I can focus a lot better, and also I can kind of not switch off but not let things affect me. I'm usually very emotional and I can withstand any kind of emotional battles and conflicts a lot better.'

The interview ended with Robert talking about how he felt about himself and how he saw the future:

> 'I feel whatever happens I could take care of myself. When somebody says – "Will you ever come off?" – I think perhaps I will – because I know perhaps deep down that there is another way, but as well I know I can't be forced into it. I can't be forced, unless I see another avenue I'm not going to stop the one I'm on. *I've* got to see it, there's no point someone saying, like there is life after death – nobody can convince me of that – just as nobody can convince me there isn't, unless I see it for myself.'

## *Kevin Cummings' experiences as a Clinic patient*

> 'I think it's wrong that I should have had to suffer doctors' beliefs as they've changed and that because I'm the patient I've got to change. Why should I suffer because I'm forced to see him? When I registered I didn't know anything about Clinics. He [Dr Stratton] was obviously fishing for patients then and so I came to his Clinic. I didn't know anything about Clinics.'

Kevin Cummings was twenty-one years old when he first went to a London Clinic and met Dr Stratton. With a few short interruptions he had remained a patient with him, and was, in 1979, still using opiates. By his own account his relationship with the Clinic and with Dr Stratton had been a central thread running through the past eight years of his life. It was summer 1976 when he came to talk to us. He wore a loose, Madras cotton shirt, jeans and sandals, his black curly hair cut to a medium length, and carried his 'works' in a small shoulder bag. Sitting in the armchair by the tape recorder, it was clear that he had definite ideas about what he wanted to tell us. He described vividly how things changed for him when policies and ideas about treatment altered over the years.

### The years before heroin

Kevin was born and brought up in a small country town not far from London. He was the youngest son in a family of four children. He recalled many disputes with his father who was, he says, authoritarian and unapproachable. By contrast, he spoke of a warm, good relationship with his mother and with his older brothers and sister.

As he grew up he began to lose interest in school work – by the time he reached his final year he truanted quite a lot, together with a few friends. He failed his final examinations and left school with no qualifications at the age of sixteen. About a year later Kevin decided to leave home and to start an independent life abroad. He emigrated to Canada and whilst there obtained various jobs. However, two years later he returned to England. He was introduced to and experimented with heroin on his journey back, when he met someone who sniffed the drug. Several months after this, while he was living with a girlfriend in London, he began smoking a great deal of cannabis. Soon he was introduced to methedrine but did not like the effects very much. By then, 1967, he was spending a lot of time with people who took drugs and he continued sniffing heroin, eventually switching from sniffing to injecting. It took a while before he realized that he was becoming addicted. This is his description of what happened:

'You see, I'd used it for nine months before I got registered. It took me nine months to get hooked, because I worked for six months, so it wasn't 'till a later point that I started mixing with addicts, I mean, up to then I was scoring weekends, and then it became weekends and one day a week, and then it became a couple of days a week and the weekend, and then it became every day. I stopped once because I thought, "Christ, you know I better not get addicted, so I had better stop". And I stopped for a week. I was all right, so I thought, "Oh well, stuff it, I'll carry on". I carried on. About three months after that, I thought "God, this is six months now I've been using, I'd better stop and see". And for three days I was all right and I thought, "Oh you know, I'm all right" and I went back. Then after nine months I tried to stop. That same day I spent four hours sweating, and the tears rolling out of my eyes, nose running, threw up my guts – terrible. I denied to my girlfriend, who was registered, that I was hooked, you know for four hours, 'till I couldn't handle it any more and she asked me what was the only thing on my mind, I said "A fix". That was when I eventually went to the Clinic, that evening. I got registered with Dr Andrew Stratton.'

### First years at the Clinic

Kevin attended Dr Stratton's Clinic from October 1968. To start with he was prescribed heroin, and he understood that the doctors believed heroin maintenance to be a feasible procedure. He was prescribed 60 mgs of heroin and 20 mgs of methadone daily. He said of Dr Stratton: 'When I first got registered he believed that a man could live his life taking heroin alone, and not affect or shorten his life in any way, or interfere with his job, provided he took heroin and not anything else.'

Kevin recalled that when he first went to the Clinic he wanted to come off heroin, but that he found it difficult to reduce his intake as an out-patient. In fact his dose actually went up in the first months of attendance. He changed his method of injecting from intramuscular to intravenous in January 1969, in order to obtain the maximum euphoric effects from his drugs. In the first months his prescription rose to 100 mgs of heroin and 30 mgs of methadone. In March 1969 he and his girlfriend were admitted to hospital and Kevin managed to get off heroin, stop injecting, and transfer to methadone linctus. He was only at the hospital two weeks and took his own discharge after being involved in an argument with another patient. One month later he returned to Dr Stratton. He had started using large amounts of heroin again and so was given an initial prescription for 320 mgs of heroin and 120 mgs of methadone daily, soon reduced to 100 mgs and 40 mgs respectively. Kevin remained on this prescription for the following eight months.

It was by then the summer of 1969, remembered by Kevin as the year the Rolling Stones played a free concert in Hyde Park and their guitarist, Brian Jones, died. It was, personally, an eventful year. His father died of cancer and Kevin and his girlfriend moved in with Kevin's mother. At the end of the year he was arrested and charged with serious assault. He was remanded on bail and the court asked Dr Stratton for a psychiatric report. The court put Kevin on a three-year probation order on condition that he attended treatment under Dr Stratton. In the following months Kevin continued to reduce his drug intake and considered coming off heroin by Christmas 1970. He began working for the first time since attending the Clinic.

It was at around this time that Phoenix House therapeutic community opened in South London. Phoenix House is a drug-free therapeutic community for addicts, established initially on the lines of the Phoenix House programme in New York. This new venture created much interest among Clinic staff. In some ways Phoenix House appealed to Kevin, though he thought that if it was useful at all it would probably be so for other people rather than for himself, and his enthusiasm waned when he heard about the programme.

> 'I believe that for a drug addict it's good to face up to what he is. But at the same time I believe that the person who wants to make him face up has got to have sufficient knowledge and discuss with the addict if he felt he could handle it. Because it's no good doing it if you're going to emotionally crack up. So I think for certain people, yeah it's fine, I knew all about Phoenix House and the whole thing and I was fortunate in that way, but – I knew it wouldn't work for me.'

Kevin was, then, unwilling to go into Phoenix House, disliking what he supposed were the methods then used.

> 'In the beginning, there was all that cutting your hair off, right? Starting at the bottom, all the washing and wiping-up, that's fine, working yer way up, that's okay. Sitting on a little kid's chair because you've been swearing too much for about three hours or for four hours with three people glaring at you and saying what a bastard you are and what a lazy shit and all this crap and you're not allowed to speak and you're sitting on a proper little kid's chair. That's to degrade you even further. And you're not allowed to speak, wearing a sign saying you're on a speaking ban for a week. I mean, when you're asleep and you wake up in the morning, your first instinct is to say 'hello'' or whatever to somebody. Those kind of things, they're ridiculous you know.'

Kevin, things continued with little change for another year though gradually his daily prescription was reduced to 30 mgs of heroin, 10 mgs of injectable methadone, and 10 mgs of methadone linctus.

### Several attempts to come off drugs

Early in 1971, Kevin asked to go into hospital again, to be withdrawn from heroin. He spent two months there and was drug-free for most of the time, except for on a number of isolated occasions. Very infrequently he went out to buy drugs, remembering that: 'Well, we cut a hole in the tennis courts with some wire cutters and went through the wood and used to go and score, you know. The hospital was a long way out but we used to go and score and come back.'

While in hospital he got a job with a building contractor, demolishing an old building at the hospital. After one week's work, he went to a public house with another patient and came back drunk, knowingly infringing hospital regulations. When he was discharged, he felt very let down and angry:

> 'The hospital was very silly. They threw me out for going over to the pub and getting drunk one night. You should let a man go out and celebrate . . . I'd got a job, I'd been working in the grounds, I'd been working in the next block to the drug unit, doing a good job with a hammer knocking down walls, right. It seems to me ludicrous, had they not done that, it is very likely that I would not be here now, because I was very happy there. I was totally off drugs and for six months I was really strong, fit, keen, and I felt really good inside myself. I was proud I'd lasted, because I'd been so ill there in the beginning, but I'd stuck it, I was really happy about that.'

This time he did not immediately return to the Clinic and Dr Stratton. He intended to stay off drugs, but after three months he turned up at another Clinic having started using heroin again. He was prescribed heroin and methadone for one month, and then entered a newly established therapeutic community, just before Christmas 1971. He still wanted to come off drugs, and found this community more appealing than Phoenix House.

> 'I went there when it had just begun. I was the third patient. It's a rehabilitation place, where you have your own room. It was built on trust. I mean if you wanted you could walk out, the station was only thirty yards away and you could get on a train to the 'Dilly, you know, and get a fix. And I never did that once. When I was in hospital, I went over the fence six times to take a fix. But when I was

at the therapeutic community, when it was built on trust, I never went once. The only time I had any drug was when, foolishly – which is their fault, but then I suppose they weren't to know – they gave us a place to clean out which was a veterinary surgeon's place. We were working away cleaning, and a friend of mine came up first with a syringe, then with the morphine, and then with the Mandrax. God Almighty, three of us who hadn't had anything, well when it's right there, it's too much. We had some of the stuff and then that was sussed out obviously. None of us had had anything (recently) so we were well smashed. So we handed it in, in two lots. We handed some of it in, and then we decided to hand in the rest.'

On the whole his nine months' stay was a very happy experience. He was able to enjoy his life without drugs and gained strength from the confidence placed in him. When he left, towards the end of 1972, he went for a holiday on the Scottish island of Iona, paid for by the community.

'I was supposed to go for ten days but I never came back because I was given 10½ grams of cocaine when I got there. I went to an island where all the freaks go . . . at Easter there was so much gear up there, it was unbelievable. I met a girl whose father was a multi-millionaire and I went with her, you know she had loads of money. She said, "Well we had better have a car", and she just bought one, and I went to her house, which I got lost in, her parents' house, it was so enormous. They had a croft on this island, and they had absolutely everything. She wanted me to go to Denmark on her father's boat with her. But I'd had enough by then; if she had given me money, her money, if she'd given it to me so I had it in my pocket and I could spend it, then it would have gone on. I went to Scotland, I went to Edinburgh, and Fife with her, and back to the island, and eventually we went down all the way to London and my home. I gave her up simply because she paid for everything, it got too much for me.'

When Kevin returned to London he was not addicted, despite the holiday in Scotland, and managed to stay drug-free for a while, and to work.

'When I came back from Scotland I was so at peace than I spent three months in a laundry just separating sheets, with a smile on my face all day. I'd never had the experience of reading a book with somebody, and I'd read a book with a chick. You know, sitting on the floor cross-legged and all that. You know I was into it, a bit of all that, Maharishi, yeah. Okay, he's making a lot of bread you know, worlds within worlds, I was into a bit of Hare Krishna then, I had a lot of books on it. I wasn't in an organization of it, but I had a lot of inner peace then which enabled me to come back to the same environment which had destroyed me time and time again and survive in it for the one and only time.'

Shortly after his return, though, he became addicted again, and by December 1973, after eighteen months' abstinence, he felt that he again needed a prescription for opiates. Previously he had succeeded in changing from his first doctor and obtaining a prescription from another Clinic, if only for one month. However, this time there was no choice but to return to his original Clinic.

### Back to the Clinic – the Clinic had changed

Although when Kevin returned Dr Stratton was still in charge, he became a patient of another doctor working there. Dr Johnson had new ideas about helping addicts which drew on contemporary radical approaches to therapy. Kevin was quite enthusiastic about these.

'He was actually working with me. I would sit on the floor with him. None of this: like the doctor sits in the chair, you sit in a chair, he's the God, you're the dog, kiss his arse and you get a script and that's all you're there for, and telling you you're a naughty boy you shouldn't do that. . . . But with Dr Johnson I had to build up the relationship with him, which was unfortunate because throughout the building up, time got wasted, and admittedly it was towards the end, when he said he was leaving, that I started to give up drugs. He said "How do you feel about it" and I said I felt angry about it, because if he had stayed I believe I would have made it, because, you see, he'd given me confidence.'

When Dr Johnson left Kevin continued to visit the Clinic for his prescription but usually spoke only to a nurse. He no longer had a regular appointment with a doctor and saw Dr Stratton only very sporadically.

In April 1975 Kevin married Sheila, who was also a drug user. Later that year he was arrested for being in possession of an offensive weapon and spent two weeks in prison, on remand. When the matter finally came to court he was given a conditional discharge. During that prison interlude Kevin's prescription was changed and he was quite furious.

'I was on three pills [of heroin] then and 20 mgs of linctus. And I'd always been straight with him [Dr Stratton] and never hassled him. He would agree with that generally. I hadn't hassled him or been on his back for more stuff – "I've run out", "It's gone down the bog", "kept the tap on and knocked the bottle over". You know all this paraphernalia. I hadn't done that. He knew that I'd been honest all the way down the line, so it was a liberty he used [the remand in prison] . . . to take my heroin away.'

Kevin noted that the Clinic policy had changed. The idea that it was harmless to maintain people on heroin for long periods had been dropped; doctors were reluctant to prescribe heroin and were working towards changing all addicts' prescriptions to oral methadone. This knowledge did not make it any easier for Kevin, who felt that he was given no choice in the matter of his treatment: 'You see, I think it's wrong because by law I have to go to him. Every time I've been off I have to go back to the same doctor that I was registered with in the first instance. . . . There's this thing in law. So I've always had to go back to Dr Stratton's Clinic.' He had a confrontation with Dr Stratton about the decision to stop the heroin:

> 'As I have said, he is God. He knows that. Because his pen is mightier than the sword, he writes the script and all that rhubarb. . . . He's a sly old fox. I've been appalled at his game, because now he's so totally different. It is a complication for him to deal with me. It would be the same for you if I'd been with you ever since the first interview. I would know about you. He gives me all the old patter now and again: that I am cunning . . . that I should be a psychiatric nurse. He was telling me that I sounded like one, that I sound just like a consultant. He said I don't want to face myself. And I said "Well I know I'm a dirty junkie, so I've faced that. If you don't give me any scripts what are you moaning about?" I mean 40 mgs of methadone is a joke for me. He gave me five pills of heroin when I first got registered. And he used the fact that I went to prison to take the rest of my script away. I had at that point given up two pills [of heroin] of my own free will for 10 mgs of linctus. And he's keeping the screws on me by saying if I went to another Clinic he would say to them that in his opinion this man shouldn't get injectable drugs. Then 99 per cent of psychiatrists reading that from another psychiatrist would blow you out. But it's only now he'll say, quite quietly, "Yes, I'll give you a transfer", because he knows now you can't get on with another Clinic. They're not taking anyone on anywhere.'

### Recent events and preoccupations

In the spring of 1976 Mrs Cummings gave birth to a premature baby who was addicted and went through withdrawal after birth. The child was taken into care by the local authority, who claimed that the couple had neglected the baby. Kevin maintained that Sheila tried to come off drugs whilst pregnant – but believed that she was not given sufficient help at the time.

> 'They expect an addict to come off after six months, carrying a baby, and to spend three months outside without taking a fix, when you've got all the pains in your back that you get from carrying a baby, plus all the aggravation from coming off stuff and knowing the relief it'll bring if you use it. How can you expect them to spend three months like that with no drugs when they have no after-care, no anything after you've been cured? And the Clinic totally lets you down in that respect. There is no after-care, there is no follow-up at all, which is a let-down for anybody going on a cure. You still need help when you come out, you don't just have a cure, and Bob's your uncle, Fanny's yer aunt, everything's solved. I mean when you stop taking drugs, you are back with the reasons, the real true reasons why you started in the first place, like you didn't get on with your dad, all those true reasons come out. So really you're back with the reasons you started taking drugs in the first place, and what have you got now? You've got nothing.'

The Cummingses were unwilling to give up their baby and were hoping he would be returned to them.

The other major preoccupation for Kevin was his relationship with the Clinic and Dr Stratton, in which he felt trapped, disillusioned, and suspicious. His main anxiety centred around the policy of changing prescriptions of heroin to methadone linctus.

> 'Now each Clinic is different, there is no common policy. Some people are getting scripts and rises, and other people are really just being fucked up. I know people who were on six grains of heroin who have been taken off. I mean taken off forcibly, it's amounted to that, that drugs have been taken away by force. They've took the drugs away, you know one pill for 10 mgs of linctus. I can tell you now on tape that when they discover, in a couple of years, how linctus is killing people and making them sick, and messing their system up much more than heroin is, then they will change back smartly. You see, for them, it's the only answer they have at present, to withdraw [addicts] from heroin. What they don't understand is that to maintain people on heroin will not injure them necessarily, right? But to maintain people on methadone linctus has harmful effects.'

Kevin felt that he could only cope by buying additional drugs as he could not manage on the dose prescribed for him; he had told the Clinic staff this.

> 'Drugs are available if you've got the money. I'm totally destroying what we've got. I'm spending it. I've done £200 in this short time. There is about £300 left. If we do that on junk, when that ends that is *the* end. Then what do I do? Do I go out and mug people? Do I sell my arse as a male prostitute, or my wife be a prostitute or lesbian, or what? What do we do? You know there's all those problems to face if you want to continue using drugs at the price today. If the Clinic was giving me sufficient for my needs I would be happy with two grains, I wouldn't say another word. Even nine pills would be fine. But to tell me that the whole policy is working towards the three months' detoxication period, then out you go, and if you should choose to come back to the Clinic because you want extra psychotherapy that's entirely up to you, well then what's the point in being there? I know I won't be able to handle that, so I've got to get some other Clinic, but where, where am I going to go?'

Kevin had never been happy, it seemed, with the way things were. He summed up what he felt about things and what it was like to be dependent on the goodwill of the Clinic staff and doctors.

> 'The doctor has got the power and that is all wrong. No relationship at the Clinic as human beings, Dr Stratton has ceased to deal with me as *me*. He can kiss my arse. At the moment I'm just in a vicious circle of what the Clinic says goes, and I have to survive by that and I can only see it getting harder and they're just cutting your throats.'

# 9

# *Coming off drugs – failure and success*

'Nobody believes that ex-addicts could ever be company directors.'
(Dave Godfrey, an ex-addict company director)

'I've always been exactly as I am now, well, not *exactly* as I am now but, I mean, I'm pretty much unchanged.'
(Tony Lyttelton, addicted for six years, then abstinent for six years)

From the vantage point of the policeman on duty at Piccadilly Circus, the ambulance crew assigned to collecting overdose cases, the doctor working in the Accident and Emergency department, or the addict who lives a life on the street, it seems unlikely that junkies ever voluntarily cease to be addicts. Those who work with them, and many addicts themselves, often subscribe to the pessimistic view that 'once an addict, always an addict'. This view could be supported by the evidence of studies that have evaluated different techniques for treating addicts, for these have usually painted a gloomy picture of the effect of treatment, with 90 per cent of abstinent addicts who are discharged from hospital or prison relapsing to drug use within one year (Vaillant 1970). However, if we step back from the first-hand engagement of addict-workers and addicts, and away from studies of specific instances of treatment, and follow instead a group of addicts over a number of years, then we find that a substantial proportion do cease to be addicted. Studies in the US and Britain have suggested that after five years approximately 25 per cent of addicts became abstinent, as do approximately 40 per cent after ten years (Vaillant 1970; Thorley 1981).

The findings of the present study are no exception, for, at the follow-up interviews, conducted seven to eight years after the initial meetings, there were forty people, 31 per cent of the original sample, who were no longer addicted to opiates and who were living in the community. The long-term view is, then, more optimistic than the short-term.

That people cease to be addicted leads to many questions. Which addicts stop using drugs? Why do they stop? How do they do it? What are the problems facing the ex-addict? Do their lives change? There are, of course, no easy answers to the questions. In this chapter we focus on some of the factors that appear relevant to describing how people achieve the transformation from addict to ex-addict. To do this we have concentrated on the forty people who were abstinent by the time of the follow-up interviews in 1976/77. They had, by then, been abstinent from opiates for an average of over four-and-a-half years, with the shortest time-span of abstinence being nine months, and the longest over eight years. The Appendix gives more detailed characteristics of those who stopped using opiates.

Was there anything special about those addicts who had come off? Were they different sorts of people from those who remained addicted? Could we have predicted, when we first saw the 128 addicts in 1969, which were likely to come off and which to continue? The answer is that this would have been extremely difficult. We know that in terms of many characteristics (such as social class, sex, work, crime, drug use, and income) those who achieved abstinence and those continuing to use opiates were undifferentiated in 1969 (*see* Appendix, p. 249). We could find only a few differences: those who stopped tended to be younger, to have a shorter history of addiction, and to have been prescribed smaller doses of drugs in 1969. We suspect that Clinic staff were more therapeutically active with these addicts, perhaps because they thought they were more likely to be successful in influencing younger, less well-established addicts, than older, more entrenched ones.

We suspect, then, that the search for prognostic indicators is unlikely to bear fruitful results, and that an understanding of how people come to be abstinent from opiates will not come from asking the questions 'What are they like?' and 'How do they differ from those who continue addicted?' Rather we suggest that inquiry should proceed along the lines of our approach in this chapter, which is to look at the circumstances and events surrounding abstinence. Just as people take many and varied routes *into* addiction, so too can they take several routes *out* of it.

### AMBIVALENCE

An addict talking to a Clinic doctor, to a probation officer, or to a research worker might have been full of good intentions about 'coming off' drugs or 'going in for a cure'. The same person may never have talked in such a way with addict friends. This is not to suggest that addicts lied about their intentions or lacked awareness of themselves. Their situation was a dual one: on the one hand they were subject to all sorts of subtle, and some not too subtle, pressures to change. They were, after all, engaged in bizarre and deviant activities and there was a whole range of people whose task was to 'do something' about addiction by helping and treating them. Every meeting between an addict and Clinic doctor, social worker, or probation officer could have become an attempt by the professional worker to persuade the addict to 'give up drugs'. Pressure also came from parents, spouses, girlfriends, and boyfriends. On the other hand, an addict had many reasons to continue using drugs. Hence, he or she was placed in an ambivalent situation between the pressures from the straight world to 'reform' and personal motivation to continue. One ex-addict, John Barnes, describing earlier unsuccessful attempts at 'cures' in hospital, showed what it felt like to be in such a situation of conflicting demands:

> 'You say this and that, and you're talking about cures, but for a junkie, at the back of his mind he's not thinking about a cure at all really. It crosses his mind because he thinks that's the right thing to think about, and the fact that he's made the effort. He goes in for a cure, but if he's got half the chance of getting a bit [of heroin] while he's inside there, that's all well and good.'

John Barnes summed up his hospitalization as a 'right waste of time'. On the ward he met some old friends; one had a 'load of H on him and another was getting a load of methedrine, another scoring up in London'. He stayed in the hospital three weeks, using drugs all the time, and then discharged himself and went to London. Much later he came off successfully during a period in prison.

Pat Chilvers, who last used heroin in 1971, also mentioned the uncertain intentions she had when she agreed to go into hospital. She consented to admission because she had nowhere to live. She thought she would prolong the withdrawal treatment as long as possible, and stayed for eight months; when first admitted she had no intention of giving up drugs for good. 'I can't think of any reason why I decided to stop. I mean I never thought I would, I thought I'd give it a try because I'd been in hospital so many times before, just for a short while and then leave again.' Nearly every addict at some time said she or he wanted to stop and yet at the same time wanted to continue using drugs. Many may have been willing to go so far as to agree to be admitted for a cure, there may have been the germ of an idea that coming off might be a good thing, but at the same time they were in two minds. They were not absolutely certain that they wanted to stop *right now*. We know that many of the ex-addicts in our sample had made prior attempts to withdraw; some of them described these earlier, unsuccessful attempts. Dave Godfrey was one. He eventually came off in 1971, but had previously been to hospital for a cure in order to persuade a court that he was willing to 'mend his ways'.

> 'I went up there and said I was an addict. I over-exaggerated it . . . manipulated everybody. So a week later I was in the London Hospital for a cure. . . . When I got there I was so negative I immediately discharged myself because I didn't need them no more and the same day I was out fixing.'

Anyway, why should they bother to stop? We saw in Chapter 7 that though very few addicts continued to get a buzz from injecting, they felt they had to use opiates in order to keep straight (*see* p. 117). This hardly seems like a major reason for continuing, but there may have been no good cause to stop. Trevor Buckton, for example, was married and had a child. He enjoyed using drugs, could not see what difference his not being an addict would make, and so did not think it was worth the trouble trying to get off. From his own point of view he had no reason to do so. 'I'm happy as I am,' he said, 'I'm not stoned all day long or anything, the only difference is that I have to fix twice a day but then that isn't that much of an inconvenience.' Drugs hardly interfered with his life. His wife no longer objected, he worked regularly, and spent time with his family. The Clinic prescribed him enough, he did not have to buy illegally, nor, therefore, spend the family income on drugs. He went on:

> 'The only time it ever has interfered with my work is through my own fault – like I've taken too much on a Saturday and had to have a fix on Sunday evening, early, which I should have had on Monday morning, and then I had to come home lunchtime on Monday. But even that doesn't interfere with my work, because I work during the morning. I can get out in the lunch hour and spend ten minutes – it's long enough to have a fix and then get back again.'

It was much the same for Jack Daniels who wondered 'Why am I still a dope addict after all this time?' In 1976 he was thirty-three and had been an addict without interruption since 1965. He lived in a bedsitter in Harringay which was still furnished in a 1960s style, with a mattress on the floor, Indian prints on the walls, joss sticks, and Rizla cigarette papers and a tobacco tin on a low table. He looked the ageing hippy. His hair was long and tied in a pony-tail, he was bearded, and wore a necklace, a scarf, tee-shirt, and sandals. A neat row of track-marks sat in the crook of his arm, no more than two inches long. He worked a few hours a day as a cleaner and was leading, by his own account, a pretty unremarkable, almost monotonous life. His main philosophy was that 'I don't want any hassles – I just want to get on with my life'. The fact that he was an addict was both a 'very big part' of his life and 'also a coincidental part'. 'I don't want to be talking about it all the time with other people. I just feel that I am a pretty easy-going guy who doesn't want any hassles in life. I am a fairly stable sort of person, I can handle drugs.' And this was the clue to his rhetorical question about why he was still an addict, for without any hassles 'I can just keep travelling around in a circle'. But why do so? Because 'I like using it you know, I'm addicted to it, very much so, well so what?' He summed up that in his opinion life was pretty boring for all of us:

> 'We jog on, we get on with it, just because I'm a dope addict it's no different for me. Sometimes I think, well "I'll use until I die" and then other times I think "well so what?" You may be sixty and still using. I just like using dope you know. My epitaph to it all is that dope addiction is no big thing.'

He saw little reason to change this style of life which he had brought from the 1960s.

Provided Clinics kept patients supplied with their minimum requirements and did not hassle them, provided there were no inordinate family or other pressures, there was, for many, little reason to stop. What would stopping have entailed? In the short run it needs time and it causes inconvenience. For Andrew Wright it would have been more trouble than it was worth. He was in his forties in 1976, and thought that if he came off drugs as an out-patient he would be moody and unpleasant at work. He believed that he needed six to nine months to really come off and could not afford to lose his job over it, nor could he take leave from work to come off as an in-patient. Wearing his dark pin-stripe suit, and looking every bit the office manager, he said:

> 'Don't think because I am so blasé when I speak about it that I don't regret every day that I ever started on it. I do. I mean if tomorrow I could be free of it I would be. You see the thing is if I went into hospital now, that job isn't going to be there for me to come out to – I mean all right I can come off, then what am I going to do for the rest of my life?'

The risks and upheaval were too big for him to be able to contemplate coming off. 'Now I use about once a day. What I have in the mornings is enough to set me up. By 10.30 when I start work you wouldn't know I've had it. It has a very good effect on me. It makes me very steady during the day. If I don't have heroin I can't do a thing. I'm completely useless.' He had a 'good flat, decent clothes, I eat well, I have a very satisfactory life, and a decent job'. The only restriction he saw was that he could not go away on business or for a holiday: 'I love travelling abroad, I love going to hot, sunny places. But I can't do that anymore. I just spend the whole of the winter in England, which I hate.'

## REASONS FOR STOPPING USING DRUGS

At any time there are some advantages in continuing as an addict and some in ceasing. The conflict between reasons for continuing and reasons for stopping is a source of tension. In retrospectively assessing their lives, many saw a shift in the balance between advantages and disadvantages as having led them to make a decision to stop using drugs.

Using opiates to feel 'normal' was not always enough for everyone; one man described how 'towards the end I was very disappointed with the effect', and Raymond O'Sullivan said how 'I didn't get a buzz at all, I wasn't getting any buzzes, once you got to the Clinic your dose was stationary, and that was it. It [the dose] had to go up to get a buzz. No I didn't get a buzz. It was just to maintain your bodily function you know.' Some realized that the fun and excitement of the drug effects had disappeared: 'I was getting older and I wasn't getting anywhere, and apart from that, things were getting worse, I had really had it. Fun had gone out of it, if you can call it fun . . . there were no kicks anymore. It was a question of having to have it rather than a choice.' Others found that they had become addicted to a drug they did not like, one person, for example, said that he had always preferred LSD and cannabis to heroin, and another realized that what he wanted were 'mind-expanding drugs not mind-contracting drugs like heroin and barbiturates which dull you'.

People became addicts, though, not only for the fun and experience of the drug effects, but also because they found the style of life enjoyable; for example, before the Clinics opened people found excitement in the uncertainty and thrill of scoring. After their opening though 'it was no fun anymore', 'it was nothing new', 'I had really had it, the fun had gone'; and for the Clinic patient 'you're more routinized than anybody working on the assembly line'. The setting up of the Clinics was, as Christina Boyd saw it, 'an absolute bore'. It focused addicts' lives because they now had to go to the chemist every morning to pick up their drugs.

> 'The Clinics are monotony, once I got off H [and on to methadone] . . . I suddenly thought ''What the hell am I doing, I'm going to be an old lady, I'm going to be in the gutter, I'm going to be in the gutter as far as how people look at me. I am a person and I'm going to be in the gutter, and I'm going to spend my whole rotten life going to

the chemist every morning. I can't do it''. And that was one of the things that decided me to get off.'

In many ways addiction is a life only for young people. Joe Henrick said that he eventually felt old among the young addicts around Piccadilly. He wondered whether he could really see himself going up to the chemist every day until he was old, and thought to himself 'am I not being like Mohammed Ali, going on just that bit too long?'

Some addicts considered continued use detrimental to their health, for veins become thrombosed and it is difficult to inject. A chaotic life style of drug use increases the risk of overdose and death. Raymond O'Sullivan knew that 'If I carried on I was going to die'. He had on occasion been near to death, he had 'tasted death', and it was 'quite a bitter taste'. Other people who stopped recalled a disgust with themselves for 'getting scruffy' and sleeping rough. 'It was degrading,' said Fred Dobson, 'I thought I'd hit the bottom of the barrel.'

Living around the West End meant that the risk of arrest and imprisonment was great. When Bill Gregor was given a six-month suspended sentence the thought of further convictions and certain imprisonment was too much for him: 'It's just playing the laws of chance, and sooner or later they're going to turn up wrong, so probability alone tells you that once you've got a suspended sentence it is then a matter of time and time alone.' For the next three years he had to remain reasonably well-behaved, 'certainly clean enough not to bring myself to the attention of the police'. Other problems were making life difficult too. He had jaundice, and his main source of income as a doorman and cinema projectionist suddenly finished.

'The financial pressures now tended to bite rather deeply because of the fall of the industry in the West End which I had been involved in predominantly over the last few years – I was working at film clubs, the old 8mm film clubs which were being shut down by the police. So my easy source of income was slowing down. I could have gone into something slightly less legal such as touting for the birds, or into something a bit heavier, as being the only way to maintain the level of income that I was expecting. The jobs in the West End were just folding, there were less of them at the time. So various pressures like that just put together the sort of feeling that enough was enough.'

He recalled that on balance it did not seem worth continuing to lead this life:

'I just decided to leave and just literally did just that. I picked up the script. I'm not even sure if I finished the last script, I don't think I did. I cashed the script and walked off with some, and just went.

> And I went to my parents' home, I just went cold turkey and I sat and sweated in bed for three days and that was that.'

Only weeks after this rather abrupt ending to his life as a drug addict Bill Gregor became a student and his life began to change. By 1977 he had been abstinent for seven years.

A further problem of continued addiction was that it interfered with other things people decided they wanted to do. On a practical level it was difficult to do simple things like go on holiday or away for a couple of days without giving advance notice to the Clinic to change the prescription arrangements. At another level using heroin prevented personal growth and change. You 'don't grow when you're on dope', said one ex-addict, 'you stagnate'. It can also interfere with relationships with spouses, parents, and children. Jenny Stock, an ex-addict, recalled:

> 'I was never at ease when I was using, I was always very, very frightened and very, very terrified. It happened very quickly over a few weeks. I got more and more frightened and more and more terrified and I just thought "Christ what the hell am I doing? I've got to stop". The relationship with Fred was ridiculous anyway, we just married too young, I was very innocent, and we weren't sexually compatible. There were a lot of things. I just got very frustrated and absolutely terrified to a point where I used to wake up in the morning and start to feel guilty. It sounds strange, but you feel guilty about fixing, especially when you've got a child, and yet enjoy it. It may be difficult to understand. And I just decided it would have to stop. So I went to see Dr Stratton and he was tremendous. I just said "I want to come off".'

### CHANGING CIRCUMSTANCES, TRIGGERS, AND INCIDENTS

It was not necessarily the strong-willed or the more coerced who succeeded in getting off drugs. The changing circumstances of addicts' lives seemed also to be part of the equation. There were many contingencies that helped to move people towards a position where they might stop, and which helped to tip the balance or precipitate change.

Some addicts literally seemed to drift with the current. Pat Chilvers, the woman who was ambivalent about going into hospital (see p. 157), had not really decided that she wanted to stop using heroin when she was first admitted. Looking back she knew that she 'quite liked the way of life, not necessarily the drugs, but I had no commitments, I was absolutely free to do as I pleased . . . I used to enjoy just walking around London.' When she wanted to leave hospital she decided to go home but her mother would not have her: relatives had come to stay and the woman did not want her addict daughter at home. The doctor suggested that she go to a community for ex-addicts and she went along with this proposal. A week after becoming free from drugs she left the hospital and joined the therapeutic community, thinking she would go there for a few days and then return to London. 'But I stayed, I think really because I couldn't be bothered to move more than anything else.' She remained there for two years.

Not every career was so explicitly one of drifting with the circumstances. About half of the people had experienced changes in their lives in the year or so preceding abstinence – for example, they had found a new job, moved into new accommodation, moved out of London, met a new boyfriend or girlfriend, got married, divorced an addict partner, or drifted away from addict friends. In many little ways, then, the world began to change.

Where abstinence has been long-planned, and approached by gradual reduction in the daily dose of heroin or methadone, the person may proceed easily to a gradual withdrawal. But there were two other approaches visible among addicts in our study. The first was where the person's social circumstances had been changing and dosages had been reduced, but where no accompanying determined intention to stop was apparent. Something more was needed to tip the balance, to turn the potential for coming off into a decision, to trigger the final move: the suicide of a friend, the death of someone in the Clinic waiting room, a final rejection by parents or spouse, an arrest with the threat of imprisonment, a bad drug effect, or a sudden deterioration in health.

The second approach was found among those people who did not plan to give up drugs and whose lives were not changing, and indeed may have been getting more chaotic. The crucial incident for these people was some external coercion, a decision made by others that led to hospital treatment, or, for six people, prison. Jack Bryant is a good example of this pattern. He had started sniffing heroin and cocaine in 1964, when he was a bass player in a modern jazz group, and had attended various private doctors before going to a Clinic. By 1972 his condition was so bad that he was admitted to a psychiatric hospital where he was maintained on methadone for most of the following three years. This was a bleak time for him:

> 'The way I look at it now is that they [the hospital] had given up on me, at my age, to be so into drugs, they'd absolutely given up on me and just thought "We'll have to just keep him ticking along until he dies". What else could people do? I mean to me it was like a terrible approach at the time, but now I think of it, they had no choice, I wouldn't give up and they couldn't help me.'

He was allowed home at the weekends, and on one particular occasion, in

1975, his mother was looking after him and the children while his wife had a holiday. That weekend he took a large quantity of barbiturates and his mother found him 'falling about', telephoned the hospital, and had him re-admitted. The hospital doctors decided to get tough with him. They kept him on 80 mgs of methadone a day for a few days and then persuaded him to reduce his dosage. He could remember that the doctor cut him down to a small amount and they were approaching a particular Sunday when it was agreed that he would stop. During this dosage reduction he lost 'a terrible amount of weight', something like two stone over three or four weeks.

> 'All I can remember, if it's any help to anybody at any time, is that I got one clear moment of thinking. You never get that when you're addicted or when you're under anything. I got one clear moment of thought where I could see all exactly as it was and I thought "Well that's it, it's got to stop, I'm not waiting till Sunday, it's got to stop here and now, and I'll start eating food, and sit down and take things easy, and start getting a life". It seems simple, but I had a hard month of physical withdrawal. I stuck it out because I'd made up my mind, I think it is as simple as that, if you make up your mind that's it, you're finished.'

By December 1975 he had stopped using opiates altogether and had not used them since.

### TECHNIQUES FOR COMING OFF

The ways in which people handled withdrawal from opiates were as varied as the processes and incidents that led to that critical moment when they were no longer using. Withdrawal can be achieved by a rapid or protracted reduction in dose of heroin, or by transfer to either injectable or oral methadone and, from there, to abstinence. The period of dosage reduction may take several years, or only a few days, or weeks. For some, the main hurdle was to stop injecting, for others it was getting off the last small dose. For yet others this last small dose, particularly if it was methadone, may seem nothing more important than cough medicine. Some people are precipitated into abstinence so quickly that they have to suffer a 'cold turkey' with no plans or aids of support; others make elaborate arrangements for the process using other drugs, getting friends to control their supply of drugs, locking themselves in a room, or going away from London. Of the 40 abstinents in our study, 21 achieved withdrawal as out-patients, 12 while in hospital, 1 while in a therapeutic community, and 6 while in prison.

Let us look at those who had their withdrawals as out-patients. Of these, seventeen had a long, gradual withdrawal over several months or years, and most were using such minimal amounts of opiates towards the end that they did not experience major withdrawal symptoms. Of the seventeen, two were injecting heroin right up to the end, two were injecting methadone, and the remaining thirteen were using only oral methadone. Generally, this group had little previous experience of abstinence – only three had had an earlier, voluntary withdrawal as hospital in-patients. George Lester, for example, planned to reduce his drugs gradually. He wanted to come off them by the end of 1974 and worked out that the best way of doing so would be to change from a prescription of injectable drugs to a combination of oral methadone pills and injections for a month or so, and then to gradually have more pills and fewer injections. In the event withdrawal was executed rather more quickly with 'one week where I was all on amps, then a middle week where I was on amps and pills, and the next week I was on all pills'. He felt that the most difficult problem he had to overcome was 'giving up the needle'; once he had done that he soon afterwards stopped bothering with the pills, in fact he forgot them altogether until he began to experience physical discomfort. He refused to consider in-patient treatment feeling that 'It's something you've got to overcome for yourself and not let someone else do it for you'. He felt that if 'someone else takes you off you are more likely to go back on'.

Four other people who achieved abstinence as out-patients had a more abrupt ending to their addiction. They had reduced their dosages over the years, but the actual coming off was unplanned and thrust on them rather unexpectedly. Elizabeth Collinson, for example, had been on 210 mgs of heroin for a number of years when, in 1972, her doctor persuaded her to reduce to 150 mgs, and to change from intravenous to intramuscular injections. During this changeover period she met a new boyfriend who was not an addict. He liked to drink and they spent a lot of time in pubs, so she soon found that she had a new circle of friends. Her boyfriend gave her 'a sense of my own worth'. She was, then, experiencing many changes in her life which were propelling her towards coming off heroin, but the actual circumstances of withdrawal were rather dramatic and happened when she and her boyfriend went to stay with his parents for a short holiday. The Clinic arranged for her to take a five-day supply of heroin, they trusted her to make it last, but as she said 'It's the usual scene, you get your five-day script to get you over the holiday and after two days it's all gone and there's no way of getting more.' By the third day she was out of drugs, and stuck in Exeter with no way of getting a new prescription. She 'felt like death' but her boyfriend said that he would not let her spoil his holiday; 'he dragged me up the hills and made me stay there all day and this went on for three days'.

> 'I suddenly thought "you've gone through it all now, what's the point of starting all over again". So we went to the chemist in London and it was absolutely lovely because I'd been going there for years and everybody on the prescription counter knew me and I said "Look, I can't actually officially cancel my script till Thursday when I go to the hospital but if I come in and ask for any don't let me do it", and they all gave a big laugh.'

She summed up: 'So it was partly the change of attitude, partly being cut down by the Clinic. If my attitude hadn't changed I would have just got it somewhere else or done my nut or something. But the fact that these things happened, and cutting down, helped.'

There were twelve people who became abstinent while in hospital and one while in a therapeutic community. Fairly typical of those who had a period of in-patient withdrawal was Tony Lyttelton, who stopped in 1973. During 1969 and 1970 his life had been 'getting worse'; in 1971 he met an old friend who was an ex-addict and this partly influenced him to stop, although there was nothing specific that he could mention as having helped him come to that view – no new girlfriend or major change in his life, 'just a gradual build up of not wanting to be on it'. He had been reducing his dose over two or three years, from 360 mgs of heroin (the dosage when he was with a private doctor) to an eventual 30 mgs of heroin and 40 mgs of methadone at the Clinic. He was working in a warehouse and 'pretty stable, I wasn't doing it for kicks anymore, it was just part of my existence to fix'. He was injecting three times a day, in the toilet at work, but he started trying to get through the day without an injection, leaving it for the evening instead of first thing in the morning. At the same time he reverted to 'skin-popping' – injecting just under the skin. For the final cure he went into hospital. In the ward he was put on methadone linctus and the plan was to 'dilute it down each day till there was nothing left'. This way, as he put it, 'you do not know when you actually stop'.

> 'They reduce it until you're just taking the flavoured syrup, and I was all right, I didn't seem to miss the fixing or anything. I didn't start to get any withdrawal feelings until I was not taking any linctus. It was a period of something like ten days after that I started getting a bit uncomfortable, I didn't have any bad withdrawal symptoms because its quite a lenient way of coming off.'

Then he began to have problems sleeping, with hardly any sleep for the first week. He was restless and 'my legs were completely tense all the time as I lay in bed, my legs were just tense, just couldn't relax'. He left hospital after six weeks, saying that he had 'had enough, I was cured and I just wanted to go home and get on with things', even though the doctors wanted him to stay for a few months, believing he would relapse if he left early. As it happened he moved away from London and had not been addicted since 1973.

There were others who had more troubled times as in-patients, though, and there was a tendency for those who were withdrawn in hospital to have had more chaotic lives than those who managed to become abstinent as out-patients. Few of the twelve who went into hospital had achieved a controlled reduction as out-patients, and ten of them had had at least one earlier, unsuccessful attempt at withdrawal as in-patients.

Six people had their last physical withdrawal in prison. In one case the person was intoxicated on barbiturates and to this day does not know why he was arrested by the police, or why he received a three-month prison sentence. For another, John Barnes, parents and spouse actively colluded with the police to have him sent to prison. He had been arrested and fined £5, and the following day he had been arrested again. He was remanded on bail for two weeks and within the first hour of release went straight back to London to score some heroin and barbiturates. He injected these on the train going home and passed out in a toilet at Tilbury Station. The police were called again and knew that it would be difficult to prefer serious charges against him. However, he had some tranquillizers on him, which he had taken from his mother. One of the CID officers visited her and both agreed that John should be charged with stealing the tranquillizers. As a result he received a six-month prison sentence. As his wife said 'it was good really, it was great, he [the policeman] spoke about it between us and said it was the best thing'. This was in 1970. He was in prison for four months, used occasionally for a few months when released, but did not become addicted again.

### BENCHMARKS

On average, those who became abstinent had first used heroin at the age of nineteen, and were twenty-one when they first attended a Clinic. They stopped using opiates at the age of twenty-five and had used heroin for just over six years. By the time they were seen by us in 1976/77 they were thirty, and had been abstinent from opiates for just over four-and-a-half years.

### FEELINGS AFTER WITHDRAWAL

Withdrawal was not the end of the process. The transformation from addict to ex-addict was not easy and required changes in nearly all areas of living. Whether the process of personal change was lengthy or abrupt, and whatever its chronology in relation to changing patterns of drug use, what had to be achieved was the movement from one style of life and way of looking at the world, to another. Susan Hughes, who we write about at length in the next chapter, put it this way:

> 'It's a fact of having lived inside your own brain for twenty-four hours a day, heroin just blanks out everything. It's a loss of personality more than anything. Something has taken over and ploughing through your body all the time and you can't live without it. When you stop, the question is "What am I going to do?"'

The main task was to reorganize life, without drugs. Jack Bryant, the bass player who spent the last three years of his addiction in a psychiatric hospital, had thought that he would never be able to stop using drugs. Some changes had already occurred in his life (for example he had begun to study music again) but much of his life was in shambles in 1975, immediately after leaving hospital.

> 'It's very difficult when you come out of hospital, absolutely clear-eyed and clear-headed and look around you after ten years of being in this vacuum. You might have read the papers, or you'd listen to the news and think, but nothing registered in that time. . . . You take in information, you educate yourself still, you read a book, you do all sorts of things, but the next day it's all gone. So last year (when I came out of hospital) it was a fair fight to get myself together, to get myself organized again, to get a routine, in order that I'm going to get myself back to the standard I was and better . . . I'm finding my feet and I'm finding that to do all the obvious things, to belong to this world, to do anything, you have to be a lot better organized . . . I suppose for the rest of my life I'll wake up every morning and tell myself how lucky I was that I got out. But at the same time you get days when you don't feel so great. You come to accept that because you realize, you think for yourself once again, you realize that it's just life you know. You must sort of go on, but you must have a routine and you must work . . . I mean its like Dr O'Neal said to me, he works at a real gut level, he said "Oh I've got great dreams too of being a millionaire and driving down the road in my Rolls Royce with my cigar. I do dream about it'. But he said "I quite like it here, because you know this is reality and I think you have to accept that too", which is true . . . I'm not extreme in anything I do now. I mean I try to get a nice, even balance into my life, and that's difficult. I might never achieve that, I might die trying to achieve it, but I'm aware that you must try to keep a balance in your life, and where I went wrong is I became extreme with the worst things possible, which were heroin and cocaine.'

As Jack Bryant pointed out, there are problems in organizing life in the absence of heroin. But there are many positive things that help this process. He 'felt like a million dollars when he stopped' because he was 'free of drugs'. Enthusiasm was enough to help him through that difficult time. Many people went through a period of euphoria at their success, understandably proud of what they had achieved. Jenny Stock was one:

> 'I never felt so proud of myself, that I was doing it myself and coming off, and it was just a tremendous feeling, absolutely tremendous . . . there was this great, fantastic feeling when I came out of hospital, and I knew that I wasn't dependent, and all your senses come back. You enjoy music – heroin dulls all your senses, everything. And suddenly you've got all these feelings and everything is beautiful and everything is – tremendous. And that lasts for about three months and then you kind of level off. Now the doctor was very good because he explained that this would happen, that you feel tremendously high but then you feel as though you're going down. But you don't really go down, it wasn't as bad as that. . . . You don't realize just how much [heroin] blocks off your feelings and your emotions until you come off, it's like coming alive again. It's a completely new experience.'

Yet, whilst on the surface the transition may appear for some people to be relatively smooth, immediate emotional problems are encountered because mood is no longer moderated by the effect of opiates. This was experienced as being unable to sleep properly, as increased nervousness, anxiety, and tension, and as feelings of insecurity, like 'a cripple who's had his crutches pinched'. It was hard, too, to shake off haunting memories of a past. Jenny Stock had nightmares:

> 'It was as though my subconscious was trying to get through somehow. It was awful, and when I had a couple of fixes after, I had a few dreams. I was walking down a very, very grotty street and in every alley-way there was the grottiest type of junkie you know, like the type who spit into their syringes because they can't be bothered to go and get some water, really dirty and grotty, blood everywhere. I had that dream. And everywhere I looked there were these dirty, grotty, really grotty people, and I realized that I was trying to escape, trying to walk faster and escape. And I couldn't escape them and I realized that it was me, those people, it was me. I was saying "Oh, all these disgusting junkies" and I'm sure that's what the dream meant, I was disgusted with myself.'

For the most part our forty ex-addicts did not seek help with such problems from Clinic staff or other specialists in addiction. As a group they were distinguished by the lack of help they received in the few months following withdrawal. Thirty-two people ceased all contact with the Clinic as soon as they were withdrawn and only three continued seeing a doctor. Five others went into therapeutic communities for several months.

### TEMPTATION TO RETURN TO DRUG USE

The majority of ex-addicts in our sample, thirty-two of the forty, never used opiates again once they had ceased to be physically dependent, but eight used heroin or methadone occasionally in the few months following withdrawal. John Barnes, whose family helped get him into prison, was fairly typical of the latter group. He spent four months in a Sussex prison during which time he regained his physical fitness. On release he went to live with his wife in Bournemouth. He soon started to travel up to his old haunts in South London, without his wife's knowledge, in order to buy heroin or methadone. He would take a day-return trip on British Rail and his absence was not noticed. He felt very isolated in his new environment, and if he went to London there was the possibility that 'I might bump into just one person I knew, and we'd start chatting and we'd shoot off somewhere and we'd score'. His financial situation – supporting himself, his wife, and child on Social Security benefits – meant that the trips were infrequent. He felt that if he had been able to go to London every week-end for three or four months he might have started using frequently and might have become addicted again. However, he found that the situation in London had changed whilst he was in prison, and he no longer found the same atmosphere there, two of his old friends had died and others had moved away. Using heroin did not seem the same because he had 'left it alone for so long'.

Those people who moved out of London had to make special efforts to obtain heroin. Bill Gregor, after coming off drugs and starting at college would journey to London to score. This happened about once a month, and then tailed off to every couple of months or so. It usually happened when 'I got pissed off with life up there [Leicester]' and abruptly, almost on impulse, 'you suddenly decide, hell, I'm going to hop on a train'. Like ex-smokers who suddenly want a cigarette, the impulse to fix emerges apparently 'out of the blue', with little or no premeditation, 'you just get up and say "right, I'm going to score." It's as easy as saying "I fancy a cup of tea" or a drink you know.'

The temptation was greater for those who stayed in London. As Jenny Stock described it, 'drug addicts are very, very funny people; if you come off and you meet somebody and they know you're off, they'll turn you on'. Knowing where to score and having friends who still used made it easier to start again. Jenny continued: 'It takes a long time to be able to say ''No'', and if someone comes up and says ''Oh well look here you are'' it's almost impossible within the first six months to say no. And then of course, I've got a great ability to lie to myself, to say ''Well I'll just have one turn on''.' Since she stopped regular use she had occasionally used methadone, mostly coinciding with particularly stressful times in her life. The most recent time was when she was having problems getting the Council to rehouse her and her children. She met an old friend who gave her four methadone pills.

> 'I had a couple of fixes, but it terrified me so much you know. I never under-estimate it. I know how much willpower I've got and how weak I am . . . I've got an incredible ability to lie to myself, but I've got an escape valve which works suddenly, I wake up, or it just suddenly happens one day and I'm just very, very frightened . . . so I do something about it.'

There were two people who, although no longer physically dependent, continued, on a long-term basis, to inject occasionally. For example, Jeremy Gophert was, by 1977, managing an office in the West End. He had ceased regular use of opiates in 1970 but had had several injections since. He had a friend who was still receiving a methadone prescription and had bought some from him every six months or so. On the last occasion it was two ampoules (20 mgs). For two of the years since withdrawal he did not inject at all, and did not think that he ran any great risk of becoming re-addicted, although the last time he had injected 'it was terrific' and 'ten times better' than when he was registered, for then it was just like taking medicine. Drugs were no longer important to his life – 'I just haven't got the time to lay about stoned' – and as time passed it became harder to dabble in this way.

> 'The way I see it now, it's so difficult to get and it's so darned expensive, but there's really no risk you know. I wouldn't end up a junkie again. The occasional joybang doesn't hurt. I've gone through all that [addiction] and I can survive one odd fix now and again.'

There are other drugs to come to terms with in the first twelve months following withdrawal. Ten people received prescriptions for, or scored, Mandrax, barbiturates, and tranquillizers, mainly in order to cope with their new sleeping problems. Thirteen found that for a few months they slipped into a pattern of heavy and problematic drinking. This might have been the first period for many years when they actually drank any significant quantity of alcohol. Thirteen said alcohol, cannabis, or other drugs were useful in coping with their mental state. It should be stressed though that very few ex-addicts continued to use drugs in a potentially harmful fashion.

## CONTINUED CHANGES

The transition from addict to ex-addict entails several changes in addition to ceasing to be addicted to opiate drugs. As we have seen, some people had begun to organize their lives in a new way whilst they were still addicted, whereas others were suddenly precipitated into abstinence, by imprisonment or other events which took them by surprise, and, subsequently, had to react more quickly in reorganizing their lives.

The problems facing the ex-addict are little different from the problems all of us have to solve – finding a source of income and a satisfying way of spending one's time, establishing somewhere to live and satisfying personal relationships and friendships. All those who stopped using opiates had made major changes in their lives (as will be seen in the Appendix) so that by the time we spoke to them in 1976/77, their life styles were markedly different from those who continued addicted.

Ceasing addiction was accompanied by new jobs or college courses. By the time they were interviewed most ex-addicts had jobs or were otherwise occupied, as students (2) or housekeepers (2), with only a few (7) in irregular employment or out of work. Ex-addicts were engaged in a wide variety of jobs: for example there were two lorry drivers, several secretaries and clerical workers, skilled carpenters and electricians, two sales managers, a company director, a computer worker, a railway porter, a musician, and two warehouse-workers. The spread of jobs did not differ markedly from that found in the general population, except for a slight under-representation among professional workers, employers, and managers, and a slight over-representation among unskilled manual, clerical, and sales workers. Most ex-addicts' incomes came from their own earnings, which was a change from earlier times when illegal sources of income were prominent. Eight were receiving unemployment benefit or social security.

Withdrawal also brought changes in patterns of friendships, for when people gave up injecting opiates they gave up seeing other addicts. For example, only four of the ex-addicts said that they had a close friend who continued to inject drugs, and none of them had recently been to Piccadilly Circus or any other meeting place for addicts. Some simply drifted away from old friends, or found that after they returned from hospital or prison many of their friends had gone. Fifteen people moved from London to live in other parts of Britain and four emigrated. Those who stayed in London had special problems in avoiding places where addicts met but, as in any large city, it proved possible to restructure the geography of social relationships. For example, Jenny Stock had been living in Camberwell, in South London, home of two Drug Dependency Clinics and the Community Drug Project day-centre for addicts. A number of addicts can be found on the pavement outside the chemist, or on Camberwell Green on warm days, and both places are meeting points known to addicts. When Jenny Stock was reducing her dose she moved a few miles away, for she pointed out, 'once you've been involved in the drug scene it's so easy to get drugs, you know where to go'. She stopped seeing her old friends:

> 'When I come to think about it, all the drug addict friends I had weren't friends at all, they didn't miss me, you don't have friends. And so I didn't tell them where I'd moved to, you have to escape from it all. You can't come off drugs and then go and see your old friends and watch them fixing-up.'

She organized her life so that she avoided places like Camberwell. She felt that for her 'there is not even a half-way mark, you've got to get right away from it, completely, because the temptation is too great'. She would no longer ride a London Transport bus if its route passed through Camberwell.

Avoiding addicts was at times difficult for people in certain occupations, for example the music business, and it was hard for two people in our sample who worked for British Rail and London Transport, as addicts used the stations where they worked. Both of them eventually gave up their jobs. Once the drift away from old friendships had begun, though, it was less and less likely that they would be resurrected. After a few months the faces and the people on the drug scene had changed, old friends had also moved on, or perhaps died. New friends who did not know the addict world were not interested in these places, and it could have been embarrassing to have been encountered by an old addict friend when in the company of someone who knew little about the former life.

It has often been cynically or pessimistically suggested that people who stop using opiates switch to depending on other drugs, but this did not happen to any substantial extent with the people we are discussing here. Many, as we have seen, had periods of heavy drug or alcohol use in the first year following their withdrawal, periods that must be seen in terms of the problems of becoming free from addiction. But when interviewed in 1976/77 (an average of nearly five years since giving up opiates) their consumption of drugs and alcohol was not much different (with the exception of cannabis) from that of a normal population sample. In the case of alcohol most drank small quantities, rarely exceeding five pints of beer a day or the equivalent in other drinks. There were two people who did not drink at all. At the other end of the spectrum there was Raymond O'Sullivan who would probably be classed as a potential problem drinker as he drank in excess of five pints of beer a day, every day, a level of drinking currently thought to be associated with eventual drinking problems. Finding, as we did, one 'problem drinker' in forty is just about what one would find in the general population.

The use of other drugs was also minimal. There were five people who were daily users of tranquillizers, anti-depressants, or sleeping tablets. All took small doses, none used them to get intoxicated, and all obtained them legally from GPs. As with alcohol, this level of drug use equates with that found in the general population (for example one national survey found that 11 per cent of the adult population were currently users of prescribed psychoactive drugs) (Dunnell and Cartwright 1972). The one drug in common use was cannabis. Three people smoked it nearly every day and another fifteen smoked it occasionally. They did not see its use as a problem, they enjoyed smoking and could see nothing wrong in it, it was a normal part of their life, nothing special, just another way to relax. For example, Wayne Jennings led a busy life as a sales executive and when he got home in the evening 'as some people like to go to the cabinet and get a scotch, I like to roll a joint and have a smoke, and then I may go out at nine o'clock and have a couple of pints'. More exotic drug use was rare: one person had recently sniffed cocaine, and another had tried some Liberty Cap mushrooms, which grow wild in Britain and have recently been discovered to be hallucinogenic.

Crime was another area of life that had changed, with none currently involved in any legal processes. None was in prison, by definition, for in this chapter we have been looking at those who were abstinent outside of institutions. None was on bail awaiting trial, on probation, or attending a therapeutic facility as a condition of sentence. Only one was subject to a conditional discharge for a previous conviction. This low level of legal involvement was reflected in the criminal activities that were reported. All were asked about 'typical' ways in which they might have recently broken the law. The greatest response was with respect to the possession of drugs: seventeen had been in possession, usually of cannabis, in the last three months. One person reported selling drugs, a small quantity to friends. None reported shop-lifting. Three said they had received stolen goods, but in all cases this was minor (for example, one had bought some paint at work which had 'fallen off the back of a lorry'). This is not to suggest that these people had been free from legal problems since they stopped using opiates, for 7 had appeared in court and been convicted on a total of 16 occasions for 23 offences. They were convicted under the drugs law (6), for theft (6), for violence (4), or for motoring offences (7). Even so, the level of convictions was much less than when they were addicted, and when these convictions are weighted against the length of time these people had been abstinent it is clear that their rate of convictions had fallen dramatically, to less than a third of what it had been when they were active addicts.

The people who stopped using opiates were, by 1977, generally healthy. One obvious consequence of ceasing to inject drugs is that infections that often accompany self-injecting are avoided, and it was not surprising to find that none of the ex-addicts had those infections commonly experienced by drug takers, such as hepatitis, septicaemia, or abscesses. However, although health hazards are reduced with withdrawal there are several ways in which former drug use may influence present health. First, there may have been physical damage that left some permanent impairment. Five ex-addicts in our sample had muscle-wasting in places where they had injected, difficulty in moving joints, or symptoms suggestive of peripheral neuritis. All attributed this damage to their former drug use. For example, Elizabeth Collinson had some muscle-wasting in the buttock that she had habitually used as a place for intramuscular injections. At least five people had lost most, or all, of their teeth and connected this with their drug use. There may have been more such occurrences, but we did not think to ask this until Christina Boyd suggested it to us. Second, it is possible that opiate addiction, or rather associated self-neglect, made people more susceptible to later infections. Six people reported severe or recurrent bronchitis since they ceased to be addicted and attributed this to previous neglect of their health. Third, several people thought that their drug use may have affected their mind: Christina Boyd reported memory loss, and two others reported occasional auditory or visual hallucinations; Mike Lunt said he had been 'more nervous' since withdrawal; and one man had been diagnosed as schizophrenic, but it was uncertain whether this condition was connected with his former drug use.

Mike Lunt, who had been off heroin for nearly seven years, felt that his former drug use had a major affect on his health, for he had since had six bouts of bronchitis, suffered some joint pains, had bad teeth, and was nervous. But he was exceptional, for most people said that they felt healthy, and were surprised that their addiction had not caused more bodily harm. John Barnes, an ex-addict for seven years, best expressed these sentiments:

> 'One thing that really surprised me is that after all that with the drugs, you would think that would really weaken somebody something terrible, a few years of that. But even when I was inside [prison] after the first few weeks when I went to prison, the first thing I done was to enrol in different evening classes. One of them was weight-training, and another gymnastics.'

He had a labouring job and was fit, healthy, and sun-tanned when we interviewed him in his council house by the coast. The only problem he had found was that when he first started labouring his hands swelled when he was working hard, especially when carrying heavy loads on a building site; he wondered whether this was because he had damaged some veins. 'It surprised me', he said, 'that after all those years of sort of degrading myself with drugs, how easy I found it to get back to what I consider a fair fitness.'

### STIGMA: HOW TO MANAGE A 'DIRTY PAST'

'Ordinariness' can be demonstrated to interviewers and contemporaries by one's current style of life, possessions, and by the things one chooses to talk about. When we talked to people who had stopped using opiates the conversations turned to politics, decorating houses, jobs, bringing up children, buying cars, and of course some reminiscence about the past. In contrast, conversations eight years previously had been about drugs, doctors, and police. Ex-addicts demonstrated that they were normal people with normal hopes and aspirations. But despite this display, these people still had to deal with their past. What sense can be made of those experiences and what do others want to make of them? Are ex-addicts stigmatized because of their past?

In the classical Greek use of the term, 'stigma' referred to bodily signs cut or burnt into the skin to show there was something unusual and bad about the moral status of the marked person. In its more recent, popular usage it is taken to refer to any attribute that is deeply discrediting. It is not the attribute *per se* that is of interest, but the way the attribute affects social relationships. Goffman (1968) pointed to three different kinds of stigma. First, there are various physical deformities of the body. Second, there are blemishes of individual character perceived as weak will, unnatural passions, or dishonesty, these being inferred from a known record of previous 'deviancy'. Third, there are the stigmas of race, nation, and religion. It is really the first two stigmas, physical deformities and blemishes of the character, that are relevant here. One important practical difference between the two is the extent and way in which individuals can control information about themselves, for hiding disfiguring injection marks and hiding a past criminal history poses different problems – one of 'visibility', the other of 'people's knowledge of one's past'.

Let us look at the problem of visible stigma first. The most common markings were 'track-marks', veins that had thrombosed from repeated injection and which appeared as dark, linear blemishes. These were commonly found on the forearms and legs and most of the time were covered by clothing. They could be concealed in other ways. John Barnes was a labourer and his arms were exposed in warm weather, but he had such extensive tattoos that it was hard to distinguish his track-marks.

Another ex-addict joined the army and at the medical inspection

> 'a brigadier, he's the one who gave me the medical, looked at my arms. The scars are pretty deep really. And he just said, "What are they?", and I just said, "Tattoo marks" because I've got a lot of tattoos. And he said "You're quite fit". I've always been pretty fit, I've been lucky really. And he just put me through. I went and swore in and a couple of days later I went up [to the training centre].'

For women, track-marks were harder to hide. They could not be covered by or passed as tattoos for these are unusual enough on women as to raise other questions of moral worth. During much of the year track-marks could be hidden by long sleeves, but could not be hidden when hot weather made long sleeves uncomfortable to wear. Susan Hughes moved to a country where the summers are hot and remembered that for the first two years she wore long sleeves even during the 95 degree summers. Eventually she gave up and wore short sleeves. Her assertive handling of people's reactions is a good example of the strategies that may be adopted to deal with inquisitive people.

The second problem for the ex-addict was that of the past being known to other people. Past addiction is recorded in various documents. Any convictions are recorded by the Criminal Record Office and people with drug convictions cannot, for example, emigrate to the US. Details of past addiction are kept by the Home Office Drugs Branch, and appear in medical records. Mike Lunt was disconcerted to discover that his NHS general practice records noted that he had been an addict. Each time he changed doctors his record cards followed him and when we talked about his illnesses and bouts of bronchitis he felt that he had not been fairly treated by his doctor:

> 'The doctors aren't very keen to see you in the surgery. It's all right until they have a look at your notes and then they are not willing to listen an awful lot. . . . This particular doctor, he started looking through my file. This was the first time I went to see him. It was about a stomach upset or something like that. He went back up [to the time spent in a rehabilitation unit]. Then he started asking about how I was and then he clammed right up. . . . He didn't give me any treatment. He said "It'll go away".'

Greg Wheeler had a different reaction from an over-solicitous GP who had studied sociology and psychiatry. He told Greg that he was fortunate to have left London, and that 'Anytime you feel depressed you come running to me. If the wife got run over by a bus or something you might go back on it.'

The existence of such records was probably not an immediate

practical difficulty for most people. The biggest problems arose from the absence rather than the presence of records, for many ex-addicts were unable to provide a suitable biography. When applying for jobs people need to provide a work history or adequate explanation for long periods of unemployment. Christina Boyd, by then in her thirties, had been unemployed for much of the time since leaving school:

> 'It's very difficult for me to get a job. I have to make up a history. I have no difficulty in making up a story, but they check. . . . So in fact you have to become a very practised liar if you want to be accepted as a good, responsible citizen. If you go in and say "I was on junk for seven years and I've come off it" they don't want to know, even though you have told the truth. . . . All the jobs that are offered at the moment are local council. So I make up "O" levels and everything. I just don't know how I am going to get a job because as soon as they check I've got years and years and years to cover. And I can't say to them, "look, I know how to work these machines" . . . I want to work and I want to earn some money. I don't mind doing filing, I'm quite responsible and sort of fairly intelligent and I won't disorder their entire organization. I'm *me*, I'm not me eighteen years back.'

We should not assume that all people with a dark past wished to hide it. Some certainly did but others were more selective. Susan Hughes was prepared to talk about her past with contemporaries, but with her father there was an unspoken agreement not to discuss the 'bad old days'. Greg Wheeler's work friends knew and 'they took the Mick out of me a few times'; a friend of Mike Lunt had seen an article on addicts in the *Daily Mirror* and said 'You used to be on drugs, didn't you?' but it was just a passing comment. Often the past is not that relevant to others.

But apart from the potential problems with friends, employers, and family, what was a person to make of a deviant past? How could one make sense of it in terms of a now different way of life? One way was to *detach* oneself and consider that the past happened to a different person, or was a separate part of life, having no connections with or relevance to the present. Ann Mullins, who had remarried since withdrawal in 1974, put it this way: 'I don't really think about it anymore. My husband would talk about it [with me] if I had reason to think about it, but it seems a whole separate part of my life really. It doesn't seem connected to me now.' When the interviewer apologized for bringing back past memories, she said:

> 'It's okay, I don't mind. They did that to me when my [first] husband was killed last year. I think that was worse. They made me go through the whole bloody mess again at the police station, which

> was a bit unfair because it was nothing to do with me, I hadn't seen him for three years. I think that was about the worst time. I don't mind talking about it, it's just that it doesn't sort of occur to me. . . . You don't really want to think about it, so you just cut it off really. Just wipe that period out.'

She was by then occupied in doing things that she wished she had done when she was younger, like trying to pursue a career in acting and dancing. 'I simply lie about my age and say "bugger it". Just drop a few years off.' She felt that she was no longer the person who was addicted. 'The only way I can explain it, is as if a chunk of my life just hadn't really existed and I've started over again. Having been fifteen [years old] something happened in between, and I've just taken up where I left off at fifteen.'

Greg Wheeler held similar, negative views about the past but his account, or lack of it, tended more towards suppression than detachment. He too had since remarried, his wife was ten years his junior and they lived in a small town fifty miles from London. He worked as a welder in a small engineering firm, the same sort of work he had done in his father's firm before he became addicted, and he and his wife were renovating the Victorian terraced house they were buying. They had just had to decide whether to buy a new car or have a child – 'we decided on the car'. We drank coffee and ate chocolate cake as Greg tried to talk about the past:

> 'That three years is just three years I've lost of my life. Quite a big bit in fact. I was getting on pretty well in the welding business [before], but I just lost three years. . . . Well I've learnt my lesson – I've experienced it and I regret it terribly. Just a stupid thing that I have done.'

He found it hard to remember much of what happened in those three years. 'I can't remember anything, you know, anymore. . . . A lot of bits of it I've tried to forget.' Like several others he found it easier to recall incidents, like the time he was arrested, than the order in which things happened:

> 'I can remember the times when I was out scoring at Piccadilly, in the car-parks, out the back, there's a side entrance to Piccadilly Station . . . I had the car parked outside there, with a girl I'd just picked up. I'd just scored. I can remember walking around the arcade and then two plain-clothes police officers came in, stopping me and taking me down to the station. I remember that. I remember telling one of my friends, go down and pick me car up for me. Those sort of incidents. While other things I just can't remember during that time I was talking about. All I can remember is going down to Dr Jackson and then going down to Camberwell Green and waiting at the chemists there to pick up my prescription.'

Right to the end of the interview, saying goodbye at the front door, he was apologizing for being unable to remember much of the period when he was addicted. Mike Lunt similarly viewed the past as a blank.

> 'When I look back now it seems so empty, that period. There's not a lot that you can remember with any sort of vividness, even people. You can remember some names and every now and then something will sort of hit you. Like when they made that [television] programme about Gail ["Gail is Dead"]. That sort of hit you between the eyes because I knew her. And now and then you come across somebody. When I first came back to London I had a job on Victoria Station and I bumped into a couple of people there. I think junkies are horrible people. They're pretty much wrapped up in themselves. I think that's why you don't remember other people's names.'

And, like Greg Wheeler, he also had problems in remembering what his life had been like: 'I've told you the truth, I can't remember a lot about them days . . . I think there's a tendency not to think about it. It's not like you look back and say "those were the best days of my life". It's a bit like a great empty space.'

A second way found to deal with a disreputable past was to *incorporate* it into one's present identity. Therapeutic communities try to do this when they translate a dubious past (addict, alcoholic) into a qualification for a future role (addict–counsellor, programme graduate). Instead of denying the relevance of the past and regretting missed opportunities, the past can be considered as something of importance to the present and a sense of continuity can be established. Raymond O'Sullivan incorporated the past by making its 'experience' an ever-present and continuing feature of his life. By 1976 he had been free of opiates for three years and had last attended a Clinic seven years previously. He was smoking cannabis and drinking every day, being the heaviest drinker among the ex-addicts in our study. He regarded drinking very much as he regarded his other drug experiences:

> 'Alcohol was purely an experience of my own. I'd experienced everything but alcohol, so I thought to myself, I'd never been a drinker till then really, so I thought I've done about everything so I'll try alcohol – and I really tried it. That was a positive thing on my part. I definitely wanted to drink a lot, I really did.'

He had had various spells when he was heavily using other drugs. When he ceased to be addicted to heroin he started injecting amphetamines and barbiturates, and continued this until 1974. He accounted for his drug use, and the continued meaning of his life, in terms of searching for experiences.

'I was taking anything that came because I wanted a thirst for experiences. Because once I'd had some heroin and some other drugs like amphetamines and, what was it, methedrine; it opens up new things within you and you want to realize what you're taking and you want to find out more, and then you realize what you're taking is not all, there are more things to take as well. So I just carried on along that sort of line, wanted to experiment you know like with myself like. You need experience of drugs because they open up your mind and your heart and your soul and release your spirit. . . . But you can't relate this you know, it's not easy to relate, besides most people don't even want to know it.'

Pat Chilvers also often thought about her past experiences. After some time in a therapeutic community she met her husband-to-be. When we met them both they were living on a small-holding, and had two children, one born just a few weeks earlier. She felt that she was still very much the same person as when addicted. She did not think that she had used heroin because of any personal problems, nor that its use had caused her any difficulties since: 'It was just something I got into, and didn't have the willpower or didn't really want to get out of it . . . I was quite content.' She and her husband did not talk about her time as an addict as he thought 'they were the bad old days', a view she did not share.

'I keep saying to him "they weren't all that bad" but I think he just goes by his experiences. . . . We never really talk about it that much. I don't think he likes me talking about it. I don't know whether it's because he wasn't any part of it.'

She said she often thought about the past and seemed to miss some of its former excitement. Was she happier now? 'I suppose so . . . I feel a bit restricted here, I think it's lack of money what does it.' Rather than experiencing the difficulties of an ex-addict, her problems seemed typical of those often experienced by mothers with two young children:

'If you haven't got money you're missing out on so much . . . sometimes I wish I never had children, you know. Just so that I could be free.'

How did the old haunts look in retrospect? Some had been tempted to go back to the once-familiar places, like tourists to their own past. 'Sometimes', said Susan Hughes, 'I wonder if I went down to the Clinic, would I recognize anybody there? Would it all be the same? Yes, it would all be the same, why bother?' She found many memories hard to erase and could still remember all the London bus routes despite several years of living abroad. 'I don't remember how to get from my parents' house to my old school, but I remember every bus that goes to Camberwell. That sort of thing just doesn't go. I remember the names of the chemists and how to get to all of them.' She was tempted to revisit Piccadilly when she returned to London for a holiday and took her new boyfriend to show him what it looked like.

> 'We got off at Piccadilly and he said, "let's go". That was it. He was so thoroughly disgusted with the way it looks, and he doesn't even know much about drunks or addicts, except what I've told him. He said to me "I think you're disgusting that you could ever have been any way involved with this kind of thing" . . . I was disgusted when I walked through, to think that I'd actually been there at one time and lived there day and night.'

Pat Chilvers, too, went to Piccadilly to see what it was like some years on, travelling up from her home in the country. What she saw made her realize that she could not return to that life style, even though she often thought of the freedom it offered.

> 'I could never go back to that way of life now. I'm too comfortable here . . . I've been up around Piccadilly since then, not looking for anything, just passing through. It makes me feel sick even walking into the toilets. . . . It all looks so dirty down there. At the time it didn't matter to me at all.'

# 10

## *Two biographies – Gillian Morris and Susan Hughes*

In our final pair of biographies we have taken two people who did not achieve an unproblematic balance between drug use and life style, who did not adopt the stable normal life of, say, Robert Jones. We have argued earlier that those who led chaotic lives were in many ways more likely to have had their addiction interrupted, for example by imprisonment, hospitalization, or the therapeutic activity of doctors; and we have indicated that such people had the most extreme outcomes, ending their addiction in death or in abstinence. The chaotic addicts were the least likely to remain addicted: they were the least successful in the sense that they did not manage to sustain their addiction. The two people in this chapter had many problems and periods of chaos when they were addicted but, like many such addicts, their outcomes differed extremely: Gillian Morris and Susan Hughes both started using heroin at around the same time, Gillian in 1965, at the age of twenty, Susan in 1964 at the age of fifteen; Gillian died in 1974, while Susan had given up heroin in 1973.

Gillian Morris' life was complicated by homelessness, overdoses, arrests, and infections. There were several occasions when she stopped injecting drugs, very often as a result of imprisonment, but she rarely lasted more than a few days after being released before she started injecting again. On another occasion she chose to make the effort herself, prompted by a probation order requiring her to live with her parents in the country. There her life began to be more placid, but eventually she visited London and returned to a full-time chaotic life in the West End. She was frequently taken to casualty departments when she had overdosed and one day in 1974 an overdose led to her death.

We have here reconstructed her life and the events leading to her death. We have spoken to several friends who remembered her and to doctors who treated her, looked at Clinic case notes and the records of casualty departments of hospitals in central London, at Home Office records, social work reports, our interview with her in 1969, and at some letters that Gillian wrote to her doctor at the Clinic.

Susan Hughes' life was also chaotic. She too had infections, had lost her teeth, and her appearance had suffered, but, unlike Gillian Morris, she did not repeatedly overdose, and was not arrested once she became a Clinic patient. Like Gillian, she had an addict boyfriend. She spent much of her time with other addicts, and most of the people in the house she shared were addicts too. She had enjoyed the fun and excitement of the early days of the drug scene in London in the 1960s, and her reputation as a tearaway. But over the years she began to think that she did not want to be an addict for the rest of her life. Her addict boyfriend was sent to prison and a new boyfriend pressured her to stop using heroin.

When we last met she was no longer an addict and was leading a life psychologically and geographically remote from the West End of London, making up time for the years she was addicted. She did not regret the experiences she had had, but wished they had lasted perhaps only two or three years, instead of the nine she had spent addicted between fifteen and twenty-four.

## *Death from addiction: Gillian Morris*

> 'This patient, who is registered with your Clinic as a Heroin addict, has been brought into our Accident and Emergency Department on twenty-five separate occasions this year, having been found in varying degrees of coma in the West End. She never remains in the Department for longer than is absolutely necessary.'
>
> Letter concerning Gillian Morris, sent to Dr Allen, her Clinic doctor, from an Accident and Emergency department in central London.

On the evening of 20 March 1974 Gillian Morris was found unconscious in the women's public lavatory at Piccadilly Circus underground station. She died the next morning in hospital of barbiturate and heroin poisoning. She was twenty-nine years old and had been using drugs for almost ten years.

She went to her Clinic two days prior to her death. The entry in the case notes reflected the pessimism felt by people who knew Gillian in the last months of her life. She was taken to casualty departments around the

West End with such monotonous regularity that these events were hardly worth noting down. That particular day she had come directly from an overnight stay in a hospital, following an overdose. She left the hospital at 9.15 a.m. to go to the Clinic. This is how the doctor recorded her attendance:

> '19.3.74. Scruffy again. Penniless. Taking barbiturates again. 2–3 daily? Not been home for weekend. Cough and chest pains. X-ray at Middlesex Hospital. Follow-up today. Decided she cannot stay at home, complaining bitterly that prescription is not big enough. Gillian says she sells barbiturates to get heroin. What is true?'

Later that evening she was again taken from Piccadilly Circus to a casualty department and she stayed overnight in hospital. Next morning, 20 March, she discharged herself from hospital at 6.45 a.m. At 6.40 that evening she was found unconscious again at Piccadilly Circus underground station and was taken to a casualty department. She was kept in hospital for recovery. At midnight she was examined and was sleeping heavily. It was decided to keep her in overnight for 'social reasons'. The next morning, at 6.45 a.m., she was examined by hospital staff and found to be dead.

### Early life

Gillian Morris was born in 1945, when her father was twenty-three and her mother twenty-two. She was the eldest child in a family of four – she had a sister one year younger, a brother three years younger, and another sister nineteen years younger. Her father was a tractor driver on a market garden. She was brought up in an isolated, rural part of Essex, going to a local primary school and then to a secondary modern school. When she was fourteen years old she was placed on probation for two years for 'breaking and entering'. Nothing more is known about this incident. At fifteen she was sent away from home to an Approved School for fifteen months, being considered in need of care and protection. She told the Clinic doctor that as a child she bit her nails and wet the bed until the age of ten, and said that she had truanted from school at least five times, for a day at a time.

At seventeen she married a local boy of the same age. She was pregnant at the time and soon after her marriage gave birth to a boy. Her marriage lasted for eighteen months, until her husband left her. She was then nineteen. While she was married she was convicted for being drunk and disorderly and causing wilful damage. After her husband left, she went back to live with her parents. Six months later she decided to leave home and move to London, leaving the baby in the care of her sister. He had been brought up by her sister ever since and Gillian never expressed to Clinic staff any desire to care for him herself. She said that she felt no emotional attachment to him, though she did remember some of his birthdays. Soon after Gillian's arrival in London in 1964 she started to share a flat with a girlfriend in Kingston. Her friend was involved in the drug scene and so she began to frequent clubs where drugs were available. She occasionally used amphetamines, then in 1965 used heroin and reported that she realized within four weeks that she was addicted. She visited several of the well-known, private GPs who were prescribing heroin to addicts in London and mentioned particularly Dr Petro. In March 1967 her girlfriend died of pneumonia associated with drug addiction and soon after that Gillian moved into a bedsitter in Westbourne Grove with her American boyfriend Robbie – also an addict. Just before the Clinics opened in April 1968, Gillian was receiving a prescription for 25 grains of heroin and 25 grains of cocaine every two days.

### Attending the Clinic

Gillian Morris was in the first wave of patients who attended the new drug Clinics in 1968. The first entry in her case notes, on 19 March records that she required an emergency prescription for 600 mgs of heroin and 600 mgs of cocaine. Four days later she was interviewed at length by the consultant.

At this time Gillian was twenty-two years old and had been using heroin for two-and-a-half years. Her American boyfriend registered at the same Clinic. She told Dr Allen that she did not want to withdraw from heroin immediately and he decided on a prescription for 480 mgs of heroin and 480 mgs of cocaine. By May of the same year she had agreed to reduce her dosage, and by August her prescription was down to 60 mgs of heroin, 20 mgs of methadone, and 210 mgs of cocaine. Already, in the first few months of the Clinic, staff suspected that Gillian was using other drugs as well. She sometimes turned up for appointments in a drowsy state and her health was beginning to suffer. She had several infections directly related to her drug use, though she was able to cope in some areas of her life. She worked for a while on a market stall in Portobello Road and continued to live with her boyfriend, although things were sometimes difficult between them. It was during this time, too, that her divorce from her husband was finally made absolute.

On 30 August 1968 Gillian was arrested, charged with illegal possession of methedrine, and remanded in Holloway Prison for two weeks. She was gradually withdrawn from drugs while on remand and was maintained on a low dose of 30 mgs of methadone while in the prison. Her Clinic records note that on one occasion whilst in Holloway a friend, concerned about her lack of drugs in prison, tried to smuggle in fifteen pills of heroin. However, the attempt was thwarted and the pills confiscated. She went to court on Saturday 7 September 1968 and was given a two-year probation order with a condition that she resided with her parents in their Essex home. She had no option but to leave London and go home. This was the first time that she stopped using heroin, but it was, however, only an interlude. Two months after the court case she and Robbie called to see Dr Allen, claiming to be off drugs and quite happy. The doctor noticed a spot of blood on the cuff of her blouse and when he enquired about it she denied that it was anything important but burst into tears and refused to look directly at him. He did not press her further but urged her to keep in touch. Gillian returned home to Essex but a month later she was picked up by the police, near her parents' home, under the influence of drugs. In November 1968 she tried to get drugs from another Clinic, but she was sent back to her original Clinic where she was put on a daily prescription for 60 mgs of heroin and 60 mgs of cocaine. According to the case notes she again had 'no desire at present to stay off drugs'.

For the next eighteen months, Gillian attended the Clinic regularly and was prescribed heroin and cocaine. She suffered from numerous abscesses and swellings and it was during this time, 1969, that she first began to use barbiturates in large quantities. Her relationship with her boyfriend showed signs of stress – rows and separations were frequent. At the end of 1969, when asked whether she enjoyed life, she replied, 'I don't expect much'. She toyed with the idea of coming off drugs though the doctor says she changed her mind from one week to the next. Her mood varied from carefree elation to being tired and worried.

In the middle of 1970, Gillian was arrested and again sent to Holloway Prison. This was for a breach of her 1968 probation order which had required her to reside with her parents. This time she was sentenced to probation with a condition of residence in a psychiatric hospital. The doctor who examined her at Holloway Prison expressed doubts about this action but the court was, apparently, persuaded by the probation officer, who arranged for her to go into hospital for addiction treatment. Predictably perhaps, this arrangement did not succeed. She was re-arrested and the court asked for a further medical report. The examining doctor wrote on 16 July 1970:

> 'She tells me that she spent four weeks in the [hospital] unit but absconded on 10th June and returned to London. She returned to taking drugs, in particular heroin, physeptone and barbiturates. She says she did not become registered again at the Drug Dependence Clinic as she had breached her probation and was afraid of being discovered. Her life seems to have been as disorganised as ever and she has again been using barbiturates intravenously with resultant

> abscesses. She has also taken accidental overdoses of barbiturates and was recently admitted to Charing Cross Hospital after falling down and striking her head whilst she was intoxicated from drugs. . . . She has no real interest in staying off drugs and in my view there is no suitable addiction unit to which I could refer her. She herself is not able to make any reasonable plans for the future. I do not feel that she can be successfully supervised on probation . . . I regret to have to say Ms Morris is really untreatable at present.'

Gillian spent a total of five months in custody during 1970. After being once again withdrawn in prison she was not allowed any drugs during the rest of her sentence. When she left prison she returned to the Clinic asking for her prescription of drugs to be resumed, for she had returned to drug use as soon as she was released. The doctor asked her what plans she had for the future, to which she replied 'I don't look to the future. I live just day by day.' A week later she was overdosing again and doing the rounds of casualty departments in the West End of London. She spent the next year or so attending her Clinic quite frequently, for some periods on a daily basis. Whenever her physical condition deteriorated she was required to collect her supply of drugs from the Clinic so that the medical staff could keep an eye on her. She also had several short admissions to hospital, primarily for barbiturate withdrawal and for treatment of her many abscesses.

During 1970 and 1971 her dependence on barbiturates grew. There was one occasion when she was found in the hospital grounds being injected with barbiturates by her boyfriend. The staff suspected that she was giving him her heroin and that together they were buying barbiturates for her to use. On several occasions whilst in hospital she refused to take her heroin pill in front of the nurses, compounding the suspicion of the medical staff.

At the beginning of 1972, Gillian's boyfriend, Robbie, died from an overdose. Although things had often been difficult between them there seems to be considerable evidence that while he was alive she relied heavily on him. There is one somewhat frantic letter, written during her friendship with Robbie, that indicates the extent to which she needed him.

> 'Dear Dr Allen,
> I am terribly sorry I missed you, but I have been very sick today I had to get in touch with Robbie. I was phoning him all day but I couldn't get hold of him until around 5 o'clock. He came around to where I'm staying and then he brought me to the hospital, I'm sorry I didn't phone the Clinic but I was a bit frightened to. I will come first thing in the morning.'

One friend observed that her life with Robbie was rather disorganized. 'They had different pads all over the place . . . never anything immaculate.' Of one particular place the friend remarked, 'It wasn't wonderful, they didn't have armchairs, there was a table, with eyedroppers and "cookers" – you know, the spoons – all that bit, and there was a bed.' Another friend described Robbie as a very well-known junkie. He was older than Gillian and had frequently been interviewed about his addiction. His picture had once appeared in the centre page of a Sunday newspaper, and the *News of the World* described him as 'King of the Junkies'. And as for Gillian? 'She was his girlfriend, she was the Queen . . . when she was Robbie's girl she was somebody' said a friend. When he died her life changed for the worse. Another friend said that she could remember meeting Gillian in the street just after Robbie died.

> 'It was very strange, she was very upset about Robbie dying. And then she had nowhere to stay. She asked me for some money to sleep. And then she was just generally out of her mind on barbs, I think, and she was in a real state. She just didn't have anywhere or anything, I mean, that was the impression I formed.'

### Coming off drugs: a nearly successful attempt

Soon after Robbie's death, in 1972, Gillian was arrested for non-payment of a taxi fare and for theft. She was remanded on bail for three weeks, on condition that she lived with her parents in the country. She appeared in court at the end of the month and was placed on probation for three years, again with a condition that she resided with her parents. Over the following few weeks she lived with them and agreed to gradually replace her heroin with methadone, starting with a reduction to 50 mgs of heroin daily. During her stay at home with her parents she wrote to Dr Allen.

> 'Dear Dr Allen,
> Just a few lines to let you know everything is okay. There is one thing however about my prescription, I've been on two heroin pills for four weeks now. I told Joe and the social worker to keep reducing my heroin as usual and put the physeptone up to replace the heroin and when I get to the end of the heroin, start reducing the physeptone the same as the heroin at two weekly intervals so when you send the next prescription you could alter it then after the Bank Holiday. Everything is going alright at home. I was twenty-seven on the 16th of this month. My mum bought me a cameo ring and my sister got me a lighter and some clothes. Well I will close now, hope to hear from you soon. Yours sincerely, Gillian Morris.'

In May, the Clinic social worker made the journey to visit Gillian at her parents' home. Despite the fact that things were apparently going quite well, with Gillian gradually reducing her heroin intake, there is a note of apprehension in the social worker's report.

> 'Gillian has now been living with her parents for eight weeks. They live in a fairly isolated area. They are, however, as Gillian remarked, only three quarters of an hour away from London by train. Gillian's grandfather and younger brother and sister also share the house. She did not appear to be discontented although she has very little to do apart from collecting her drugs every day. This takes her about one hour, leaving the house at 8.30 am every day. The rest of the day she spends around the house, helping her mother and walking the dogs. Her married sister and her two children live quite nearby, so she sees them quite often. She has also seen her ex-husband and her nine year old son while she has been there. Gillian is concerned about her drugs being cut, and admits to being "frightened" about her heroin being cut down – she wants to change to ampoules of methadone instead of linctus. Throughout the interview she was tense, anxious and trembling, and also quite ill at ease. She knows very few people around that area, most of the friends she did have, have married and moved away. Gillian talks as though she plans to stay there permanently, referring to next year's summer holiday with her parents, but I do not feel it is far from her mind to return to London where she is more at home. Her physical health is much improved – she has gained a considerable amount of weight. She has, however, an abscess on her hand from injecting, which has been treated by her GP. She is anxious that someone should visit her again after she loses all her heroin pills: about one month's time.'

She was still with her parents in the summer and seemingly contented. She wrote:

> 'Dear Dr Allen,
> Just a few lines to let you know how I am, everything seems okay right now. In two weeks time my parents are going to Spain for a fortnight, my brother and grandfather will be at home with me and a girlfriend is on holiday so we are going out days, I might go to a pop festival with my brother. At last we have some summer. I have been sunbathing and have got quite tanned, well gone red as a tomato, let's hope I turn brown. Concerning my script, at the moment I feel okay about it. Naturally the crucial point is yet to come; anyway all one can do is hope for the best. Well I will close now, hope to hear from you soon. Yours sincerely, Gillian Morris.'

Dr Allen remarked that the contrast between his patient in London and at home was extraordinary.

> 'Compared with *here* [the Clinic] – Gillian usually filthy, open sores on her ankles – *there*, it was all trees and chintz curtains and Gillian bringing in tea on the tray, and sitting in front of the window having afternoon tea, looking all neat and tidy and dressed up in a trouser suit, playing the hostess.'

By late summer Gillian had come off heroin and was using methadone. She then expressed fears about her parents going on holiday for two weeks, leaving her with her brother and grandfather. She asked the doctor for extra ampoules of methadone to cover the time her parents were away. They left for their holiday on 30 August and a few days later she and her brother bought two 50 pence tickets for a rock concert in London. She went home after the concert, but the following Monday she left again for London. According to the probation officer, Gillian and her grandfather 'couldn't get on'. In London, she took some heroin and barbiturates and was soon 'in a very bad state, drowsy, weepy'. The Clinic had her admitted to hospital, but she was discharged from the ward after one week because she was 'not behaving in an acceptable way and was under the influence of barbiturates and with multiple inflamed injection sites'. Three weeks later she told Dr Allen that she had no regrets about returning to heroin and to London – 'This is my life, I just want to live from day to day.' The chaos in her life returned, and four weeks later she was arrested on theft charges. She spent a few days in Phoenix House therapeutic community for assessment, but when she refused to join for a longer period the court sentenced her to six months' imprisonment.

### The last months

Gillian Morris saw in the 1973 New Year in Holloway Prison. Again she was withdrawn from drugs and we learn about her state of mind at the time from a number of letters she wrote to people at the Clinic. In one to the Sister, dated February 1973, she expressed doubts about her ability to stay off drugs.

> 'I was quite expecting "time" when I went to court because I refused Phoenix House. I was lucky though, I got six, six months all to run concurrent. I get out on the 15th February – roll on. Christmas wasn't too bad though, we had nice food, chocolates and fags and a present from the officers, talcum powder, soap and fags. When I get out the welfare worker here is trying to get me into a hostel, there is one in Hackney I'd like to get into but I don't know yet what I'm

> going to do. The object of the unit is to try and help us to think about staying off drugs when we get out but I really don't think I'll be able to make it and I really don't want to try and fool anybody by saying positively that I'm not going to take drugs because it's not that easy and also considering I'll only be here for about five and a half weeks and as Dr Allen always said I would be a compulsive drug addict, if I can get it I will take it.'

When she was released she managed to stay off drugs for only a few days, and after less than a month she was back at the Clinic. After this her life began to look rather like that of a chronic, skid-row alcoholic. In May 1973 she was sentenced to a one-year conditional discharge for 'violent behaviour'. In June she was arrested for loitering at Euston railway station and remanded at Holloway Prison. During that time she wrote again to Dr Allen.

> '19.7.73
> As you know, I am in Holloway again (all down to barbs). The reason I'm writing is to let you know what I want to do about this court case. I've been remanded for three weeks for medical and probation reports. I saw the Probation Officer today and he told me he would recommend probation, so I'm keeping my fingers crossed, but as I breached (my probation) in the past, it might be a bit dodgy. One good thing, my parents want me home. He also said from reading previous reports he thinks it will be very hard for me to stay off drugs. I think this and I know the court will too but if I want to get registered again it wouldn't make any difference to my probation order, if I want to leave home, as long as I contact the Probation Officer of my change of address it is okay.'

In August she was convicted for begging. In November she arrived at the Clinic with double layers of clothes and told the doctor that she was 'skippering' (sleeping rough). A week later she was arrested for obstruction, and fined a 'pound or a day'. Her hair was infested and she had black eyes from fights. She lived at various hostels and passed her time at day centres for homeless people. She was frequently intoxicated when she arrived at the Clinic. Eventually the case notes change from recording those occasions when she arrived stoned to recording those when she arrived 'sober'. Throughout this time she had abscesses and infections on her hands and feet. When she had few useful veins left in her arms and legs she started injecting in her umbilical vein. Many of the prescriptions that she received from the Clinic included antibiotics for infections. Over the years she had also sustained physical damage from fights and falls.

The last few months of her life were perhaps no different from the years preceding her death. But the frequency of overdoses increased and her life became more chaotic, with the Clinic staff feeling less optimistic that the process might be stopped. In the last two weeks of her life she was taken to casualty departments on at least eight occasions. It seems that there was a general agreement among the staff, which she shared, that she was bound to die if she continued to take drugs in the sort of quantities and in as disorganized and chaotic a way as she did. The doctors had discussed with her the possibility that she would kill herself and had made various therapeutic efforts. Given that it was not possible to place her under secure conditions to forcibly prevent her using drugs, what could any doctor have done? Dr Allen summed it up: 'There was a limit to how much pressure you could put on Gillian, you could put pressure on her in the sense of refusing to give her a prescription, or put pressure on that you would report all misdemeanours to the law or her Probation Officer.' The doctors recognized that these threats would have little effect. There was agreement that Gillian would be alive today if she had been in a secure hospital or a prison for a long period of time, but all pointed out the ethical problems of such action. One doctor who treated her still had colour photographs of her abscessed forearms in his office. He remarked 'everything was tried and nothing worked'. Despite this she was held in great affection by the staff of the Clinic. Dr Allen recalled: 'Everyone here spent hours with Gillian, either washing her sore ankles or putting plasters on them, or 'phoning people on her behalf, or trying to bring her round when she was a bit too far gone on barbiturates.' He remembered her affectionately:

> 'I can sort of picture her coming down the corridor, leaning slightly forward, holding a cup of coffee and spilling half of it as she came, perhaps a little bit slurred on barbiturates, and coming in a very friendly sort of way. She would never be aggressive. She would sometimes plead, in a sort of tongue in cheek way, to get a bigger prescription knowing full well she wouldn't get one. . . . Whereas you just didn't like a lot of chaotic people – they were unpleasant – Gillian was never unpleasant, she was never malicious, and there was something likeable about her the whole way through.'

One of Gillian's friends wrote to Dr Allen when he heard of her death. The following is an extract from the letter:

> 'I am writing to you about Gillian Morris. It was a great shock to me to hear that she was dead. I was told two weeks ago but couldn't accept it in my mind . . . Gillian and I were friends and I went to meet her outside the chemist on Monday and waited half an hour

before I was arrested and taken to the local police station. . . . I had looked after her a few days previously and had taken her to the Charing Cross Hospital where she stayed for part of the night. . . . I have had two friends now that have died of overdoses. Gillian was really kind to me in the 'Dilly. I had few friends and Gillian and I spent a lovely sunny afternoon sitting on a milk float in Shaftesbury Avenue. She always gave me strength to go and tried hard in her own way to help me as I was just as sick as her. I am trying to come off heroin and make do with a mild drug but I was really addicted to heroin. . . . I would like to come and visit her grave if you could send me the address.'

## *How Susan Hughes got off heroin*

For some people the decision to give up using heroin was extended over several months or years, accompanied by tentative attempts to reduce the dose and by gradual changes in life style. Others were precipitated into abstinence by a prison sentence. Still others, like Susan Hughes, made a relatively sudden decision and within a few weeks had managed to stop. We interviewed her in 1977, in the living room of her parents' house in Finchley, where she was staying for a short holiday. She was by then living abroad and had not used heroin since the winter of 1973/74.

### Turning on to heroin

Susan Hughes was born in 1949 and was brought up in North London. She had been a bright student at school, attending a Catholic convent to the age of ten and then a Jewish school where she stayed until she did her 'O' Level examinations. She was allowed to take these a year early, at fifteen, and it was hoped that she would stay on to take 'A' Levels. By this time she had come across people in North London who were using drugs and had first tried heroin at the age of fourteen. She was also becoming involved in the fringes of the emerging rock music scene, knowing members of several rock groups, and on one occasion dancing on 'Ready Steady Go', the television rock-and-roll show. With so much excitement around her she could not face the prospect of a further two years at school. She decided to study art instead and, in 1965, enrolled as a part-time evening student at an art college, thinking she would take 'A' Level art in this way. This did not avoid the problem of facing a two-year course though, and after a short while, Susan stopped attending the evening classes and got herself a job: 'I wanted the money then so I went to live in Hampstead, which is where it all started.'

She was by this time addicted to heroin – she said that she was addicted by the age of fifteen – and was very involved 'in the London drug scene' in the mid-1960s. Part of its attraction was the glamour and the excitement. Chasing around London looking for a doctor to prescribe heroin was an adventure in itself. Lots of other things happened too. During the first year of work she found herself pregnant. She decided to have the child, which was adopted soon after birth. She also found herself coming up against the law and was twice arrested and charged, once for theft of cheques and once for possession of drugs. She was helped by 'Release', which Caroline Coon had opened in 1967 to give legal advice on drugs charges. The first time she was given a conditional discharge, and on the second occasion was placed on probation for two years.

Like many other people who started using heroin in the 1960s, she sometimes received prescriptions from the handful of doctors in London who were willing to prescribe heroin. She recalled Dr Petro with mixed feelings:

> 'He was a treasure that man. He at one time was a very, very clever man. He was Alexander Fleming's pupil at the time Fleming discovered penicillin. In his more lucid moments he was very interesting to talk to. But then, you know, he'd made it on other people's misery to such an extent that you can't really forgive him for it. I feel he was responsible for an awful lot of deaths and unhappiness. If he didn't have enough money to go gambling he'd come down and say "Do you want to buy a script off me for ten bob", and he'd give you five and five [grains of heroin and cocaine] or whatever you wanted. The next day you went back to get another five and five and you'd find it was £5. At which point you sort of think "well, this guy is making money out of my miseries".'

### Attending the Clinic

Susan, like Gillian, was one of the first patients to attend the Clinics when they opened in 1968. She was then eighteen, and, like many addicts, suddenly found herself in the limelight. There was a lot of publicity about the new Clinics and journalists were looking for addicts to help them with their news stories. Susan Hughes' boyfriend was a television cameraman and, as we have seen (p. 83) Susan was used by a television company in a programme on the new Clinics.

She had been getting 480 mgs of heroin, 480 mgs of cocaine, and 200 mgs of methedrine a day from Dr Petro, but Dr Jackson at the Clinic in South London would not give her as much as this:

> 'He gave me six [grains] of heroin, six amps of methedrine, and six grains of cocaine a day. He automatically cut you down whatever you told him you were getting – he knocked a few off – which is fair enough because everybody told him they were using more than they got anyway. You see, you can have the spare to sell and at that time we had to pay for the prescriptions anyway.'

The Clinic doctor very soon cut out the cocaine altogether, and a few months later cut out the methedrine. Two years later, in 1970, Susan was down to 240 mgs of heroin, and then to 180 mgs, with 50 mgs of methadone and barbiturates.

At this time Susan was living in Shepherd's Bush with her boyfriend, Tony Bishop, who was also an addict in our study. They attended the same Clinic, where they were treated very much as a couple. Most of their time was spent with other addicts. Susan only worked occasionally, in part-time jobs, and made some money selling her paintings. Things stayed very much the same for the next three years.

> 'Nobody really encouraged me to get off. The doctor would say "Okay, we'll cut you down a pill this week" and fine, that was all right. I'd go back next week and he would say "How about another one?" I'd say "No, leave it at that". Every six weeks he would go "Come on, you're going to be reviewed – down another pill".'

Susan was as good as any other patient in finding reasons why her dose should not be reduced and in giving excuses for getting extra drugs from Dr Jackson.

> 'You keep stringing it out: you go back and say "I lost my script, give me another script. Somebody stole my script." And nobody can lie as well as junkies can lie. They will tell you everything under the book. Some of the things they say: "Oh, the dog ate it." The things you come up with. The doctors must have heard some of the most fantastic excuses: "Oh I'm going away for the weekend, can I have my script out three days early?" At first the doctor will write it, and then you go back two days early for your next one: "You can't have it." "Well, I'm going to die, you've got to give it to me." And rather than go through the aggravation they do prescribe. Looking back at it, I think it's a wonder he just didn't come up with a machine gun and shoot the lot of us.'

Like many others, Susan was not able to keep up the life of an addict without running into problems. By 1972 she was using barbiturates and recalled that she was making a 'rapid decline', that she was losing weight, that her teeth were rotten, and that she had not visited her family for six years.

> 'My hair was horrible. You know, I still wasn't in as bad a mess as the majority of them. I still maintain that I did look after myself better than most of the addicts did, because after a couple of years most people started to look terrible. I don't think I looked like a junkie until the very end – then I started to look terrible.'

### Changes

Around this time there was an incident that Susan thought was related to her decision to change her life. She was in the crowded Clinic waiting room one Friday morning when one of the other patients died 'in front of my eyes'. She remembered seeing lice crawling in the hair of the dead woman. But other things were happening too that, in retrospect, turned out to be important. In early 1973 Alec, who was not an addict, moved in to share the flat with Susan and her boyfriend Tony. She went out with Alec on a couple of occasions and then, within two weeks, Tony was arrested and remanded in Brixton Prison. She was left with Alec, who began to take Tony's place. Alec took a tough line on her addiction: 'He said "Why don't you get off? Look at yourself in the mirror, look at what a bloody mess you are, you're ruining yourself. You have enough brain to do something, you've got talent, why don't you use it?" And he just nagged me constantly.'

Susan considered that it was due to Alec that she really got off heroin. She thought that if she had stayed with Tony she would have remained addicted, as would Tony (he too came off heroin). She also knew that she was not getting younger, that 'I was going to end up dead or I was really going to end up looking like one of the really bad cases'. At that point she thought that she had been addicted for 'so many bloody years' that she should try a change.

> 'It was just absolute tiredness. Getting fed up with all the bullshit, with people selling you dope, and looking like a mess. And getting on the train – everybody would look at you. It was just absolute boredom and sheer pissed-offness I guess, it got to that point. I wasn't enjoying fixing any more. I didn't get anything out of it. I just had to have it to keep myself from going raving mad.'

Tony was sent to prison and spent the time in Wandsworth. He had looked after Susan and in a sense had facilitated her addiction, for example by collecting her prescriptions when she was too sick to move. Alec wouldn't do anything like that. He forced her to start leading a more regular life, beginning with basic things like making sure she ate proper meals.

### Coming off

So Susan was beginning to get bored with the life she was leading and it was, anyway, beginning to change under Alec's influence. Two months after meeting they married and took a spring-time honeymoon in South Wales. She took two weeks' supply of methadone pills and an ounce of cannabis with her. She told the Clinic doctor that she was going to stop:

> 'I knew I was going to. I didn't know it was going to be quite as bad as it was. I thought it was going to be pretty grim but you know, I suppose it was a masochistic trip really and I knew I had to do it then. . . . If you're on your own you have a chance of getting out of it. If you're mixing with them every day in the Clinic you stand no chance at all unless you've got fantastically strong willpower and mine wasn't that strong. I had to get away from them so Alec took me down to Wales, or I took him down to Wales. He left me by a beach and I was too sick to move . . . I was just in a sleeping-bag and it was bloody freezing. It was in April, it was just the week we got married. It was my honeymoon. I was in a sleeping-bag. I was so ill, I was screaming, of course nobody could hear me. It was very quiet down there. I was about ten miles from the nearest town. I couldn't have walked that ten miles to save my life, literally, I had to stay there.'

Alec gave her some drawing paper and pencils and said 'Now, draw yourself better' and left her there. She did some sketches whilst she was going through withdrawal and remembered the old castle up one side of the beach and the wild horses on the other side, and that it was a 'beautiful place to put somebody to get them off drugs'. She still had a drawing of the view from the cliff. Alec stayed in a camp-site three miles away and brought her food every day. She was stuck by the beach because she was too weak to climb the cliff to get back up. Finally, five days later, he helped her back and said 'I think you might just about be cured now.' At that point all she thought was 'Just give me a fix', for all she wanted was some heroin. Then she thought 'What's the point? You've gone through five days of hell now you might just be beginning to get better.'

This, then, was how Susan actually withdrew from opiates. She was by then twenty-four, and had been addicted for most of the previous nine years. From this time she was no longer dependent, though not all her problems were solved by one week in Wales. She and Alec returned to their Shepherd's Bush flat, in a house where there were a number of other people using heroin and methadone. She had been supplying some of them but no longer had a prescription. They started getting heroin from other people, and she would see them injecting or getting high and would feel 'Oh God, do I ever want a fix.' So tempted, she started to use heroin again. At first she injected only about once a week but this soon increased to twice weekly. She did however inject intramuscularly rather than intravenously. She wanted a prescription again and went back to the Clinic, asking to be taken on as a patient. Knowing her intentions, Alec had written a letter to Dr Jackson asking him not to prescribe because he thought that she could manage without. Dr Jackson complied with Alec's wishes.

### After heroin

Over the next eight months she injected less frequently. During this time she gradually switched to drinking and soon had drinking bouts that started on Friday and went through the whole weekend. She would buy a bottle of spirits, drink until she was drunk, then pass out. She would start again around the middle of the next day. The bouts were really determined by her financial situation. Usually she started on a Friday night because she had been paid – she had now started work.

> 'If you had £2 you could either buy a fix which would last you an hour, or you could buy a bottle of booze which would last you possibly twenty-four hours. And I'd say to myself "this is all the money you've got, what are you going to do?" And if somebody came round with a fix I'd sometimes buy that first and then afterwards I'd wish I hadn't so I used to try and tell myself "Go on, go out and buy the booze, it's better for you to buy the booze than to buy the fix". And then somebody would always have a bit of dope laying around, we smoked a lot. And that was really the way it worked.'

It was, as she said, 'a fight' to stay away from heroin whilst living in that house. Towards the end of that year, though, she and Alec had a stroke of good luck. Alec's parents, who lived abroad, wanted the young couple to join them and sent airline tickets so that they could both travel. They left England early in 1974. A few months later Susan managed to get a job in the civil service, a job she had held ever since. But her problems were not over as her drinking increased.

> 'I mean, there everybody drinks. They are an alcoholic nation. For the first six months, when I lived with Alec, we drank all the time. We broke up over drink – he got very drunk one night and broke my nose which didn't help so I left him and went off to live with some friends. This was about three months after we got there. I used to drink every night, every day.'

She would go to work, come home at night, and drink until about two o'clock in the morning. This was about a year after she had stopped using heroin. The heavy drinking went on for about six months. She did not get hangovers until one night 'I was so sick, I thought that I was going to die'. She went to a hospital and told the doctor that there was something wrong with her. He said, 'Yes you've got a hangover.' Since that time she had not drunk so much or so frequently. If she did drink to get drunk she felt ill. 'I'm so sick the next day. I don't know whether it's a flashback to anything but I just feel I'm dying. I can't drink too much now. It's great. It's a safety valve.'

### Present problems

When we met, Susan said she still drank, but not in the way she had previously. She took one or two drinks most evenings and about once a month went out and got drunk, but regretted it the next day.

She and Alec had separated amicably a few months after emigrating. Not long after he drowned when surfing. She continued in her job and had many friends, including a new boyfriend. She was still abroad and had not injected any drug since she left England in 1974. But it had not been easy in that time:

> 'It took me a hell of a time to get used to living a normal life again afterwards. I'd sit there and think "Oh God all I want is a fix" and this was up to a year afterwards. I'd sit there and think "I'd just love to feel a fix right there now". Well now it doesn't bother me so much. It doesn't bother me at all really. If I get depressed I don't think "God I'd love a fix". I think instead "Oh God I'd love a nice smoke, or I'd like a drink or something". I can go and get that and it's not harmful to me. If it's there, if somebody comes around with an ounce of pot and says "Roll yourself one", fine. It's not hurting me and it's not hurting them. I'm not tempted to go out and beat someone over the head or kill somebody. I'm not going to get in a car and be incapable of driving, whereas with alcohol, alcohol is dangerous and I only drink at home. If I'm drinking, I get drunk on my own. I'll sit in a corner and finish the bottle off and that's it. I'm not hurting anybody.'

It was her pride that helped prevent her returning to heroin, and her pride, she thought, that had helped her to get off in the first place. She still sometimes looked in the mirror and recalled what she had looked like. She told herself that if she went back on heroin, she would look terrible within a couple of weeks.

> 'I wouldn't want to spoil what I've got now and go back to having to sleep on bomb-sites and in doorways and go to Piccadilly and talk to

those people who smell a bit funny, and they look a bit dirty, and they've got things crawling in their hair. I felt that I could take on the world when I first got off. After a couple of years I was so proud of actually getting that far. I thought well I can do anything now. If I can beat that monkey, I can beat anything.'

There were other problems, as well as alcohol, that had continually to be faced. She occasionally ran into people who suspected that she once was an addict. She was an attractive person with shoulder-length hair, well-built, very chirpy and vivacious, wearing jeans and short-sleeved T-shirts. The old injection track-marks were just visible on her arms. When she went abroad she wore long sleeves but it became too hot in the summer to do this comfortably. She no longer let her track-marks worry her though, and did not try to hide them, having learnt how to handle people's inquisitive remarks.

'When I first went to work somebody said to me "What are those marks?" I said "What do you think they are?" He said "Were you a junkie?" I said "Yes, so what are you going to do about it. Mind your own business". Sometimes I'll say that I was fed intravenously for ten years. I think it's ignorant to point it out. If it's one of my contemporaries it's fair enough because they obviously know. But when one of the old men comes up and says "What are those marks on your arms?" it's just being bloody nosey. Well at that point I'll say "Why don't you fuck off".'

How did she view those nine years of addiction?

'I feel that I've missed the best years of my life. But then I don't regret it. It's strange, to me it was all experience, I could never be that low again. Looking back and thinking to myself, "God, you let yourself get right down there". I regret I spent so many years. If it had been two or three it would have been different. But it was nine odd years. That's what really does it to me, but then I found when I got off I hadn't aged as much as I thought I was going to . . . I found that people said to me "How old are you – twenty-three?" I'll be thirty next year. I thought, my God, if these ten years catch up with me I'm going to look like I'm forty when I'm only thirty. But it didn't seem to work quite that way. I don't feel I'm as old as I am. I have two of my younger sisters – one of them, she's married with two kids and to me she's about forty to look at and the way she acts. I think – I could have been like that. I'm glad I'm not. I'm glad I had the experience. I think it teaches you a lot about other people, what you're prepared to do, how society looks at you, and now I tend to look down at people a bit myself.'

She had gradually re-established contact with her family and was staying with them on holiday when we talked to her. For six years she had had little contact with them except through her probation officer who occasionally telephoned her mother to say that Susan was still alive. When she was addicted she was too ashamed to go home. She had younger sisters and knew she looked 'pretty dreadful' when addicted, and that when, at earlier times, she had occasionally gone home there had been problems. She recalled that her sisters would say 'Why isn't Susan at home yet?'; 'Why does she come in and go to sleep on the sofa?'; 'Why does she look so bad?'; 'Why has she got those funny marks on her arms?'

When she stopped using heroin she realized how distant she was from her family and wanted to return to see her parents and sisters. Her mother had had her fifth child and Susan had not even known of the pregnancy. Being addicted had been fun and romantic but had resulted in ignoring her family. She felt that she had since gained her independence and that her mother and father could now respect her. She thought she had to make amends for the problems she caused them when she was on drugs.

> 'It was a guilt trip, it's getting over a guilt trip and it's still there. I'm still trying to get over the guilt trip because I felt very guilty. I used to have very bad nightmares that my mother and father would catch me fixing in shop corners or that I'd be on the underground having a fix and trying not to let anybody see and then they'd come up and pass me, and that used to really worry me. Now I can come home and know that I'm in perfectly good physical health and that I can look after myself.'

However, those days were rarely discussed between Susan and her family. Her father never mentioned them. One of her sisters did and made jokes about them. Her mother told us that they still frightened her. Susan went on at length about her feelings of guilt.

> 'I didn't live at home the whole time I was on drugs because I couldn't bear to see them looking at me and knowing what I was doing to them. Now I can come home, I can go swimming, I can play with the kids and not feel guilty. I now feel that I don't have to hide myself from them. I'm probably doing it with too much of a guilt feeling but that's something you can't help. I feel that I want to give them things all the time to prove that I can now look after myself. I feel that I want their approval. Yet it never bothered me before. Now I want them to tell me what they think, that I'm doing well. That makes me feel better.'

# Part Three
# *Future prospects*

# 11

# *Treatment and policies in the 1980s*

The British 'system' for the treatment of addiction is a loose collection of ideas, policies, institutions, and activities. There is a legal framework within which Clinic doctors and other staff work, but the translation of this into day-to-day practice leaves considerable room for individual initiative and interpretation. This reflects a position of compromise between the various parties involved – government, civil servants, and doctors – and also the strength of the medical profession's claims to clinical freedom. There have been few overt guidelines or policy directives from the DHSS or Home Office designed to help in the interpretation of the legislation or indicating the ways in which the Clinics could or should be run. In this respect the British 'system' is unlike the methadone maintenance programmes in the USA, which are tightly controlled by licensing regulations specifying choice of drug, form of treatment, and dosage to be prescribed. In the UK such matters are left to the discretion of individual clinicians.

This loose policy has allowed considerable flexibility in response to the problem of drug dependence. However, it makes it difficult to answer the question 'Does the policy work?' because, with various aims and approaches accommodated within the 'system', it is difficult to specify what it is that is meant to be 'working'. In the Clinics we find different treatment approaches and, inevitably, treatment policies that have changed considerably since the Clinics were first established back in 1968. If people from other countries look to Britain for advice in dealing with their own problems of drug use then they should be advised that the first question should not be 'does the British "system" work?' but 'what do you want a drug policy to achieve?'

As we have already described, the Clinics were established in a political atmosphere that called for control over addicts and doctors. It was hoped that over-prescribing would be curbed once specially licensed doctors, working mainly within the NHS, took on the task of treating addicts. Implicit was the idea that 'competitive prescribing' would undercut and diminish the black market. So one aim of the policy was the social control of the drug problem. But there was a second aim, proposed by clinicians rather than civil servants: to continue to treat addicts. But even among the clinicians there were disagreements as to what treatment meant. Was the aim to maintain people on opiates or to help them towards abstinence? The conflict between social control and treatment, and the various views on treatment, were nothing new. Such disputes can be found in the debates about the nature of addiction since the end of the last century.

### THE CLINICS AND DRUG CONTROL

Can the British approach be considered successful in controlling the drug problem? At the beginning the policy embodied in the 1967 legislation seemed to be succeeding, for supplies of heroin derived from overspill prescriptions became scarcer and black-market prices rose. But the following decade saw considerable changes in the pattern of illegal drug use in the country and in the type and availability of drugs on the black market. Worldwide political changes have resulted in Third World heroin – from the Golden Triangle in South-East Asia and, more recently, from the Middle East – reaching the London market at prices that are as low, relatively, as those in the 1960s.

Press reports echo those of the 1960s in pointing to the problems of drug addiction. Interviews with addicts in Subway 4 at Piccadilly Circus underground station still make newsworthy stories. 'It started simply with pot. But before long Annabel was hooked into running heroin for the Triads. God knows how it will end, but it will be nasty' was the heading for a *Guardian* report on the 'hard drug scene' (10 March 1977). The *Sun* ran a similar report on 'Britain's junkie jungle' – 'an evil trade in death – and it's going on right here on your doorstep' (12 April 1977). And there are reports on private doctors who prescribe for addicts, similar to the press reports on the junkies' doctors of the 1960s. 'Mayfair doctor, aged 76, faces probe on drugs' reported the *Evening Standard* (13 July 1979), after a journalist's investigation into the prescribing of Diconal for addicts.

There is agreement between police, customs officers, doctors, voluntary agency workers, Home Office and Department of Health officials, and researchers that in the last ten years the extent of opiate addiction has increased. The main public source of data continues to be the Home Office reports on the number of known addicts. These statistics are compiled from doctors' notifications. It has been a statutory obligation since 1968 for all doctors to notify the Home Office of any person whom they consider to be addicted to a drug appearing on a list of mainly opiates (cocaine, dextromoramide, diamorphine (heroin), dipipanone, hydrocodone, hydromorphone, levorphanol, methadone, morphine, opium, oxycodone, pethidine, phenazocine, piritramide). People who use opiates but are not considered addicted are not counted when the statistics for addiction are compiled (though they may go into a Home Office file of 'suspects'). Addicts who do not come into contact with doctors will not be counted because, obviously, they are not notified and, in addition, there are undoubtedly doctors who see addicts but who for one reason or another do not notify the Home Office. The statistics are probably 'best' for those addicts who come into contact with Clinics or with doctors in the legal and penal system. These various limitations to the Home Office data are acknowledged by the Home Office and others (Johnson 1975; Institute for the Study of Drug Dependence 1980). The data are, however, commonly used as indicators of trends of the absolute extent of addiction.

We have previously given the statistics on the addicts known to the Home Office from 1935 through to 1968, up to which date notification was not statutory (*see Table 2(2)*, p. 36). What have been the trends since then? As will be seen in *Table 11(1)*, there has been a steady increase since 1969 in the number of addicts known to the Home Office and, as there is no reason to think that the notification system has become more efficient in recent years, this trend is generally taken to indicate an underlying increase in addiction. The first line of *Table 11(1)* gives the *number of addicts known to be receiving drugs* at the beginning of each year and the tenth line gives the number known to be receiving drugs at the year's end. From 1969 to 1980 the total number receiving drugs had doubled. Those 'known to be receiving drugs' were those in receipt of opiate prescriptions. This included patients at Clinics, as well as some who received prescriptions for opiates other than heroin and cocaine from other doctors. Line 5 gives the *total number notified in any one year*. In 1980 this totalled 5116, although the year's end total for those receiving drugs was 2849. Therefore, even accepting the limitations of the data, we can see that there was a considerable number of people who were known to be addicted but who were outside treatment services in any one year. It will also be seen (line 4) that since 1969 the number of *new notifications* had risen, and was usually almost as large as the beginning of year total. For example, in 1980, 2669 addicts were known at the beginning of the year, and there were a further 2447 new notifications that year. Of the new notifications, two-thirds (1606) were previously unknown to the Home Office.

Table 11(1) *Narcotic drug addicts known to the Home Office, UK, 1969–80*

| | *1969** | *1970* | *1971* | *1972* | *1973* | *1974* | *1975* | *1976* | *1977* | *1978* | *1979* | *1980* |
|---|---|---|---|---|---|---|---|---|---|---|---|---|
| 1 addicts known to be receiving drugs at 1 Jan. (= line 10 of previous year) | | 1462 | 1426 | 1549 | 1617 | 1816 | 1967 | 1949 | 1874 | 2016 | 2402 | 2669 |
| persons notified during the year by medical practitioners: | | | | | | | | | | | | |
| 2 not previously known | | 711 | 774 | 800 | 807 | 870 | 922 | 984 | 1109 | 1347 | 1614 | 1606 |
| 3 known in earlier years | | 484 | 562 | 587 | 599 | 566 | 536 | 541 | 622 | 753 | 778 | 841 |
| 4 total notified during year (= lines 2 + 3) | | 1195 | 1336 | 1387 | 1406 | 1436 | 1458 | 1525 | 1731 | 2100 | 2392 | 2447 |

| | | | | | | | | | | | | |
|---|---|---|---|---|---|---|---|---|---|---|---|---|
| 5 total number of addicts notified (= lines 1 + 4) | 2881 | 2657 | 2762 | 2936 | 3023 | 3252 | 3425 | 3474 | 3605 | 4116 | 4794 | 5116 |
| persons no longer notified as addicts at 31 Dec.: | | | | | | | | | | | | |
| 6 removed by reason of death | | 74 | 58 | 65 | 61 | 77 | 68 | 63 | 40 | 60 | 50 | 73 |
| 7 admitted to penal or other institution | | 1157 | 1155 | 1254 | 438 | 388 | 484 | 513 | 442 | 484 | 553 | 431 |
| 8 no longer seeking treatment | | | | | 708 | 820 | 924 | 1024 | 1107 | 1170 | 1522 | 1763 |
| 9 total no longer recorded (= lines 6 + 7 + 8) | | 1231 | 1213 | 1319 | 1207 | 1285 | 1476 | 1600 | 1589 | 1714 | 2125 | 2267 |
| 10 addicts known to be receiving drugs as at 31 Dec. (= lines 5 − 9) | 1462 | 1426 | 1549 | 1617 | 1816 | 1967 | 1949 | 1874 | 2016 | 2402 | 2669 | 2849 |

*Note:* *For 1969 only the total number of addicts notified and the year-end total is given by the Home Office. Figures for years prior to 1969 are given in *Table 2(2)*, p. 36. The notification system was changed in 1968, making it obligatory for doctors to notify addicts. The year totals given in *Table 2(2)* are roughly comparable with line five of the above table.

*Sources:* Home Office Statistical Bulletin (1981); Judson (1974); Institute for the Study of Drug Dependence (1980).

Whichever measure is taken – the total number of addicts known to be receiving drugs, the total number of addicts notified in any year, or the total number of entirely new notifications in any year – the trend is the same, showing a gradual increase in the number of notified addicts since 1969. But what can one deduce from the numbers in *Table 11(1)* about the extent of addiction? The Home Office data reflect the system for collecting the data as well as the extent of the problem that they are taken to represent. There are perennial attempts by Home Office civil servants, voluntary agency and Clinic workers to estimate how many addicts there 'really' are. It is, of course, crucial for policy-makers to estimate the real extent of the problem, especially when the distribution of scarce resources is at stake. Apart from the practical problems of trying to arrive at some census of drug addicts, there are considerable definitional problems. The notification system provides legal definitions of who is to count as an addict, but it is likely that people use various methods of estimating how many addicts there 'really' are. Observers usually end up by guessing that the real extent of addiction can be arrived at by multiplying the Home Office data. For example, a senior Home Office Drugs Branch official thought that there were roughly three times as many addicts as the Home Office figures reported, and Patrick Jenkin, Secretary of State at the DHSS, estimated the total number of narcotics addicts at 10,000 (twice the number of notified addicts) with a further 10,000 using barbiturates (*Drug Link* 1980b).

Home Office statistics on seizures of drugs by the police and customs indicate that Britain now has a sizeable black market in heroin (and other drugs). Back in 1968 there was virtually no trade in illegally imported heroin. The first major seizure of smuggled heroin came in 1971 when 1.14 kgs were confiscated by the authorities. The following year heroin seizures amounted to over 13 kgs, including a single seizure by the customs of over 7 kgs from Hong Kong. Seizures have continued to increase and reached a maximum of over 60 kgs in 1978. Since then they have dropped somewhat, declining to 45 kgs in 1979. However, this is still a massive amount compared with the insignificant seizures in 1968 (Ashton 1981). By the late 1970s the main source was Iran. *The Sunday Times* (24 February 1980) quoted a Home Office official, saying that 'Britain has entered the international big league in heroin. Last year the customs police recorded a 260 per cent increase in the amount of material entering the country. That was exceptional, but there is no doubt that we are in the first division.' The article went on to say that what worried the authorities was that Britain, once a transit point for heroin on its way from the Far East to other parts of Europe and the USA, had now become a market itself. Police sources believed that the heroin was brought into the country largely by middle-class Iranians using heroin as a means of transferring their wealth from a politically troubled Iran. In April 1980 William Whitelaw, the Home Secretary, reported in a written answer in the House of Commons that seventy-one Iranian nationals had been convicted of, or apprehended at port of entry, for offences involving heroin in 1977, 1978, and 1979 (SCODA 1980).

The availability of heroin is also demonstrated in street prices. The Institute for the Study of Drug Dependence has calculated that illicit imported heroin of 20–80 per cent purity 'retailed' for £40 to £80 per gram in 1975 and that with inflation the price would have been £65 to £103 per gram in 1979. But in that year official sources recorded the price of 20–100 per cent pure heroin as ranging from £50 to £100 per gram. Given the higher average purity of the Middle-Eastern heroin on the British market in 1979, the effective price drop is greater than the overall prices suggest (Ashton 1981).

What does this evidence tell us about the success or otherwise of the British 'system' in controlling addiction? It is clear that the 'system' has not stopped the spread of addiction and that hopes that the Clinics would contain the extent of addiction have not been fulfilled. However, a more generous interpretation might be to argue that the numbers of known addicts are not large in comparison with those of the US and many Western European countries, and that the 'system', although not controlling the problem, has resulted in a slower spread of addiction than there might otherwise have been.

## THE CLINICS AND TREATMENT

Have the Clinics been successful in treating addicts? We can look at this question with the aid of the data collected from our ten-year follow-up. We have seen what happened to one group of addicts who came to the Clinics when they first opened. They may, of course, have been different from addicts who came into treatment later in different historical circumstances, but this, of course, could only be determined by follow-up of other cohorts. What happened to the addicts in our study from 1969 through to 1979? The results are summarized in the Appendix (*Table A(3)*), though we shall consider them in some detail now.

We found that, by 1979, 15 per cent had died. Perhaps this level of deaths is much lower than either the addicts or the doctors might have foreseen ten years ago. But it could be considered a high death rate for a young population under medical treatment. All died from causes related to their drug use.

A majority of the survivors, 47 per cent, were no longer attending Clinics. If we exclude those who were in prison, we would estimate on the basis of the evidence collected that *38 per cent of the original sample were abstinent from opiates ten years on.* The evidence is that their abstinence was successful and that they did not have problems with other drugs. We found that on the whole those who were abstinent had few problems with their lives; in most respects they were ordinary people leading ordinary lives. We consider that this figure of nearly 40 per cent successfully abstinent will surprise many people. It is certainly a much more optimistic result than many would expect. For whatever reasons, and by whatever routes, these people managed to stop their addiction, and it can now be shown with certainty that a substantial proportion of opiate addicts do manage to successfully stop using drugs. Opiate addiction, then, is not irredeemable.

There were 38 per cent still attending Clinics after ten years (a group similar in size to those who were abstinent). Some, but by no means all, did not have major problems with their addiction and many (30 per cent of the sample) had received prescriptions for opiates without interruption for ten years.

The interpretation of these results depends on what one expects of treatment: that it should supply a cure, aiming to free addicts from addiction, or be a measure helping addicts to lead a reasonably normal life on drugs. On the one hand there is reason for optimism because after ten years 38 per cent were alive and abstinent. As this sample was representative of patients receiving heroin at London Clinics we can generalize the result to predict that around 40 per cent of all patients who received heroin at London Clinics in 1969 are now likely to be abstinent. This rate compares favourably with success rates for other psychological and addiction problems. What we cannot tell from our study is how far this rate is attributable to therapy and the efforts of Clinic staff.

On the other hand, as a similar-sized group failed to become abstinent this may suggest a gloomy outcome from a treatment point of view, if abstinence is the aim. The implication of this statistic is that, if similar results are to be expected for successive intakes, nearly 40 per cent of patients taken on in any one year will still be patients ten years later, suggesting growing case-loads. This has significant consequences for planning the scale and content of treatment. However, if one conceded that abstinence cannot be expected of all patients and that there is room for maintenance treatment, then we need not necessarily take this group as indicative of treatment failure, but would rather look for evidence of how they led their lives. As we show in the Appendix (pp. 245–51), and as we have argued elsewhere in this book, despite drug use some of those who continued to be addicted for many years evidenced few problems.

### AT THE CLINICS 1980–81

We revisited Clinics in the winter of 1980/81. We went to nine of the

London Clinics and spoke to doctors, nurses, and social workers, asking them to look back over the last dozen years and to tell us about the current problems facing them. We enquired about how their treatment aims had changed and developed, and asked them to speculate about the future of work in this area of medicine. We also talked with people at the Home Office Drugs Branch, the Metropolitan Police Drugs Squad, the Institute for the Study of Drug Dependence, and members of the Standing Conference on Drug Abuse.

Statistics from the Department of Health show the average annual number of out-patients attending drug Clinics in London to have risen from 830 in 1971 to 1023 in 1978, an increase of 23 per cent, with similar rises elsewhere in Britain (*see Table 6(1)*, p. 94). In talks with Clinic staff, there seemed to be general agreement that the length of time between people becoming opiate dependent and appearing at the Clinics had not changed substantially over the past ten years – impressions confirmed by the Home Office statistics on known addicts. A picture emerged that showed current newcomers to Clinics to be in their mid- to late twenties and to have, generally, been using opiates regularly for two to three years or more. Home Office statistics show that current known addicts are on average older than those of ten years ago. The most frequent ages of known addicts in 1979 were twenty-five to thirty-one, accounting for 51 per cent of the total; nine years before, in 1970, the ages nineteen to twenty-four accounted for 51 per cent of the total. Addicts aged thirty or over in 1979 accounted for 43 per cent of the total compared with 28 per cent in 1970 (Home Office 1981).

The Clinics were established to cope with opiate-dependent patients and, on the whole, people who were not dependent on opiates were not accepted for treatment. There were exceptions, and some had tried to develop special facilities for non-opiate users, but such efforts had not always been successful, perhaps because many non-opiate users arrived under the impression that they would be prescribed drugs, and when this did not happen, ceased to attend.

The Clinics may not have altered much in the last decade in respect of the types of patients taken on, but there were other discernible changes. There was, by 1980/81, more of a sense of order and calm about them. It seemed that fights and arguments in waiting and consulting rooms were more rare. The 'fixing' rooms, which saw many of the dramas of broken syringes, broken and lost ampoules, and the surreptitious exchange of drugs, had disappeared. Staff had succeeded in creating a sense of order in their work, to a large extent by the successful enforcement of rules. A psychiatrist put it this way: 'Rules are essential, although this is against one of the basic tenets of medicine. They are necessary in the drug field, one needs to be able to say "I can't do this because this is the rule".'

There had also been a refinement of the decision about the initial dose to prescribe. Long gone were the days when the doctors decided on the first dose by halving the patient's request. Some Clinics had introduced unilateral policies regarding doses, for example, they prescribed a set amount of methadone, such as 40 mgs, to all new patients. In other Clinics the amounts were more negotiable, but still often within limits; for example, one had a maximum ceiling for new patients of 80 mgs of methadone. In 1977 the average daily dose of methadone for patients attending NHS hospitals was 62 mgs (Ashton 1981). Most new patients were prescribed oral methadone only, a policy change that we discuss below. It is worth noting how small these doses are in comparison with the early days at the Clinics when it was not uncommon for new patients to receive doses of several hundred milligrams of heroin.

One doctor's methods for assessing the minimum dose required by a new patient were indicative of the changes that had occurred. She described the procedure:

> 'They come after a fast of drugs of a minimum of 12 hours. I then dose them with methadone mixture in 10 mg steps, and they remain here for half a day . . . I dose them to get some idea of how much they can take. Out of the people I have dosed, I had sixty, there were four who were not dependent at all physically and had very adverse effects from a 10 mg dose. . . . The others were divided into "low" and "high" dose people, but there is something extremely odd about tolerance – there isn't any sharp measuring point. I try to make prescriptions individual, and as a result we have some low dose people on 20 to 40 mgs, but I think we could go on dosing them to very high dosages – because I am sure that people can take a lot more than they need. You can't tell until you have tested who will turn out to be a high or low dose.'

Such interests in elaborate assessment are often tied to consultants' views as to the nature of addiction. This doctor felt that hopes for the future treatment of addiction lay in understanding the biochemical structure of the brain and in studying physiological processes. Another consultant, by contrast, argued that such elaborate assessment procedures were unnecessary because he saw addiction not as a pharmacological problem but as a social and psychological one. Consequently, offering an addict a nominal dose of drugs would be sufficient basis for beginning a therapeutic relationship. Some doctors still agreed to give new patients injectable drugs for a short period of time, with the provision that the patient subsequently accepts the notion of abstinence. One argument in support of this approach is that short-term prescribing of injectable drugs is a way of attracting patients to treatment and keeping them interested for a sufficient time during which a therapeutic relationship can be established.

In line with the trend to formalize initial treatment there had also been a formalization of the treatment plan, instituted in some Clinics as a treatment 'contract'. The contract, which may or may not be written, is an outline of the treatment aims and plans, giving the proposed time schedule for the patient *en route* to total abstinence from opiates. The contract is an expression of a new treatment goal. The notion of long-term maintenance had been abandoned in these Clinics, and patients were, and still are, accepted for treatment on the assumption of their being willing to become abstinent. New patients were generally seen quite frequently, maybe once a week, and therapeutic endeavour was certainly maximized at the beginning of a contract. If a patient failed to achieve abstinence within the specified time the contract was open to re-negotiation. This formalization of the treatment plan was based on psychological theories of learning and behaviour modification in which it is reasoned that repeated injection simply reinforces addiction and, therefore, maintained patients are unlikely to be motivated to change. In addition to the therapeutic rationale, a contract had an obvious advantage for staff: it gave less room for argument, bargaining, and negotiation which earlier characterized the consultation. It was one response to the problem of how to treat new patients when the old 'dinosaurs' fill the Clinic case-load. Contracts for specified time periods lessen the chances of the long-term burden of maintained patients.

New treatments may be born out of pragmatism as much as reasoned plans. For example, one argument given for group therapy was that a lack of clinical time and scarce facilities were making the provision of individual treatment very difficult. 'We just can't see them individually', said one nurse. 'There are eight people in a group and you see them for an hour. It's a weekly group and you can see eight at a time and you have two workers to a group.' But there was also a treatment rationale: 'we are much more confronting now, we say "what are you going to do with your life?" The drug is a minor thing and we are willing to help sort out your life.'

### CONCEPTUAL CHANGES AT THE CLINICS: FROM MAINTENANCE TO CONFRONTATION

One consultant summed up his ten years' experience by saying that 'We are doing much the same as we did in 1968, only better'. This view from the inside conceals some distinctive changes in the way in which staff saw their work. We have already indicated that there had been reforms in treatment practice; behind these were some significant conceptual changes.

As already discussed, a major consequence of the policy formulations of the late 1960s was the inherent contradiction for Clinic workers between control and treatment. In the first few years, the task of controlling the drug problem came to overshadow the task of treatment. In the mid-1970s there was a growing sense of frustration at the Clinics. Those engaged in treatment began to ask themselves to what end they were offering addicts prescriptions for opiates. Staff viewed their vocation as a therapeutic one, and only reluctantly abandoned notions of treating people. They resented having to act like 'policemen with white coats on', as one junior doctor put it. Many had, by 1976, come to argue that there was a conflict between social control and treatment. For example, many doctors saw that for controlling the drug problem a maintenance policy might be best because it attracted patients to Clinics and provided them with drugs. But maintenance conflicted with therapeutic ideals, for patients who were maintained, it was argued, were not changing, and were not being cured of their addiction. Maintenance maintained the *status quo*. A handout from one Clinic, given to visitors in 1976, outlined this problem:

> 'We feel that while the policy is reasonably satisfactory from the viewpoint of society, there is doubt as to whether a legitimate prescription for injectable drugs is in the long term interests of the individual patient. Our observations suggest that while such a prescription alleviates the immediate problem of obtaining drugs it reduces the motivation and energy needed to change the individual's situation and he frequently resumes illegal drug use in addition to his prescription after a period of some months. It might be argued that regular increases in the maintenance prescription would prevent such relapses into illegal drug use but we believe this would be at the cost of further reducing the individual's ability to cope constructively with his psycho-social problems.'

Increasingly, staff thought that although prescribing heroin and other injectable drugs had been a reasonable course of action in the late 1960s and early 1970s it was no longer relevant. Doctors started to question their own motives and the historical heritage that they had hitherto accepted. One consultant remarked:

> 'In the early days we were primarily prescribing Clinics and we were set up to clear up the mess of the late 1960s. We were told: "You will prescribe" but as the years have gone by I began to think that prescribing is of lesser and lesser importance. . . . We have maintained by default. Ten years on we have people maintained, but they are created by me and people like me in other Clinics. They nearly all have been getting drugs on tap from the Clinics longer than they were even getting them before they came to the Clinics. I certainly don't want that to continue. It seems pointless.'

A doctor at another Clinic similarly expressed concern about the therapeutic pessimism of maintenance:

> 'I hate admitting that anybody's being maintained because I think that if one openly declares that you're running a maintenance programme for anybody then it's so easy just to stop talking to them, and stop caring about people and stop helping them over crises and stop doing any supportive case-work, it's so easy just to opt out of that and say "well there's your ration book, show your face every couple of weeks, and if you're not dead you carry on drawing it".'

Another consultant turned to the same theme. Simply prescribing to addicts was the easiest and in some ways the cheapest response, but was it justifiable?

> 'We should help our patients with more rigour and with greater energy for the morale of patients, staff, and society. . . . If one doesn't one is committing someone to life with something he is abusing and it's really substituting the black market with prescribed drugs. I don't call that maintenance, I call that a non-intelligent response.'

Staff also argued that containing addiction by judicious prescribing was not practical. First, by the mid-1970s it had become apparent that prescribing could not undercut the black market. It may have been, as some have argued, that legal prescriptions for opiates delayed the advent of a large-scale, organized black market, but in the long run it was not to be stopped. Prescribing was in any case always limited to the opiates, and these were only some of the drugs that were used. Second, Clinic doctors argued that controlling addiction was not an appropriate role for them, and ought to be left to legislators and law enforcers. Third, there was the practical issue, as one doctor said, of how to maintain people on injectable drugs when eventually they have no veins left into which to inject.

Meanwhile, some Clinics were beginning enquiries into their work. By the mid-1970s one or two had tried to institute a non-injectable policy, in other words, prescribing only oral methadone for their new patients. In the midst of this questioning appeared the results of a study that compared the effects of prescribing heroin against prescribing oral methadone. The study was conducted at University College Hospital Drug Dependency Clinic between 1972 and 1976 (Mitcheson and Hartnoll 1978; Hartnoll *et al.* 1980). It was designed to compare two groups of patients who approached the Clinic seeking heroin prescriptions. These, in clinical terms, qualified for and were randomly assigned to a treatment of either injectable heroin or oral methadone. The findings indicated that at twelve months those who were given prescriptions for heroin were more likely to have continued in treatment, whilst those who were offered methadone were highly likely to have ceased contact. At twelve months, 74 per cent of those who received heroin were still patients, but only 29 per cent of those who were offered methadone were still in attendance. The methadone group were also more likely than the heroin group to have discontinued regular opiate use.

The authors summed up their findings saying that 'the provision of heroin maintenance may be seen as maintaining the *status quo*, although ameliorating the problems of acquiring drugs' (Hartnoll *et al.* 1980: 882). 'By contrast', they concluded, 'refusal to prescribe heroin (and offering oral methadone instead) may be seen as a more active policy of confrontation that is associated with greater change' (Hartnoll *et al.* 1980: 883). They showed that refusal to prescribe heroin was associated with a considerably higher abstinence rate, but at the expense of an increased arrest rate and a higher level of illicit drug involvement and criminal activity among those who did not become abstinent. There were no differences between the two groups in terms of non-opiate use, employment, or health. Then they came back to the problem that had been a central issue all along. As the authors pointed out:

> 'The long-term implication of this approach [prescribing oral methadone] is that although it is more "therapeutic" in terms of discouraging continued drug use, it also leaves a group of heavily drug-involved people outside of clinical "control". This prospect might be considered undesirable to society, both because of the criminal activities of this group and because they form the basis of a potentially expanding illicit drug subculture. . . .
>
> In relation to policy in the United Kingdom, the results do not provide strong evidence that entirely justifies continuing the policy of maintaining addicts with injectable drugs, nor do they show that present policies are a clear failure in terms of the British drug situation. The differences between the two groups, although often statistically significant, are not startling. . . . The results do suggest that there is a conflict between a policy that would maximise the numbers who achieve abstinence and a policy that would maintain greater surveillance over a higher number of drug users and ameliorate their total preoccupation with illicit drug use and criminal activity.'
>
> (Hartnoll *et al.* 1980: 883)

The caution expressed in the published results was not paralleled in the reception the research received. Most of those we spoke to had not read the particulars of the study, nor did they know much of the finer detail of the results. However, they knew of the study and had taken it to show that it was more therapeutic and 'confrontational' to offer oral methadone than injectable heroin, which served to 'maintain the *status quo*'. It seems to us that to some extent, as so often happens in medicine and more generally in science, it did not matter to clinicians what the precise results were. What concerned them more, as several consultants indicated, was that here was scientific justification for a policy change that was already emerging from the work context.

So during the mid-1970s the clinicians' views became reoriented towards therapy. The switch to prescribing only oral methadone to new patients, initiated in a few Clinics in the early 1970s and in the majority from around 1975/76, was seen by doctors as a step in a therapeutic direction. The change can be seen in the increase of methadone linctus and tablets prescribed since 1976 and the corresponding decrease in prescriptions for methadone ampoules (*see Table 6(2)*, p. 100). Quantities of prescribed methadone linctus and tablets exceeded ampoules in 1978. We are told that there are now only three London Clinics that will consider prescribing injectable drugs to new patients. This is a major change since 1968, when between 60 and 80 per cent of patients were prescribed heroin (*see Table 6(3)*, p. 102). In 1980 only 7 per cent of patients were receiving heroin (Home Office 1981) and we may surmise that most of these were older patients.

This shift in policy gave many staff a renewed sense of hope and purpose. Combined with a therapeutic contract it seemed a fruitful approach. New patients, to paraphrase the words of one consultant, would not be committed to a life on heroin or injectable drugs; they would be confronted with the idea that they should become abstinent. Other doctors pointed to the benefit of reduced risks of infection, and the control pay-off that there was less likelihood of patients being able to sell, or receive a good price for, oral methadone.

## PROBLEMS AND DIFFICULTIES AT THE CLINICS

Various problems concerning the new approaches to treatment have been suggested by those both within and outside the Clinics. The first criticism is that the Clinics have narrowed their objectives by implicitly selecting their clients. In the early days people attended because they wanted a regular supply of injectable drugs. Now that these are unlikely to be supplied, the people who go to Clinics and who stay with them may either be those who actually seek treatment or those who, for various reasons, including pressure from other agencies such as courts, are willing to accept oral methadone. Even of those who find their way to Clinics, only a minority stay – the University College Hospital study found that only 29 per cent of those offered oral methadone were still in treatment contact after twelve months. So what is happening to all the people who do not come, or who come and shortly thereafter terminate treatment?

Critics argue that there are many people – casual users of opiates, barbiturate users, 'polydrug' users – for whom treatment facilities are unavailable. Such criticisms are substantiated by the evidence of Home Office notifications, which show that in 1979 nearly 1000 of the 1614 new addicts were notified by doctors working outside the Clinics; by the evidence that each year there are nearly twice as many addicts known to the Home Office as there are in treatment; and also by a study of accident and emergency departments, which indicated that many people treated for overdoses are drug-dependent and yet not in contact with Clinics (Ghodse 1976). Many find their way to other agencies or to GPs willing to prescribe methadone or, the current favourite, Diconal. Such evidence may be taken to mean that there are many people who 'should' be going to Clinics, but who, for one reason or another, do not present themselves or are not accepted for treatment. The newsletter of the Institute for the Study of Drug Dependence (*Drug Link* 1980a) concluded that 'by and large, the Clinics are fully occupied with the relatively settled old-timers, left-over from the era of the old time street junkie', and that, to some extent, they 'have become a backwater of our social response to drug abuse dealing with a problem that no longer reaches the heart of the UK drug scene'.

The second criticism is also about the narrowing of objectives, in that the Clinics have reduced the range of treatments on offer. We have remarked on the flexibility allowed by the British policy over the years in granting considerable clinical freedom to consultants. But what has emerged recently is a more consistent British 'system' than in earlier years. One consultant who adhered to the oral methadone policy admitted that treatment had become stereotyped and that giving everyone similar quantities of drugs and disregarding their special characteristics was a 'cul-de-sac' response. Treatment is often determined by fiat, rather than being tailored to the problems of the individual. One consultant said that he disliked this 'authoritarian' position which dictated therapy. A similar point was made by a clinical psychologist from the Maudsley at a meeting of London drug Clinic doctors in 1980:

> 'Instead of a greater sensitivity to the individual differences between addicts, we find an increasing tendency to treat all addicts the same way – to try to force all addicts to conform to our ideas about treatment. Instead of selecting individuals for different treatments, Clinics are tending to set up rigid and inflexible systems.'
>
> (Gossop 1980: 3)

The third criticism is that the doctors are now acting as if they can ignore the wider setting of drug use. Having retreated from the idea that they are involved in social control, it is suggested that the Clinic doctors are making possible the rapid growth of the black market by making legal drugs harder to obtain. Some critics suggest that the oral methadone policy was a mistake because it intensified the black market, and they raised the possibility that there could be a link between the policy and the rise in addict notifications to the Home Office.

However, the changes in approach may not be the dramatic departure from past practice that the critics claim them to be. The Clinics do still define their work primarily in terms of prescribing drugs. Looking back over the years since 1968, one consultant commented:

> 'When we opened we were just dishing up drugs and nothing else, not refusing to prescribe to those who should not get drugs, but we neither tried nor offered alternatives. It may have seemed flexible yet it was rigid, in the sense that we did not offer anything except a lot of drugs. Now we are also rigid in that we give just one type of drug, in linctus form. We have always been drug oriented. We have always just looked at prescribing. This is what we should get away from.'

### CLINICS AND RESOURCES

The impression of calm purposefulness at the Clinics was also somewhat misleading, with staff restricted by their limited resources and the financial crisis facing the NHS. The Clinics were originally financed with special funds made available to Hospital Boards by the Ministry of Health (later the Department of Health). With the reorganization of the NHS in 1974 they became the financial responsibility of Area Health Authorities, the basic administrative units of the health service. There are ninety-eight Area Health Authorities in England and Wales, serving geographical areas with average populations of half a million. The Clinics now have to compete for local funds with other branches of medicine. One can see how financial administrators, in seeking to save money to accommodate government limits on health service expenditure, might turn their attention to Clinics. It is difficult to estimate the costs of the Clinics as NHS Areas rarely release detailed costings of separate sections of the health service, but in 1977 it was estimated that the total cost of the Clinics and allied services for England and Wales came to £1.5 million, of which £300,000 was the cost of drugs. This money is now under threat. 'We end up being simply the bottom of the pile' was how one consultant put it.

At one time it was envisaged that there would be one social worker for every 25 Clinic patients. However, the Advisory Council on the Misuse of Drugs, in their *First Interim Report of the Treatment and Rehabilitation Working Group* (1977), showed that social-work staffing ranged from one social worker to every 22 patients to one for every 163, with an average of one to 64. So far, the cash restrictions have had their main impact on staffing. Many consultants talked about the difficulties of staff recruitment. Vacancies are frequently 'frozen', and with the severe shortage of nursing staff in the NHS, posts in Clinics are often given a low priority. No Clinic has yet closed, but there were plans to shut down an in-patient ward at one hospital which has nearly one-third of the beds for addicts in the whole of London. Staffing problems are compounded by limited career opportunities. Many doctors who became interested in addiction in the 1960s are still working at the Clinics. Undoubtedly, this enabled them to develop a body of knowledge and practice but, on the negative side, a number admitted to feeling battle-weary, having seen generations of addicts come and go and experiencing a strong feeling of *déjà vu* with respect to the ploys and promises of patients. It is a weariness that borders on despondency.

In contrast to the relative stability of the senior medical staff the rest of the treatment team tends to be a movable feast. The career prospects of junior medical staff are small. A long-time observer of the Clinics at the Institute for the Study of Drug Dependence said 'There's not really much future in drugs for an ambitious psychiatrist. . . . there's room for about two or three people at any one time who will be seen as the intellectual leaders in the field.' This area of medicine is not expanding and promotion is often dependent on the retirement of senior doctors. Thus, many prefer to seek their careers elsewhere. In some cases junior hospital doctors work in Clinics for a short spell as part of their training. Staff turnover is possibly no greater than in other branches of medicine, but it highlights the chronicity of patients who attend through numerous staff changes.

A final problem with current funding is that Area Health Authorities are primarily interested in providing services for people in their own localities and many accord a low priority to the treatment of addicts. There are now 34 Clinics, 14 in the London area, which suggests that nearly two out of three Area Health Authorities have no special facilities for the treatment of addicts. Areas with Clinics often seek to impose geographical catchment areas, and are reluctant to treat people from outside their areas. This has led to considerable gaps in services, even in the South-East, which is relatively better served than the rest of the country. The problem may become more acute from 1982 when it is proposed to change the structure of the NHS by replacing the existing Area Health Authorities with much smaller District Health Authorities.

Several consultants saw a viable future only if funding arrangements were radically changed, with funds being separated from the Area Health

Authorities and specially ear-marked for the treatment of addiction. They argued that addiction is a national problem and cannot be funded as a local issue.

The Conservative administration of the early 1980s responded to the crisis in the UK economy by emphasizing the limits to state intervention. This led to cuts in expenditure in the health and personal social services. In a radio interview in 1981 the Secretary of State at the DHSS, Patrick Jenkin, stated his belief that funding of drug treatment should be left to local communities, arguing that it was impossible to determine the needs of each area from a central point in London (*File on Four* 1981). And Timothy Raison, Minister of State at the Home Office, told a meeting of the Standing Conference on Drug Abuse in the previous year that 'there is a limit to the contribution which can be made by central and local government', and stressed the importance of the voluntary field (SCODA 1980). These statements would seem to raise serious questions about the future of the Clinics.

### PROSPECTS FOR THE 1980S

As we have shown in our examination of the response to addiction over the last hundred years, there coexist competing views on the nature of addiction and the appropriate response to it. This was true in the 1890s, in the 1920s, in the 1960s, and is still true today. The British 'system' has never been a purely penal or medical one, it has rather been a blend of two philosophies, with one or other view dominating in different periods. Even in times when the medical view was held to be dominant, for example in the 1920s, medical work was always conducted within a legal and penal framework. The 1920s saw not a victory for medical dominance in the field of addiction, but an *entente* between doctors and the state.

The present situation seems to presage a new balance between medical and penal approaches. The doctors have viewed the first years of the Clinics as unsuccessful in terms of treatment, and have drawn back from the idea that their work is important for social control. Their disappointment and pessimism have led to a narrowing of the way they now define their task, and they have tried to reformulate their views so that therapeutic pessimism is countered with new talk of therapeutic zeal. There is a sense of retreat from earlier ideas. But the Clinics are only one part of the 'system'. Government departments are also reassessing what has happened since 1968, have also concluded that the Clinics have not been successful, and are using this evidence not to reformulate treatment plans, but to suggest a shift in emphasis, back to control.

Two arguments are presented at a governmental level. The first is that there should be a rethink about the work of the Clinics and a new initiative for them. Some would like to see the Clinics expanding their work and taking on patients who have hitherto been excluded. Those who argue for this emphasize that the Clinics should readopt their earlier role and responsibilities for the social control of the wider drug problem. They argue that the current increase in the extent of addiction and the buoyancy of the black market are related to the narrower task that the Clinic staff have set themselves.

The second argument runs counter to this and, whilst also putting the emphasis on control, suggests that the Clinics should have a less important role to play than that of the police and customs. The base of this argument lies in government policies in the early 1980s which aimed at a reduction of state involvement in the provision of medical and social services, made visible in cuts in government expenditure. Accompanying this has been a new emphasis on law and order, with increased expenditure on policing and a philosophy of stronger penalty, especially for young offenders. This general shift from welfare and caring to penalty is the setting within which we may detect changes in the government's approach to the problems of drug addiction.

The difficulties of working with addicts, and the apparent lack of immediate therapeutic success, are being used as arguments not for more effort and understanding, but for a withdrawal from the field. A senior Home Office official has been quoted as saying that the whole approach to drug addiction is now in question. Up to now 'the aim has been rehabilitation', in other words the work of the Clinics, but 'we can't afford this anymore. All we can do is to support these people for a time. But once they're hooked, they have effectively passed a death sentence on themselves' (*The Sunday Times* 24 February 1980).

A major statement of the government's views on addiction was put by Patrick Jenkin at a meeting at Phoenix House in 1980 (*Drug Link* 1980b). He argued that 'as with so many health problems, prevention is very much better than cure', and then told the audience that in preventing drug abuse 'our first and most vital line of defence is obviously the police and the customs. They do a magnificent job in limiting the availability of dangerous drugs and without their efforts our drug problem would be infinitely worse.' The statement illustrates how, in discussions about drug use, medical concepts are fluid and open to considerable slippage of meaning. To talk of prevention in terms of policing is rather distant from the common medical usage of the term.

The new governmental analysis of the situation is, then, a return to a strong view of policing as the central element in the social response to drug addiction. The language of government policy no longer gives a prominent place to doctors; it is no longer they who are seen as playing a key part in controlling addiction. The poor return on treatment, compared with the claimed success of policing and customs work, was a theme raised again by Patrick Jenkin, later in his speech: 'I do not have to tell you', he is reported to have said, 'that all this [treatment and research] is of course in competition for scarce public money with other more immediate and perhaps more obviously popular needs.' In times of financial stringency the Minister gave a clear indication of how the money should best be spent:

> 'While no one would for one moment question the value of the customs surveillance of our ports or the police campaign against traffickers, or, I hope, the health education effort to persuade people of the dangers of drugs, it must be very evident to those in this hall that the same cannot always be said about research or still more about the efforts to rehabilitate drug abusers.'
>
> (Drug Link 1980b)

The current treatment policies favoured by many Clinic staff would be entirely encompassable within the type of policy proposed by the Minister. His proposals would not mean a total disengagement of doctors from the field, rather a reduction in their relative role. A government seeking to save money in the NHS would welcome any redefinition of a therapeutic role that meant fewer patients would apply and fewer resources be needed. The doctors' own narrowing of their task is, then, consonant with the narrowed medical task envisaged by the Minister.

From the standpoint of the beginning of 1981 the prospects for the Clinics look uncertain. We now have thirteen years' experience of the Clinics and that experience is viewed equivocably by those within the Clinics and by others outside. The conflict between treatment and control is still there, and, if anything, is once again highlighted, with many doctors arguing for a narrowed, predominantly therapeutic task, and government departmental officials arguing for a new initiative on controlling the drug problem. At the beginning of the 1980s, then, we seem to be facing the start of a new balance being argued between treatment and control.

# Part Four
# *Appendix*

# Appendix
## *A ten-year study of heroin addicts in London*

### RESEARCH AND THE SOCIAL RESPONSE TO ADDICTION

The second half of the 1960s was a period of intense activity for legislators, civil servants, doctors, and others concerned about the growth of drug use in Britain. As we have shown in this book, the social response took the form of legislation for new controls and penalties on drug use, and of new treatment policies – the setting up of the Clinics. Another way in which modern governments respond to social problems is to initiate research. Information and knowledge, it is often argued, are crucial to understanding and ameliorating social problems. The research on which this book is based can be seen as part of this response to the problem of drug use. In 1967 the Minister of Health announced in the House of Commons that a unit would be established to conduct research into addiction. This, the Addiction Research Unit, was established at the Institute of Psychiatry in 1967 and financed by the Ministry of Health. It was conceived by its Director as an interdisciplinary unit, staffed by psychologists, psychiatrists, social workers, social psychologists, statisticians, and sociologists, working in several areas of addictions, such as cigarette smoking, alcohol use, and drug addiction.

Our study on opiate addiction was carried out under the auspices of the unit, and was designed to look at what happened to people who were given prescriptions for heroin – research especially relevant as heroin would, from 1968, be prescribed under more controlled conditions by doctors working in Drug Dependency Clinics. Neither clinicians nor policy makers were certain of the likely impact of the Clinics. Would, for example, addicts who were prescribed regular, steady quantities of heroin be able to lead relatively normal lives, or would they remain chaotic and disorganized? To get some idea of the effect of the Clinics we decided to interview patients to find out what sort of lives they were leading. We approached London Clinics and in 1969 drew a representative sample of patients who were being prescribed heroin. It is the people in this sample who appear in this book.

After the initial survey in 1969 we decided to follow these people to see what would happen to them over the years, and have managed to follow them across a ten-year period, from 1969 to 1979. Some of the follow-up material was derived from official records, more from the personal contact we made in 1976/77 with the survivors of the sample. In this chapter we present the data in the form of a longitudinal study, describing the status of the people at various points. Using the material in this way allows us to see how, in basic behavioural terms, these people changed over the years.

### THE SAMPLE IN 1969

Between March and November 1969 we took a sample of one in every three patients who were attending 13 of the 15 London Drug Dependency Clinics and who were being prescribed heroin. There were 128 people in the sample, 93 men and 35 women. We managed to interview 111 (86.7 per cent) of them. At that time about 45 per cent of the patients at these London Clinics were being prescribed heroin. The London Clinics accounted for about 80 per cent of all Clinic patients in England and Wales. The sample selected by us therefore constituted about 12 per cent of all the Clinic patients in England and Wales (*see Figure A(1)*).

When we first interviewed them in 1969 the addicts were, on average, twenty-five years old and reported using heroin for an average of five years. There were considerable variations, the shortest reporting having used heroin for less than a year and the longest for over thirty years. They first used heroin at an average of nineteen-and-a-half years, with a range from fourteen to forty-eight years. Despite this wide range, over 90 per cent had first used heroin before they were twenty-five years old (Stimson and Ogborne 1970).

Most of the addicts had first used heroin in that period in the 1960s when there had been a general increase in the use of heroin in Britain – the increase that informed and influenced the policy discussions and decisions that culminated with the establishment of Clinics. The people in the sample were both representative of the patients at the Clinics in 1969, and reflective of the changing pattern of addiction in the 1960s. This is shown graphically in *Figure A(2)*. The majority (86 per cent) of the addicts we spoke to had first used heroin in the 1960s, mainly between 1962 and 1967. There were a few who had started long before this, the earliest being

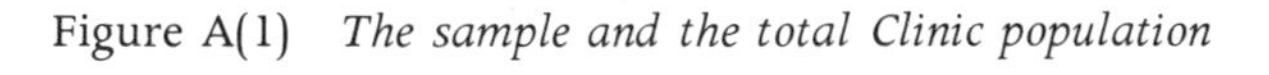

Figure A(1) *The sample and the total Clinic population*

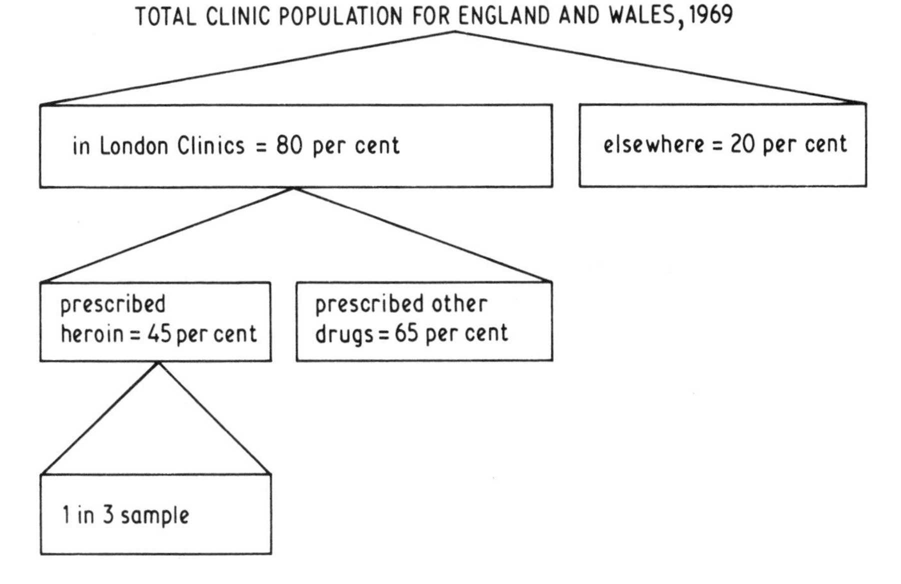


*Note:* This sample is representative of all patients who received prescriptions for heroin at London Clinics. It constituted approximately 12 per cent of the total Clinic population for England and Wales for 1969.

in 1939. Many of those who started before the 1960s were Canadian addicts who lived the first years of their addiction in Canada before coming to Britain in the 1960s. *Figure A(2)* shows the cumulative number who had used any drug, and had used heroin, for successive years from 1939 up to the opening of the Clinics in 1968. The data are given for the 111 addicts we interviewed in 1969. On the same chart we have plotted the total number of addicts known to the Home Office Drugs Branch for the years 1958 to 1968. The slopes of the two curves are remarkably similar, which we interpret to suggest that our addict sample was typical of the total known addict population for these years.

The people we interviewed were receiving prescriptions for heroin and in 1969 the average prescription was for 140 mgs. There was a wide range with the smallest amount prescribed being 10 mgs, and the largest 1140 mgs. Heroin was not the only drug prescribed, and the majority of these Clinic patients (82 per cent) were also prescribed methadone in ampoules, pills, or linctus. The prescription of both drugs at the same time reflected what were then two common Clinic strategies: first, the prescription of methadone linctus as a reserve for occasions when the addict patient used up the prescribed heroin too quickly; second, and more importantly, a treatment approach that attempted to transfer the

Figure A(2) *Year of first use of any illegal drug and of heroin, shown cumulatively for the interviewed sample of heroin addicts. Also shown, to a different scale, is the number of heroin addicts known to the Home Office for each of the years 1958–68*

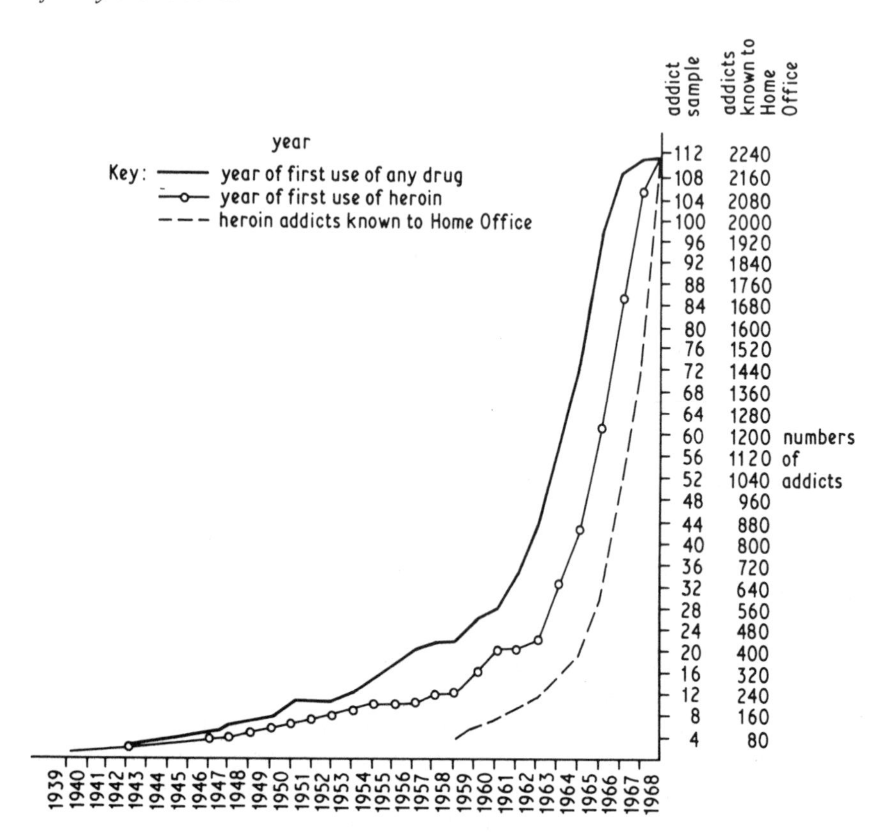


addict from heroin to methadone by substituting a certain amount of heroin with a certain amount of injectable methadone, the long-term aim being to transfer the patient to oral methadone and subsequent abstinence.

Many other drugs were prescribed, with nearly half the patients receiving prescriptions for sedatives and hypnotics (for example barbiturates). Few people reported restricting their drug use to the drugs prescribed by the Clinic – only 16 per cent said that they did this. In *Table A(1)*, we give the numbers being prescribed different categories of drugs and the numbers reporting using them. The range of drugs used suggests that it is not entirely accurate to refer to these people as *heroin* addicts. Certainly the majority preferred heroin to all the other drugs that were available, and they were selected to be interviewed by us by virtue of the fact that they were prescribed heroin, but it is clear that these people were prepared to use a wide variety of drugs.

Table A(1) *The sample in 1969: drugs prescribed and reported used during the month preceding interview**

| | prescribed | | used | |
|---|---|---|---|---|
| | no. | % | no. | % |
| methadone | 91 | 82 | 95 | 86 |
| other opiates, e.g. morphine, opium, pethidine | 0 | 0 | 23 | 22 |
| amphetamine, amphetamine/barbiturate mixtures and other stimulants | 14 | 13 | 49 | 44 |
| sedatives and hypnotics | 51 | 46 | 83 | 75 |
| tranquillizers | 5 | 4 | 19 | 17 |
| cocaine | 14 | 13 | 32 | 29 |
| cannabis | | | 68 | 61 |
| psychedelics | | | 13 | 12 |

*Note:* *Based on interviewed sample, n. = 111 (total sample n. = 128).

If asked to construct a composite picture of the heroin addict patients in 1969, it would be something like this:

> 'The typical addict patient was male, twenty-five years old, born in this country, single, likely to have been separated from one or both parents, and left secondary modern school at fifteen. He started using drugs at sixteen, heroin at nineteen, and had used heroin for about five years. Before he started using heroin he was convicted for an offence that was not to do with drugs. He was unemployed or only casually employed, and supported himself from a variety of sources including crime. In addition to heroin he received methadone on prescription. However, he did not confine his drug use to the drugs that were being prescribed for him. He had a great deal of contact with other addicts, injected in their company, and did not inject in a sterile manner. He attempted abstinence but had chronically relapsed, and was often in hospital for the treatment of conditions associated with drug use.'

Useful as this composite picture is, it is a distortion, for a closer examination of the 1969 data revealed much variation in experience and behaviour. For example, with employment: a third were employed and had been for the previous three months, while a contrasting, similar-sized group were unemployed, and had been for the previous three months.

With income: 22 per cent reported income from employment as their only means of support in the previous month, whilst just over a third had an illicit source of income. With crime, 20 per cent admitted to no criminal activity at all in the previous three months, a third were involved in criminal acts covered by the drugs laws, and a further third reported, in addition, some stealing or acquisitive criminal activities. With injections, whilst only 11 per cent used sterile techniques, nearly a third used their disposable syringes once only, as is medically desirable. Last, whilst few knew no addicts at all, only a half knew forty or more.

While treating the sample as a whole suggests that the addicts were typical socially disorganized individuals, this composite approach proved untenable on closer examination as there was in fact a range of behaviour and experience among the addict patients: not all suffered social and physical complications with their addiction. It was this diversity that we focused on in 1969, developing a typology of four distinctive patterns of behaviour (Stimson 1972, 1973). One group, who we called the 'stables', suffered the fewest social and physical complications of addiction. These addicts worked and had legitimate incomes; they avoided other addicts and tended to use their drugs at home, alone. They appeared to have the most control over their drug use in that they tended to restrict it to prescribed drugs. They avoided physical complications and had been hospitalized less often than the other addicts. They had the lowest rate of criminal activity (those that did report breaking the law reported mainly offences against the drug laws) and the least criminal convictions. They were residentially stable, ate and slept regularly, and in appearance tended to be conventional and well-dressed.

Those who we called the 'junkies' were the opposite. They did not work and tended to support themselves by stealing and hustling. They were highly involved with other addicts, and if they had relationships with members of the opposite sex these people tended to be drug users too. Their drug use was carried on in public places and with other people. They did not restrict it to prescribed drugs for they used extra heroin and other black-market drugs. They showed little heed for sterile injections and had many physical complications and hospitalizations. They had a high rate of criminal activity, which included drug-related crime, stealing, and other acquisitive activities. They reported a high incidence of convictions and institutionalization for offences. They were residentially unstable and ate and slept poorly. In appearance they were unconventional and unkempt.

A third group, who we called the 'loners', had some of the characteristics of the junkies, but when interviewed they were distinguished from them by their low rate of criminal activity, their low involvement with other addicts, their support from Social Security benefits as opposed to hustling and stealing, and a lower rate of physical damage and complications. They used their drugs alone, sometimes buying them in addition to those prescribed, but never buying much extra heroin. They appeared to have cut themselves off from the drug scene and had almost as little contact with other addicts as did the stables, though they were not involved in the conventional world of work. The name loners seemed appropriate. They had unstable living arrangements, ate and slept poorly, and were unconventional in appearance.

The fourth category, the 'two-worlders', had a somewhat intermediate status, having some of the characteristics of both the junkies and the stables. Like the junkies they had a high rate of criminal activity and were very involved with other addicts. They tended to use drugs with other addicts, taking extra heroin and other drugs that were not being prescribed for them by their Clinics. They had a high rate of convictions but, while the junkies tended to have been imprisoned, the two-worlders were more likely to have been placed on probation. Like the stables, they were employed and had fairly legitimate incomes, and like them avoided physical complications and hospitalizations. They were also residentially stable and ate and slept regularly. Last, like the stables, they were, when interviewed, relatively conventional in appearance.

The numbers in each of these groups are shown in *Table A(2)*.

Table A(2) *The sample in 1969 categorized: numbers in each group*

| | *'stables'* | *'junkies'* | *'loners'* | *'two-worlders'* | *total* |
|---|---|---|---|---|---|
| females | 8 | 5 | 8 | 4 | 25 |
| males | 25 | 13 | 22 | 16 | 76 |
| total | 33 | 18 | 30 | 20 | 101* |

*Note:* *Missing data prevented the classification of 10 interviewed and 17 non-interviewed people.

This typology was constructed on the basis of the behavioural data that had been collected in the 1969 interview. The importance of this sort of analysis lies not so much in any permanent or distinctive boundaries we might infer, but rather in the emphasis it gives to the fact that the addicts were a varied bunch of people who had achieved diverse ways of living while addicted to heroin. Such a finding contradicts many of the stereotypes about heroin addicts, and renders problematic an understanding of the relationship between the pharmacological effect of a powerful drug and the way in which people manage to lead their lives whilst addicted (*see also* Chapter 7).

### FROM 1969 TO 1975

The Home Office has, since about 1935, kept files on those persons known to be addicted to various drugs. Up until 1968 these files were derived from routine police examination of prescription records kept by pharmacists, and from voluntary information supplied by doctors, hospitals, prisons, courts, and the police. The 1967 Dangerous Drugs Act provided for the compulsory notification of people addicted to heroin, cocaine, and various other drugs, it being incumbent on doctors seeing people addicted to these drugs to notify the Home Office (*see* p. 207). The Home Office keeps records of all those who have been statutorily notified. For those who attend Clinics the information comes to the Home Office mainly via two-monthly returns on addict patients made by Clinics. This inform-

Table A(3) *The sample at follow-up, 1969 through to 1979: Clinic attendance and death*

| *year* | *data source* | *attending Clinic* | | *known dead* | | *not attending Clinic* | |
|---|---|---|---|---|---|---|---|
| | | *no.* | % | *no.* | % | *no.* | % |
| 1969 | first interview | 128 | 100 | | | | |
| Oct. 1970 | Home Office records | 99 | 77 | 3 | 2 | 26 | 21 |
| Oct. 1971 | Home Office records | 76 | 59 | 8 | 6 | 44 | 34 |
| Oct. 1972 | Home Office records | 74 | 58 | 8 | 6 | 46 | 36 |
| Oct. 1973 | Home Office records | 73 | 57 | 8 | 6 | 47 | 37 |
| Oct. 1974 | Home Office records | 63 | 49 | 12 | 9 | 54 | 42 |
| Oct. 1975 | Home Office records | 65 | 51 | 12 | 9 | 51 | 40 |
| 1976–77 | follow-up | 55 | 43 | 15 | 12 | 58* | 45 |
| July 1979 | Home Office records | 49 | 38 | 19 | 15 | 60** | 47 |

*Note:* *Six of these in prison. **Five of these in prison. This information was not tabled for earlier years.
*Source:* Adapted from Wille (1981b).

ation, coupled with that from prison medical officers and from other notifying doctors, was useful in providing some minimal details profitable to a follow-up study.

Between 1969 and 1975 we used these records to see what happened to the sample (Ogborne and Stimson 1975; Thorley, Oppenheimer, and Stimson 1977). For each person we noted whether they were still attending a Clinic and, if so, whether they were being prescribed heroin and/or methadone; if they were not attending we noted whether they were alive or dead. Our findings are summarized in *Tables A(3)* and *A(4)*. In broad outline the Home Office material can be read as showing that there was, over the years, a steady decline in the numbers attending Clinics so that by 1975 only about half of the original sample were still patients. Each year also saw a steady increase in the numbers known to be dead.

Table A(4) *The sample at follow-up, 1969 through to 1979: distribution of Clinic-attending patients by prescription*

| *year* | *attending Clinic* | *receiving heroin with or without methadone* | | *receiving methadone only* | | *not receiving opiates* | |
|---|---|---|---|---|---|---|---|
| | | *no.* | % | *no.* | % | *no.* | % |
| 1969 | 128 | 128 | 100 | — | — | — | — |
| 1970 | 99 | 72 | 73 | 25 | 25 | 2 | 2 |
| 1971 | 76 | 56 | 74 | 17 | 22 | 3 | 4 |
| 1972 | 74 | 52 | 70 | 20 | 27 | 2 | 3 |
| 1973 | 73 | 47 | 64 | 24 | 33 | 2 | 3 |
| 1974 | 63 | 41 | 65 | 20 | 32 | 2 | 3 |
| 1975 | 65 | 41 | 63 | 21 | 32 | 3 | 5 |
| 1976/77 | 55 | 35 | 64 | 20 | 36 | 0 | 0 |
| 1979 | 49 | 24 | 49 | 25 | 52 | 0 | 0 |

*Source:* Adapted from Wille (1981b).

In 1969 we predicted that the stable addicts would be less likely than the others to change, for better or worse. They were the least likely to have had their addiction interrupted through imprisonment. They presented themselves as able to function reasonably well when using heroin and it was expected that this would give staff less reason to take them off it than if they were leading more socially disorganized lives. Their pattern of drug use was unlikely to lead them to physical complications that, if not resulting in death, might result in the Clinic doctor stopping the prescription. Since they rarely scored on the black market, saw few addicts, and seldom visited Piccadilly, they were less likely to be arrested. They were more positively inclined towards Clinics, which suggests they were less likely to run into conflict with staff. They saw themselves as able to manage on heroin and not in need of any help. In other words, in 1969 they seemed to avoid most of the hazards of addiction. It might have been expected therefore that they would be more likely than other addicts to successfully remain addicted. This was indeed the case. In 1973, when we compared the status of each of the four groups, the stables showed the least change of all – they were most likely to still be prescribed heroin or methadone and least likely to be dead, in prison, or not attending a Clinic (*Table A(5)*).

Table A(5) *Status of the four groups of addicts in April 1973*

| | *'stables'* | *'junkies'* | *'loners'* | *'two-worlders'* | *total* |
|---|---|---|---|---|---|
| attending Clinic | | | | | |
| prescribed heroin | 17 | 9 | 6 | 6 | 38 |
| prescribed methadone | 8 | 3 | 4 | 4 | 19 |
| not attending Clinic | 6 | 3 | 15 | 8 | 32 |
| dead | 1 | 2 | 4 | 1 | 8 |
| in prison | 1 | 1 | 0 | 1 | 3 |
| not known | 0 | 0 | 1 | 0 | 1 |
| total number | 33 | 18 | 30 | 20 | 101* |

*Note:* *Missing data prevented the classification of 1 non-interviewed and 10 interviewed people.

### THE PERSONAL FOLLOW-UP IN 1976/77

Home Office records do not tell us the precise current status of all heroin addicts. The important question, which the records cannot answer, concerns the people who are neither dead nor at Clinics. Whether or not these people have ceased to use heroin or other drugs cannot be known from the records. Some may well be using drugs illicitly and undetected. For example, from Home Office records we learnt that, by October 1975, 40 per cent of the sample were not attending Clinics. Thus, whatever the strength of the records as a source of data, we were presented with their undeniable weakness: they told us nothing about the precise current status of almost half our sample. This gap suggested that the record follow-ups needed to be complemented by personal follow-up. We therefore designed a follow-up study in which we tried to trace and recontact all the survivors in the sample we had originally interviewed in 1969. We did this follow-up between June 1976 and November 1977. It is from these interviews that the personal material in this book has been drawn.

By December 1977 we had managed to follow-up 124 (97 per cent) of the original sample of 128. We made personal contact with 107, most of whom were interviewed. The interviews, the majority of which were tape-recorded and several hours long, were a mixture of structured questions and open-ended discussions, covering past and present drug-taking and a wide range of personal, social, and medical aspects of people's lives. We traced, but did not manage to contact, two people, though obtained some contemporary information on them from other sources. There were four people who we were unable to trace, and fifteen had died. We managed to collect additional material from hospital case notes, Home Office records, criminal records, voluntary agencies, spouses, and friends.

Tracing, contacting, and interviewing was lengthy and time-consuming and we had to be discreet in our enquiries as, at first, we had little idea of what these people would by then be doing, and feared that our efforts to contact them might be an unwelcome intrusion into their lives. Some were easy to trace because they were still attending Clinics, but for many others the last-known contact had been some years before. Among the various agencies and sources we consulted were Clinics; birth, death, and marriage records in the UK and elsewhere; the NHS central register of patients; GPs; hospitals; addict welfare agencies; prisons; the Mental Health index of patients admitted to psychiatric hospitals; hostels and reception centres; relatives and acquaintances; and we also called at old addresses. Nearly 400 letters were sent. Seven of the people were living abroad, 78 were living in Greater London, 26 were living in other areas in the British Isles, and two cases were not known about. To date, this study is the longest personal follow-up of a sample of British heroin addicts. The average time from the first interview in 1969 to the follow-up one in 1976/77 was 7.6 years (Stimson, Oppenheimer, and Thorley 1978).

### People still attending Clinics in 1976/77

Over the years the number attending Clinics declined so that at personal follow-up there were only fifty-five who were still patients. (This was almost the same as the number, fifty-two, who were not at Clinics and who were living in the community.) Six people were in prison when they were interviewed and had all been using opiates at the time of their arrests. Five of the people still attending Clinics were in hospital when interviewed.

### Death

Eleven men and four women had died and were, on average, thirty years old when this happened. We looked at hospital case notes, death certificates, and coroners' inquests and found that they were all dependent on drugs when they died.

### Drug use

All the people were asked about their use of drugs over the twenty-eight days preceding the follow-up interview and their answers are summarized in *Table A(6)*. Forty people had stopped using opiates and were living in the community. Sixty-two were still using opiates. Five people who were in prison were abstinent from opiates. We were uncertain of the drug use of the remaining six people, although for reasons which we discuss below we think that they were not using opiates.

### People using opiates

Fifty-five of the 62 people continuing to use opiates were still attending Clinics and receiving daily prescriptions for heroin or methadone, or both. Nearly all of these 55 people were injecting drugs and only 5 confined their use of opiates to oral methadone. Heroin alone was prescribed for 13 people, whose average daily dose was 220 mgs. Methadone alone was prescribed for 20, the average daily dose being 70 mgs. Seven of these 20 people received only oral methadone; all the others also received some form of injectable methadone. Twenty-two people received both heroin and methadone, and their average daily doses were 140 mgs of heroin and 60 mgs of methadone. The highest opiate prescription was for 500 mgs of heroin with 150 mgs of methadone daily, and the lowest for 10 mgs of methadone.

Six people who injected opiate drugs were not attending Clinics. Three of these were using opiates every day and we therefore supposed that they were physically dependent. Another one used opiates at least once a week; the remaining two had injected opiates only once in the previous twenty-eight days and had in fact maintained an intermittent use of opiates for some time, without resuming physical dependence. This shows that few people in this sample continued to use opiates without attending Clinics.

### People no longer using opiates

At least forty people were no longer using opiates and were living in the community; a further five were abstinent and in prison. Those living in the community and not using opiates had last been physically dependent an average of five years previously, with a range from nine months up to over eight years. More information will be found in *Table A(7)*.

Table A(6) *The sample at personal follow-up, 1976/77: drugs reported used during 28 days preceding interview; results given for 113 people (88 per cent of sample) alive at follow-up*

| | | attending Clinics | | in prison | | others | | total | |
|---|---|---|---|---|---|---|---|---|---|
| | | *no.* | % | *no.* | % | *no.* | % | *no.* | % |
| opiate users | injectors of opiates | 50 | 39 | | | 6 | 5 | 62 | 48 |
| | oral methadone and other opiates | 5 | 4 | 1 | 1 | | | | |
| people abstinent from opiates | daily drug use | | | | | | | 45 | 35 |
| | 100 mls alcohol | | | | | 1 | 1 | | |
| | tranquillizers, hypnotics, and anti-depressants | | | 1 | 1 | 5 | 4 | | |
| | cannabis | | | | | 3 | 2 | | |
| | occasional drug use | | | | | | | | |
| | cannabis | | | | | 15 | 12 | | |
| | stopped using drugs | | | 4 | 3 | 16 | 12 | | |
| no. with uncertain drug use | | | | | | 6 | 5 | 6 | 5 |
| total | | 55 | 43 | 6 | 5 | 52 | 41 | 113 | 88 |

Table A(7) *The sample at personal follow-up, 1976/77: people abstinent from opiates – number of years abstinent*

| no. of years abstinent | less than 1 | 1 | 2 | 3 | 4 | 5 | 6 | 7 | 8 | total |
|---|---|---|---|---|---|---|---|---|---|---|
| no. of people abstinent | 2 | 5 | 3 | 6 | 4 | 4 | 7 | 8 | 1 | 40 |

It has been suggested that people who achieve abstinence from opiates may switch their dependence to other drugs, so we were particularly interested in what sorts of drugs these people were by then using. In all, we found that there were nine people out of the forty who were using some sort of psychoactive drug every day, but the type of drugs and the manner in which they were used were not different from what would be found in a similar age group in the general population. There was only one person who could be considered a heavy drinker, and he was drinking 100 mls or more of alcohol every day (100 mls of alcohol is contained in five pints of an average English beer), a level of consistent drinking considered to be associated with long-term physical damage. Five people were using low doses of tranquillizers, anti-depressants, or hypnotics which were prescribed for them by GPs. They were not used for intoxication. Three people were smoking cannabis every day. A further fifteen used cannabis less frequently than this. There were sixteen people who used no psychoactive drugs at all (*see Table A(6)*).

There will be some researchers who doubt the veracity of self-reports on drug use and who would argue that perhaps the people we saw did not tell us the truth. The interview material we obtained finds support in the results of a third interview (Wille 1978, 1981a). A sample of the people who were no longer using opiates were interviewed again a year later, by Wille, and asked, without being forewarned, for a urine sample. Of the twenty-four people contacted, twenty-three gave samples and when tested these yielded negative results to tests for opiates, methadone, cocaine, methylamphetamine, amphetamine, methaqualone, nitrazepam, other benzodiazepines, and barbiturates.

We have found in this study, then, that people who have been addicted to heroin and who then stop do not replace their dependence on heroin by dependence on other drugs.

There remains the question about the six people on whom we had incomplete information. Were they likely to still be using opiates or had they stopped? We think that they had almost certainly stopped. None of them had attended Clinics in the UK or Ireland since 1974 or earlier, and none had a conviction for a drug-related offence since 1969 – both of which indicated to us that they were unlikely to have still been using opiates. We spoke to one, on the telephone, who told us that he was not using opiates, but then we lost contact with him. One emigrated to a country where opiate use is rare and would be extremely hazardous for an immigrant, and his mother told us that he had stopped using drugs. The mother of another told us that her son had stopped using drugs but had been drinking large quantities of alcohol when he had last visited her, two years previously. One severely ill woman had returned to the USA and the doctor at the Clinic she had attended thought she was unlikely to have still been alive; however, we were unable to find any record of her death. If, as this evidence suggests, these people were not using opiates, then the total number of people in the sample who had ceased to be addicts and who were not in prison rises to forty-six.

### A YEAR BY YEAR SUMMARY: 1968–75

When we interviewed people in the follow-up of 1976/77 we tried to chart their activities for each of the years from 1968 up to the follow-up. We used what we came to call a 'life chart' on which we plotted each year the number of months that people were addicted, what drugs they were using, whether they were at a Clinic, the time spent in hospital, prison, or work. We supplemented the interview information with data from Clinic case notes, Home Office records, records of convictions kept by the Criminal Records Office, and information from relatives and friends. We tried to arrive at the best estimate for each person of the amount of time spent each year in each of the activities, and managed to do this through to 1975, the last complete year before the follow-up. The data were then cumulated for the complete sample so that we arrived at the total 'person–months' for each year. In other words, there were 128 people in the sample, so for each year there were 128 × 12 person–months, a total of 1536. We then plotted, for each full year from 1968 to 1975, the number of person–months that the aggregated sample was engaged in the various activities. This provided a graphic portrayal of the sample's activities over the eight years.

The first life chart (*Figure A(3)*) gives the summarized drug use for the sample. In this chart 'heroin' means that the person was receiving a prescription for heroin, with or without other drugs; 'methadone' that the person had a prescription for methadone but not heroin; 'illegal opiates' that the person was using opiates without prescription; 'other drugs' that the person was using non-opiate drugs. 'Abstinent' is the residual category of those who were not using any of the aforementioned drugs. It will be readily seen from this chart that the number of person–months in abstinence increased over the years and that the number of person–months in receipt of a prescription declined.

Figure A(3) *Life chart, 1968 through to 1975, showing person–months of drug use*

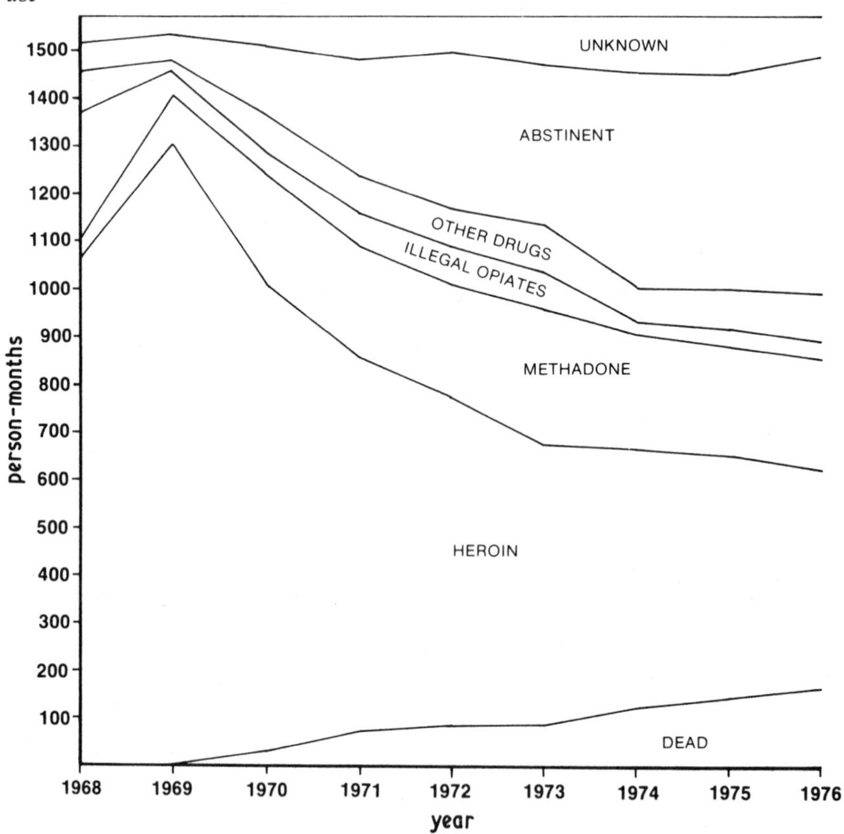


The next summary life chart (*Figure A(4)*) plots the institutional status of the sample and gives the number of person–months spent in prison, hospital, or as a Clinic patient. 'In community' is the residual category, describing all those person–months not spent in any of the aforementioned institutional categories. It will be seen that the number of person–months spent as Clinic patients declined.

The final life chart (*Figure A(5)*) gives the employment for the sample. First we have excluded, at the bottom of the chart, those months taken up by those who were dead, in prison, or in hospital. Then we have charted the number of person–months spent employed or unemployed. It will be seen that the proportion of months spent employed increased relative to the months spent unemployed.

Figure A(4) *Life chart, 1968 through to 1975, showing person–months in contact with institutions*

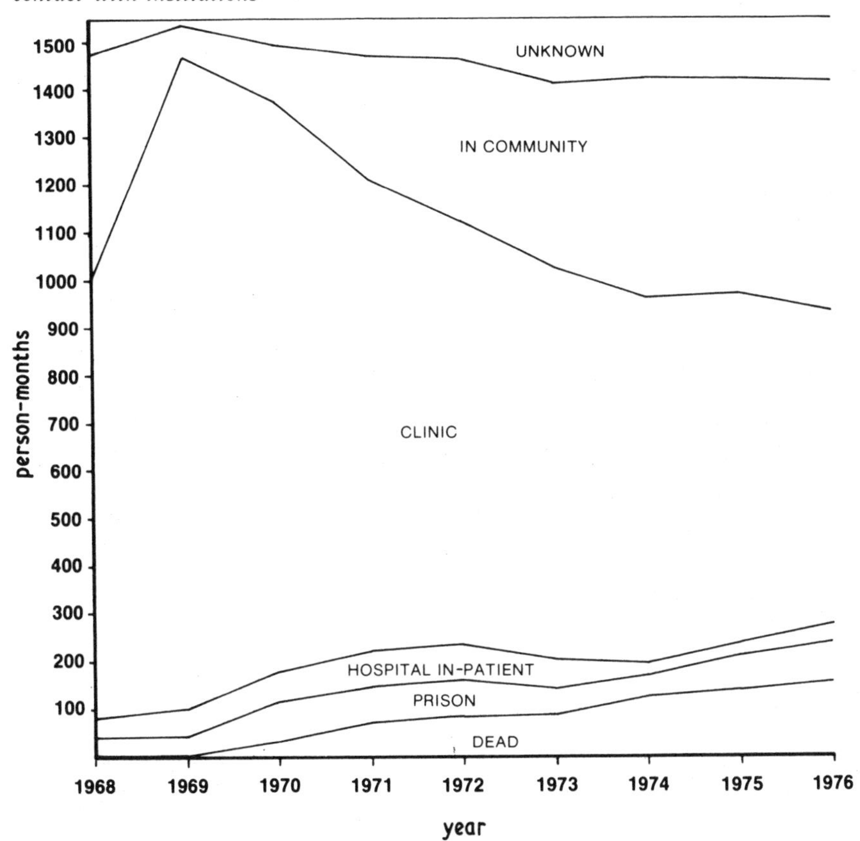


## DIFFERENCES BETWEEN THOSE WHO STOPPED AND THOSE WHO CONTINUED

There were several major differences between those who had stopped using opiates and those who were still addicts. The general trend was for those who had stopped to have made major changes for the better in their lives (Oppenheimer, Stimson, and Thorley 1979). Those who stopped were little involved in legal or illegal use of drugs and were more likely to be drinking 'socially'. No medical examination was undertaken, but those who stopped were more likely than those continuing addiction to have reported that their health was 'good' or 'excellent' and, predictably, none of them reported conditions such as abscesses, septicaemia, or hepatitis which are normally associated with drug use. As for crime, those who stopped were less 'involved' with the law (in the sense of being on remand, on a suspended sentence, conditional discharge, or probation)

Figure A(5) *Life chart, 1968 through to 1975, showing person–months in employment*

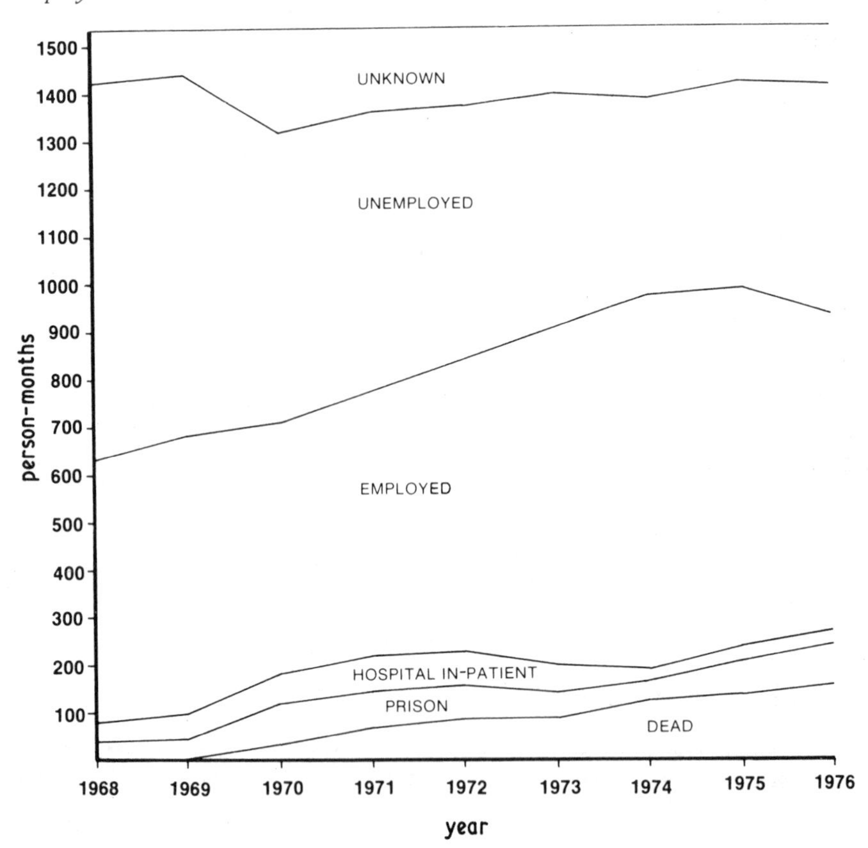


than those who continued to use opiates. They also reported less often breaking the law with respect to shop-lifting, illegal possession of drugs, or selling drugs. Their pattern of friendships had also changed, for those who stopped using opiates had tended to change their friends, few still having addicts among their close friends. None of those who stopped had recently visited Piccadilly Circus or any other well-known centre of drug trading. As for their work and living conditions, more of those who stopped were working and more had been in continuous employment than those who remained addicted. They were also more likely than those who had continued to use opiates to have had legal sources of income, and to have been in permanent accommodation. The comparisons between those who had stopped and those who continued addicted are shown in *Tables A(8)* to *A(11)*.

Table A(8) *The sample at personal follow-up, 1976/77: drugs used and prescribed during month preceding interview (differences between opiate users and abstainers)*

| | *users (n. = 61)* | | | | *abstainers (n. = 40)* | | | |
|---|---|---|---|---|---|---|---|---|
| | *prescribed* | | *used* | | *prescribed* | | *used* | |
| | *no.* | % | *no.* | % | *no.* | % | *no.* | % |
| opiates | 55 | 90 | 61 | 100 | | | | |
| tranquillizers | 14 | 24* | 17 | 29* | 6 | 16* | 8 | 21* |
| amphetamines | 5 | 9 | 19 | 33* | | | | |
| cocaine | 3 | 5 | 6 | 10 | | | 1 | 3 |
| hypnotics | 12 | 20* | 22 | 37* | 3 | 8 | 4 | 10 |
| cannabis | | | 25 | 43* | | | 19 | 49* |
| drugs obtained illegally | | | 26 | 43* | | | 5 | 12 |
| alcohol | | | | | | | | |
| 100 mls daily in past 28 days | | | 4 | 7 | | | 1 | 3 |
| no days exceeding 100 mls | | | 23 | 40* | | | 22 | 61* |

*Note:* *Because of missing data, n. for these percentages is slightly less than 61 for users and 40 for abstainers. Percentages are based on known numbers.

Table A(9) *The sample at personal follow-up, 1976/77: health (differences between opiate users and abstainers)*

| *health* | *users (n. = 61)* | | *abstainers (n. = 40)* | |
|---|---|---|---|---|
| | *no.* | % | *no.* | % |
| good or excellent | 29 | 51* | 28 | 76* |
| poor or very poor | 10 | 18* | 4 | 11* |
| in the last three months | | | | |
| abscess at injection sites | 8 | 13 | 0 | |
| abscess elsewhere | 5 | 8 | 0 | |
| septicaemia | 1 | 2 | 0 | |
| hepatitis | 2 | 3 | 0 | |

*Note:* *As note to *Table A(8)*.

Table A(10) *The sample at personal follow-up, 1976/77: crime (differences between opiate users and abstainers)*

| | users (n. = 61) | | abstainers (n. = 40) | |
|---|---|---|---|---|
| | *no.* | % | *no.* | % |
| on remand, suspended sentence, conditional discharge, or probation | 14 | 23 | 1 | 3 |
| criminal activities (in last 3 months) | | | | |
| shop-lifting | 12 | 21* | 0 | |
| illegal possession of drugs | 42 | 72* | 17 | 46* |
| obtained things by false pretences | 6 | 11* | 0 | |
| received stolen goods | 7 | 12* | 3 | 8* |
| sold drugs | 14 | 24* | 1 | 3* |
| one or more of the above | 42 | 72* | 19 | 51* |

*Note:* *As note to *Table A(8)*.

Table A(11) *The sample at personal follow-up, 1976/77: employment (differences between opiate users and abstainers)*

| | users (n. = 61) | | abstainers (n. = 40) | |
|---|---|---|---|---|
| | *no.* | % | *no.* | % |
| employment | | | | |
| full-time or part-time employed, student, or housewife | 38 | 62 | 33 | 83 |
| worked previous 13/13 weeks | 27 | 45* | 27 | 71* |
| worked 0/13 weeks | 24 | 40* | 7 | 17* |
| worked 52/52 weeks | 23 | 39* | 22 | 58* |
| income (previous 4 weeks) | | | | |
| own earnings | 40 | 66 | 33 | 85* |
| social security | 20 | 35* | 6 | 17* |
| unemployment benefits | 4 | 7* | 2 | 6* |
| sickness benefits | 6 | 11* | 0 | |
| any benefits | 28 | 46 | 8 | 20 |
| any 'hustling' (borrowing, shop-lifting, stealing, selling drugs, money from friends) | 24 | 39 | 5 | 13 |

*Note:* *As note to *Table A(8)*.

When we compared their characteristics in 1969 there were few differences between those who were to eventually stop using opiates and those who continued, just as there were few differences in their pre-drug-addiction backgrounds. We compared the two groups on numerous single characteristics, such as social class, sex, employment, crime, drug use, and income, and found that for the most part they could not be differentiated either in 1969 or on earlier attributes (Oppenheimer, Stimson, and Thorley 1979). The only differences that we found were that those who stopped using opiates were younger, had a shorter history of addiction, and had been prescribed smaller doses of drugs in 1969. The lack of earlier differences between the two groups indicates that it would have been difficult to choose individual characteristics of prognostic value, and, second, that the later differences found between the two groups were related to withdrawal from opiates. It was those who had stopped using heroin and methadone who had changed between 1969, when we first saw them, and 1976/77, when we saw them for a second time. Those who stayed on heroin and methadone hardly changed at all over those years, for better or worse (the only change we detected was an improvement in sterile injection techniques).

## 1969 TO 1979: THE FIRST TEN YEARS

We continued to keep track of these people through the Home Office records (Wille 1981b) and our last record search, in July 1979, enabled us to summarize their outcome after a period of ten years. In 1979 their average age was thirty-five years and a mean of 15.4 years had elapsed since their reported first use of heroin. The Home Office records for the sample indicated a continued decrease in the number attending Clinics, a continued increase in the number dead, and an increase in the number not attending Clinics (*Table A(3)*, p. 236). By July 1979, 49 of the sample were still patients attending Clinics, 19 had died, and 60 were no longer attending Clinics. Thus, after ten years, the majority of them were no longer Clinic patients.

### Those not attending Clinics

The evidence of the personal follow-up in 1976/77 was that the majority (88 per cent) of those who were recorded by the Home Office as no longer at Clinics nor in prison (and not dead) were not continuing as 'hidden addicts'. The information from our most recent examination of the Home Office files showed that the number of abstinent addicts continued to increase. In July 1979, fifty-five were no longer at Clinics nor in prison. If we assume that 88 per cent of them were abstinent, the number drug-free by 1979 was in the region of forty-eight: therefore the *ten-year abstinence rate* is estimated as *38 per cent*. The Home Office data also told us something more about the stability of the abstinence of those who were not using opiates in 1976. Forty abstinent people were interviewed in 1976/77 (these were the abstinent group in the above comparisons) and only one had re-attended a Clinic by 1979, another one was in prison. The remaining thirty-eight had not changed, as far as the records indicated, by 1979. The six people about whom we were uncertain in 1976/77, because we did not have complete information, had not since appeared in the Home Office records, a further indication that they were likely to be abstinent.

There were six people who used illicit opiates in 1976/77 but who did not receive a prescription. Four of these were back at Clinics in 1979, that is all the daily users and one of the occasional users. Five of the six people who were in prison in 1976/77 were back at Clinics in 1979. In all, 48 of the 58 people who did not attend a Clinic in 1976/77 were still not attending in 1979, one of them being in prison.

It would appear that those who achieved abstinence were likely to continue so. By 1979 the average period of abstinence from opiates was more than six years. Looking at the changes over the years from 1969 it would appear that there were dramatic changes immediately after the Clinics opened. For example, the biggest decline in the numbers attending Clinics occurred in 1970 and 1971 and thereafter the decrease was smaller. Of the 44 people who were not attending Clinics in 1971 (*Table A(3)*), 21 remained abstinent to 1979. The following eight years showed a continuing, though smaller, increase from 44 to 60 in the number of people who stopped attending Clinics.

### Those still attending Clinics

Of the 49 people still attending Clinics in 1979, 25 received methadone only, the other 24 were still receiving prescriptions for heroin, either alone or together with methadone. The majority (38, i.e. 30 per cent of the original sample) had received prescriptions for opiates continuously over the ten years since 1969 and there were 20 people (16 per cent of the original sample) who had been prescribed heroin without interruption for the ten-year period.

On average, these people had been using opiates for more than fifteen years and it would be realistic to regard them as chronic addicts. However, the majority, especially those who continued to be prescribed heroin, led lives that were reasonably unproblematic. This was demonstrated in the personal follow-up in 1976/77 when it was found, for example, that 62 per cent of the continuing opiate users were employed (*see Tables A(8), A(9), A(10), A(11)*).

The evidence would support the contention, argued elsewhere in this book, that the successful addict, the person who continues addicted, must avoid various hazards such as infection, arrest, and antagonizing Clinic staff. We have shown earlier in this Appendix that those whom we called stables in 1969 showed the least changes over the years. We would not have anticipated that our typology would be useful ten years later, and were surprised to find that our predictions concerning the 1969 stable addicts continued to be confirmed. In 1979 this group of addicts was more likely than any other group to be still receiving prescriptions for heroin and to have received such prescriptions without interruption over the ten-year period. In contrast, those who led more chaotic lives in 1969, those we called the junkies, were not represented at all in the group of continuous heroin users ten years later (*Table A(12)*).

Table A(12) *The status of the four groups in 1979*

| | *'stables'* | *'junkies'* | *'loners'* | *'two-worlders'* | *total* |
|---|---|---|---|---|---|
| total in group in 1969 | 33 | 18 | 30 | 20 | 101* |
| no. receiving heroin prescriptions continuously from 1969–79 | 11 | 0 | 4 | 2 | 17 |

*Note:* *Missing data prevented the classification of 1 non-interviewed and 10 interviewed people.

### Death

Nineteen people, 14 men and 5 women, died in the ten-year period. All of them were dependent on drugs at the time of their death at a mean age of thirty-one. The deaths were evenly distributed over the ten years and yield a death rate, based on the total sample at inception in 1969, of 14.8/1000 yearly. (If calculated on the basis of the active addicts only, the death rate would be higher.) In eight cases the cause of death was respiratory failure due to opiate and/or barbiturate poisoning; four people died from renal diseases, one from bronchial pneumonia, one was found dead with cut wrists, one died from carbon monoxide poisoning from a faulty room heater, and one burned to death at home. For the three remaining people the coroners' verdicts contained no further information than 'addiction to drugs'.

### Clinic mobility

Eighteen patients out of the total of 128 changed Clinics in the period 1969–79.

### CONCLUSIONS FROM THE LONGITUDINAL STUDY

In this chapter we have approached the question of 'what happens to heroin addicts' using information from highly structured interview questions and official records. We found that over the years the number of people remaining addicted declined, so that after ten years a majority no longer attended Clinics and 38 per cent had ceased to use heroin and other opiates. When they ceased there were considerable changes in their lives, and, generally, they did not turn to other drugs or alcohol as a substitute for their former addiction. This evidence gives reason for optimism about the outcome of addiction. On the other hand, a similar proportion, 38 per cent, remained Clinic patients: a majority of these had received prescriptions without interruption for ten years.

# *References*


Advisory Committee on Drug Dependence (1968) *Cannabis*. London: HMSO.

Advisory Council on the Misuse of Drugs (1977) *First Interim Report of the Treatment and Rehabilitation Working Group*. London: unpublished mimeo ACMD (2)/28 April.

Ashton, M. (1981) Personal communication.

Banton, M. (1959) *White and Coloured*. London: Jonathan Cape.

Beard, W. (1970) Here and now. *World Medicine* 23 September: 9.

Berridge, V. (1977) Fenland opium eating in the nineteenth century. *British Journal of Addiction* **72**:275.

—— (1978a) Working class opium eating in the nineteenth century: establishing the facts. *British Journal of Addiction* **73**:363.

—— (1978b) War conditions and narcotics control: the passing of Defence of the Realm Act Regulation 40B. *Journal of Social Policy* **7**(3):285.

—— (1979a) Morality and medical science: concepts of narcotic addiction in Britain, 1820–1926. *Annals of Science* **36**:67.

—— (1979b) Opiate use and legislative control: a nineteenth-century case study. *Social Science and Medicine* **13**a:351.

Blumberg, H.H., Cohen, S.D., Dronfield, B.E., Mordecai, E.A., Roberts, J.C., and Hawks, D. (1974) British opiate users: 1 People approaching London drug treatment centres. *International Journal of the Addictions* **9**:1.

Bradshaw, S. (1972) *Drug Misuse and the Law*. London: Macmillan.

*British Medical Journal* (1963) Addiction to amphetamines. **2**:5354–355.

—— (1965) Control of drug addiction. **2**:1259–60.

—— (1967) Centres for the treatment of drug addiction. **2**:498. This article was subdivided into three contributions as follows: Bewley, T.H., Advantages of special centres; Connell, P.H., Importance of research; Chapple, P.A.L., Treatment in the community.

Burroughs, W. (1969) *Junkie*. London: New English Library.

Central Office of Information (1979) *Prevention and Treatment of Drug Misuse in Britain.* London: HMSO.

Compilation Group for the History of Modern China (1976) *The Opium War.* Peking: Foreign Languages Press.

Connell, P.H. (1966) What to do about pep pills. In T. Raison (ed.) *Youth in a New Society.* London: Rupert Hart-Davis.

Crowley, A. (1922a) *Diary of a Drug Fiend.* London: Collins.

—— (1922b) The great drug delusion. Author given as 'A New York Specialist'. *The English Review* **34**:571.

Dangerous Drugs (Notification of Addicts) Regulations (1968) London: HMSO.

Dangerous Drugs (Supply to Addicts) Regulations (1968) London: HMSO.

Departmental Committee on Morphine and Heroin Addiction (1926) *Report.* London: HMSO.

De Quincey, T. (1978) *Confessions of an English Opium Eater* [1821]. Harmondsworth: Penguin Books.

Dole, V. and Nyswander, M. (1965) Methadone treatment for diacetylmorphine (heroin) addiction. *Journal of the American Medical Association* **193**:646.

*Drug Link* (Newsletter of the Institute for the Study of Drug Dependence) (1980a) Controlling addiction: the role of the Clinics. **13**:1.

—— (1980b) Phoenix AGM hears major government policy statement. **14**:1.

Dunnell, K. and Cartwright, A. (1972) *Medicine Takers, Hoarders and Prescribers.* London: Routledge & Kegan Paul.

Edwards, G. (1969) The British approach to the treatment of heroin addiction. *Lancet* **i**:768.

Emboden, W. (1972) *Narcotic Plants.* London: Studio Vista.

*File on Four* (1981) BBC Radio Four. 18 February.

Frankau, I.M. and Stanwell, P.M. (1961) The treatment of heroin addiction. *Lancet* **ii**:1377.

Ghodse, H. (1976) Drug problems dealt with by 62 London casualty departments. *British Journal of Preventive and Social Medicine* **30**:251.

Gillespie, D., Glatt, M.M., Hills, D.R., and Pittman, D.J. (1967) Drug dependence and abuse in England. *British Journal of Addiction* **62**:155.

Glatt, M.M. (1966) A review of the Second Report of the Interdepartmental Committee on Addiction. *Bulletin on Narcotics* **18**(2):29.

Goffman, E. (1968) *Stigma.* Harmondsworth: Penguin Books.

Gossop, M. (1980) A plea for flexibility in the treatment of drug dependence. Unpublished mimeo. Bethlem and Royal Maudsley Hospital.

Harrison, J.B. (1854) The psychology of opium eating. *Journal of Psychological Medicine* **7**:240.

Hartnoll, R.L., Mitcheson, M.C., Battersby, A., Brown, G., Ellis, M., Fleming, P., and Hedley, N. (1980) Evaluation of heroin maintenance in controlled trial. *Archives of General Psychiatry* **37**:877.

Hayter, A. (1968) *Opium and the Romantic Imagination.* London: Faber & Faber.

Hewettson, J. and Ollendorf, R. (1964) Preliminary survey of one hundred London heroin and cocaine addicts. *British Journal of Addiction* **60**:110.

Home Office (1981) Drug addicts known to the Home Office, 1980. *Statistical Bulletin 6.*

Huc, E.R. (1865) *The Chinese Empire*. London: Longman. Quoted in A. Fields and D. T. Tararin (1970) Opium in China. *British Journal of Addiction* **64**:371.

Institute for the Study of Drug Dependence (1980) *UK Official Statistics Relating to Drug Abuse*. Supplement to *Drug Link* **13**.

Interdepartmental Committee on Drug Addiction (1961) *Report*. London: HMSO.

—— (1965) *Second Report*. London: HMSO.

Johnson, B.D. (1975) Interpreting official British statistics on addiction. *International Journal of the Addictions* **10**(4):557.

—— (1975) Understanding British addiction statistics. *Bulletin on Narcotics* **27**(1):50–1.

Judson, H. (1974) *Heroin Addiction in Britain*. New York: Harcourt Brace Jovanovich.

Kerouac, J. (1972) *On The Road* [1957]. Harmondsworth: Penguin Books.

*Lancet* (1965) Drug addiction. **ii**:1113.

Leary, T. (1970) *The Politics of Ecstasy*. London: Paladin.

Leech, K. (1973) *Keep the Faith Baby*. London: SPCK.

Ministry of Health (1967) *Treatment and Supervision of Heroin Addiction*. HM (67) 16. 7 March. London: Ministry of Health.

—— (1967 and 1968) *Treatment and Supervision of Heroin Addiction: Precautions Against Misuse of Prescriptions*. F/D121/22 and F/D121/22B. London: Ministry of Health.

Mitcheson, M.C. and Hartnoll, R.L. (1978) Conflicts in deciding treatment within drug dependency clinics. In D. J. West (ed.) *Problems of Drug Abuse in Britain*. Cambridge: Institute of Criminology.

Ogborne, A.C. and Stimson, G.V. (1975) Follow-up of a representative sample of heroin addicts. *International Journal of the Addictions* **10**(4):1061.

Oppenheimer, E., Stimson, G.V., and Thorley, A. (1979) Seven-year follow-up of heroin addicts: abstinence and continued use compared. *British Medical Journal* **2**:627.

Roth, J.A. (1963) *Timetables*. Indianapolis: Bobbs-Merrill.

Schur, E.M. (1963) *Narcotic Addiction in Britain and America*. London: Tavistock.

SCODA (Standing Conference on Drug Abuse) (1980) *Newsletter*. October: 9.

Spear, H.B. (1969) The growth of heroin addiction in the United Kingdom. *British Journal of Addiction* **64**:245.

Stevenson, D. (1965) In *Medical News* 3 December, Vol. 165:1.

Stimson, G.V. (1972) Patterns of behaviour of heroin addicts. *International Journal of the Addictions* **7**(4):671.

—— (1973) *Heroin and Behaviour*. Shannon: Irish University Press.

Stimson, G.V. and Ogborne, A.C. (1970) Survey of addicts prescribed heroin at London Clinics. *Lancet* **i**:1163.

Stimson, G.V., Oppenheimer, E., and Thorley, A. (1978) Seven-year follow-up of heroin addicts: drug use and outcome. *British Medical Journal* **1**:1190.

Stimson, G.V. and Webb, B. (1975) *Going to see the Doctor*. London: Routledge & Kegan Paul.

Thorley, A. (1981) Longitudinal studies of drug dependence. In G. Edwards and C. Busch (eds) *Drug Problems in Britain*. London: Academic Press.

Thorley, A., Oppenheimer, E., and Stimson, G.V. (1977) Clinic attendance and opiate prescription status of heroin addicts over a six-year period. *British Journal of Psychiatry* **130**:565.

Trocchi, A. (1966) Problems and pseudo-problems. *Mental Health* Autumn. Quoted in Silberman, M. (1967:75) *Aspects of Drug Addiction.* London: Royal London Prisoners' Aid Society.

Vaillant, G. (1970) The natural history of narcotic drug addiction. *Seminars in Psychiatry* **2**:486.

Wikler, A. (1952) A psychodynamic study of a patient during self-regulated readdiction to morphine. *Psychiatric Quarterly* **26**:270.

—— (1965) Conditioning factors in opiate addiction and relapse. In D. M. Wilner and G. C. Kassebaum (eds) *Narcotics.* New York: McGraw-Hill.

Wille, R. (1978) Preliminary communication: Cessation of opiate dependence – processes involved in achieving abstinence. *British Journal of Addiction* **73**:381.

—— (1981a) Natural processes of recovery. In G. Edwards and G. Arif (eds) *Drug Dependence in Socio-Cultural Context.* In press.

—— (1981b) Ten-year follow-up of a representative sample of London heroin addicts: clinic attendance, abstinence and mortality. *British Journal of Addiction* **76**:259.

Zacune, J. (1971) A comparison of Canadian narcotic addicts in Great Britain and Canada. *Bulletin on Narcotics* **23**(4):41.

# *Index of addicts and ex-addicts*

The following people are mentioned in the text:

| | | |
|---|---|---|
| Hollis, Mick | Addict: patient at Clinic | 82–3, 117 |
| Howell, Bennett | Addict: patient at Clinic | 72, 89–90, 118–21 |
| Hughes, Susan | Ex-addict since 4.73 | 7, 83, 86, 137, 168, 177–78, 181–84, 194–202 |
| Humphreys, Nick | Addict: patient at Clinic | 73–4 |
| Jennings, Wayne | Ex-addict since 4.70 | 69–71, 174 |
| Jones, Robert | Addict: patient at Clinic | 7, 116, 130, 137–44, 183 |
| Lester, George | Ex-addict since 10.75 | 165 |
| Lunt, Mike | Ex-addict since 7.70 | 175, 177–78, 180 |
| Lyttelton, Tony | Ex-addict since 6.73 | 155, 166–67 |
| Martini, Brenda | Addict: patient at Clinic | 129–30 |
| Milford, David | Addict: patient at Clinic | 74 |
| Morris, Gillian | Died 3.74 | 7, 116, 137, 183–94 |
| Mullins, Ann | Ex-addict since 8.74 | 178–79 |
| O'Sullivan, Raymond | Ex-addict since 6.73 | 71, 75, 160–61, 173–74, 180–81 |
| Platt, Trevor | Addict: patient at Clinic | 83–4 |
| Rose, Marty | Addict: patient at Clinic | 77–8, 135 |
| Rossi, Pete | Addict: patient at Clinic | 89, 133–34 |
| Stock, Jenny | Ex-addict since 7.73 | 162, 169, 172–73 |
| Tunstall, Lew | Addict: patient at Clinic | 122, 124, 129 |
| Wheeler, Greg | Ex-addict since 2.71 | 69, 177–80 |
| Wright, Andrew | Addict: patient at Clinic | 78–9, 134, 159–60 |
| Wrighton, Louise | Addict: patient at Clinic | 76–7, 124–25 |

# *Name index*

# *Subject index*